To Mr Hughes
From Pamela and Michael

THE
MIRACLE OF
MAN

A SURVEY OF HUMANITY'S UPWARD
MARCH THROUGH THE AGES

By HAROLD WHEELER
HON.D.LITT., F.R.HIST.S.

ODHAMS PRESS LIMITED, LONG ACRE, LONDON, W.C.2

THE WORLD'S FIRST ARTISTS AT WORK

Even in the Stone Age man did not "live by bread alone." Undoubtedly the first artists, wh
by the light of chalk lamps, depicted on cave walls the animals they hunted, were moved
considerations of magic, but their marvellously accurate and lifelike representations were
first and hesitating advance along the road that led to Raphael and Michelangel

CONTENTS

REVEALED BY THE EYE OF A GIANT TELESCOPE

A nebular region south of Zeta Orionis. A great projection of dark matter is cutting off light from behind. According to some experts dark nebulæ are composed of minute particles of fine dust expelled from the sun and the hotter stars by radiation pressure, and are held in space when repulsive forces on both sides are nearly equal. On one occasion 850 nebulæ were discovered in a single exposure. This wonderful photograph was taken at Mount Wilson Observatory, California, with the aid of the 10-in. reflector telescope, until recently the largest astronomical instrument in the world, the exposure being three hours. The camera has enabled man to acquire much new and valuable knowledge of the heavens.

,WORLDS IN THE MAKING

Some nebulæ are dark, while others are luminous or shine by reflected light. Whirling gaseous masses known as spiral nebulæ are believed to be worlds in process of formation.

CHAPTER 1

IN THE BEGINNING

Man looks at the universe. Five hundred billion worlds in the making. Great thought— or great machine? The fate of the universe. The sun and its planets. What are sun spots? Their effect on the earth. Celestial chemistry. Mars and Jupiter. Is there life beyond the earth? The moon. Meteors and star-dust. The laboratory of outer space. What the spectroscope reveals. The structure of the universe. Molecules, atoms, electrons. Matter becomes energy. Discoveries of the modern physicists.

I F IT were possible to annex the stars, and they were equally shared, each of us would become a property holder of some consequence. We might even claim a place in a gilt-edged volume on *The Landed Gentry*. There would be at least sixty stars apiece for the 2,000 million men, women and children who inhabit the earth. So Sir James Jeans assures us.

This is not to infer that the world is over-populated. People are merely badly distributed. Accommodation for all could be found on the little Danish island of Bornholm. It is quite pleasantly situated in the Baltic, and has an area of 225 square miles.

But there would be standing room only.

The dwelling-place of the human race is no more than a speck in a universe of such colossal proportions as to stagger the most lively imagination. Many of the suggested celestial colonies are no more solid than gas. What we understand by life would therefore need to be much modified if it were to exist in such circumstances.

The extent of territory would vary. The owner of Betelgeuse, for instance, would be the proud possessor of broad acres. The volume of that glowing mass is 27 million times as great as our sun; its diameter is 300 million miles. We should not receive

5

quite so many callers as on the earth. That might be an advantage. Although Sirius is comparatively near, it is 51 billion miles away from the scene of our present and immediate activities.

Man's search for an explanation of the origin of himself and of the universe has led him along a myriad tangled paths. None has proved a broad highway, nor has the going been easy. Every mountain top scaled was to be the end of the journey. But each has proved to be no more than a summit with a further vista.

Life Cramped by Ignorance

The opening passage of the Bible, the text-book of multitudes of kindly folk, starts with a dogmatic statement that admits of neither compromise nor denial. To attempt either is mere foolishness, because lack of proof is not necessarily want of truth. "In the beginning God created the heaven and the earth." So positive a claim is a fact or a challenge. It depends on the attitude of mind of the reader.

The inquisitive who would exact an answer to the problem of how God came into existence must accept the First Cause as something granted. Not all the pryings, and gropings, and peerings of science and philosophy, of believer and agnostic have added to or subtracted from the bold assertion of the unknown writer of an unknown age.

The biologist, armed with microscope and test-tube, has not yet discovered the origin of life, neither has the compiler of dictionaries adequately defined its meaning. Theologians discuss the minutiæ of its significance, and agree to differ.

Fear of the Unknown

It may be that the near-men, the creatures of Piltdown, Heidelberg, Neanderthal and Rhodesia, our cousins many times removed, questioned themselves regarding these puzzling matters. Their heart-searchings were intermittent and elemental, no doubt, but deeply implanted. That their lives were cramped by reason of their ignorance of what are now termed natural laws seems beyond dispute.

The present writer, though appreciating to the full the cause of thunder as now taught in every infants' school, is still made unhappy in a storm by the explanation offered by a nurse in his early childhood. Crash and flash were God's way of warning naughty boys to mend their manners.

If such were the abysmal ignorance of an average person when the nineteenth century was drawing to its close, when the world was ringing with the discoveries of Tyndall, Darwin, Wallace and Huxley, what must men's imaginations have conjured up in the long era that preceded the dawn of intelligible utterance, perhaps half a million years before?

Though many animals regard natural phenomena with easy indifference, individual members of a species react in different ways. Some dogs, for instance, are terrified by a thunder-storm; others take not the slightest notice of it. Fear of the unknown has dogged the generality of humanity since the dawn of history, and there is no reason to believe that the distant relations or remote forebears of our race were less afraid of the altogether inexplicable than their humbler animal counterparts.

Life Omnipresent in Nature

Danger stalked them by day; terror lurked in the shadows of the night. Experience, often bought at first hand, was purchased at heavy and even tragic cost. Were there not hideous cries in the howling of the wind? They must be caused by an invisible being. Somebody and not a mere something must fan the crimson frightfulness of the volcano, must hurl the hot stones and fling up the stinking, smouldering mass of molten lava that vomited from the mouth of the vent and spread grey ruin and fiery death in its wake.

All seemed endowed with life. Little enough was friendly. Few things seemed stable; most of them changed. The clouds that floated lazily overhead gave way to threatening black masses that outvoiced the roars of the jungle in their growling, and were riven by flashes of blinding fire that set the forest ablaze.

Even the great ball in the sky was uncertain in its behaviour. It acted strangely. It came and went, sometimes glowing with genial warmth, sometimes scorching and searing and burning, and sometimes giving very little heat at all. Water, cool and refreshing to touch and taste, became on occasion as hard as rock, so that one could walk on it. Mists blotted out the landscape. Rain stung. Stones stood still or rolled. Dust danced. Gems that sparkled on the grass in the early morning disappeared when they were touched.

In winter soft flakes of snow fell gently and apparently harmlessly, but they piled

EXPLORERS OF THE UNIVERSE

(Above, left) Sir Isaac Newton. He held that gravity is a force, whereas Einstein regarded it as a property of space, which he believed was curved. (Above, right) Sir William Herschel, who in 1781 discovered Uranus, the first planet to be added to the solar system since classical times. The discoverer mistook it for a comet. (Below, left) Sir James Jeans, O.M., Secretary of the Royal Society, who won public fame by making astronomy popular. (Below, right) Dr. Robert Andrews Millikan, American Nobel prizeman, famous for his investigations on the electron, who believes that creation still continues in stellar space

themselves outside the dank cave that was the home of near-man and locked him in or shut him out. Avalanches crashed down the mountain-side, dealing death and destruction. For the most part it was a pitiless world, though perhaps its almost human denizens knew neither hope nor despair. They were "of the earth, earthy."

Let it be said at once that no branch of science speaks today with the cocksureness of fifty years ago. Science now makes suggestions rather than deliberate statements. It voices contradictions; indeed, rather courts them. It is less positive than it was, for the alleged truth of today is apt to become the untruth of tomorrow.

Mechanical Explanation Abandoned

In the nineteenth century it was freely stated that everything had a mechanical explanation and that the future was predestined; "mechanical determinism" is the correct scientific term for this view. Hermann von Helmholtz, the distinguished German scientist, went so far as to assert that "the final aim of all natural science is to resolve itself into mechanics." Such a statement is far from true today.

Commenting on the matter, Prof. J. S. Haldane said that "the attempt to analyse living organisms into physical and chemical mechanism is probably the most colossal failure in the whole history of modern science." Inward and spiritual forces, "feelings which are outside the world of measurable things," are allowed to play a part in the universe.

"Universe" is a little word with a big meaning. "The whole creation, embracing this and other worlds and everything comprised in space, considered as some sort of a unity or system." So runs the definition in the dictionary. It could hardly be more comprehensive.

We are accustomed to regard the figures glibly given by the Chancellor of the Exchequer when introducing a budget in the British House of Commons as reaching "astronomical proportions." They are negligible when compared with figures as the astronomer and physicist know them. On the authority of Sir James Jeans, "the total number of stars in the universe is probably something like the total number of grains of sand on all the seashores of the world."

But what of the universe as such, for the stars are no more than its bits and pieces? Dr. Edwin P. Hubble, of the Mount Wilson

Observatory, gives the diameter of the universe as 6,000 million light-years, a light-year being a convenient unit of measurement employed by astronomers in an attempt to prevent their statistics occupying too many lines in their notebooks. A light-year is the distance light travels in twelve months at the rate of 186,300 miles per second.

As though these statistics were not sufficiently staggering, the same distinguished authority adds that some of the 500 billion nebulæ, or worlds in the making, are receding into space at the rate of from 30,000 to 40,000 miles a second. Thus it would appear that the universe is expanding. There is so much space between stars and nebulæ that the total amount of matter "may be visualized," according to Dr. Hubble, "as corresponding to a grain of sand in each volume of space equal to the volume of the earth."

Strange that a speck which the average man usually disregards as of no consequence, unless he happens to get one in his eye, becomes of importance as a unit of measurement to those who deal with the colossal. The term "speck" is used advisedly, and in its ordinary sense, because a grain of sand is really a mountain when contrasted with the minute atoms of which all matter is built up.

Great Thought—or Great Machine?

There are two schools of thought regarding the ultimate fate of the universe. One, typified by Sir James Jeans, holds that it is slowly running down. The other, of which Dr. Robert Millikan, a Nobel prizeman, is an exponent, denies so tragic an ending to the great adventure.

"Science," says the latter, "finds the hand of the Creator still at work in stellar space, and rejects the pessimistic theory of the existence of only a disintegrating process, by which the universe will eventually burn itself out. There is an abundance of hydrogen out in interstellar space that is busying itself breeding heavier and commoner elements out of its atoms. The radiant energy leaking from the stars is probably constantly replenishing the hydrogen supplies as fast as they form the heavier atoms—just another finger pointing to the conclusion that the Creator may still be at work." In a word, the universe is both breaking up and being rebuilt.

Sir James Jeans says that "In general the universe seems to be nearer to a great thought than to a great machine. It may

TREES AND CROPS → MEAT AND MILK → HUMAN ENERGY

DEAD TREES UNDER PRESSURE

MINERAL ENERGY

BOILER HOUSE STEAM PIPE TURBINE DYNAMO A MODERN LIVING-ROOM

THE SUN AS UNIVERSAL PROVIDER

The sun is the supreme energizing machine. It is a universal provider. In a very real sense a mutton chop is part of its bounty. The fallen trees of the forest, changed in form and substance, store up sunshine, absorbed millions of years ago, in the form of coal for future service either as a direct source of heat and light or as a generator of electricity.

MAN—A*

MOLTEN MASSES DISGORGED BY VESUVIUS

Lava which flowed from Vesuvius during the eruption pictured on the opposite page. The cones of volcanoes are usually built around the vents by accumulations of the molten materials which are flung up. Some active volcanoes are still below the level of the sea.

well be that each individual consciousness ought to be compared to a brain cell in a universal mind." He adds that the universe "shows evidence of a designing and controlling power." The thought, it must be inferred from the writings of this eminent authority, is that of a pure mathematician.

Expanding for Ever

"It is widely held that matter slowly changes into radiation," avows Sir Arthur Eddington. "If so, it would seem that the universe will ultimately become a ball of radiation, growing ever larger and thinner and fusing into longer and longer wave lengths. In about 1,500 million years it will double its radius, and its size will go on expanding in this way in geometrical progression for ever."

Sir Ambrose Fleming, who did so much to develop radio, sums up his belief as follows: "There seems to be proof that the physical universe is not in itself eternally enduring but is, as it were, wasting away and moving towards a state in which some fresh act of creation will be required if physical phenomena, as we know them, are to continue. It is not, therefore, self-produced or self-maintained, but the result of a creative power, and requires a continually operative directive agency.

"There are unquestionably in the physical universe things that stimulate our appreciation of order, beauty, adaptation, numerical relations, and purpose in our minds—we who are thinking, feeling persons—and hence the qualities which excite these psychic reactions must have been bestowed on the universe by a sentient intelligence at least as personal as ourselves."

Let us leave the physicists and astronomers to continue their intricate jig-saw puzzles—they are unlikely to complete them yet awhile—and approach within 93 million miles of the stage on which man plays his part. There, radiating the light and heat without which the earth would be a stark, dead world, is the sun, the supreme energizing machine and lordly governor of that space in which we live, and move, and have our being.

The Sun as Universal Provider

It is a universal provider. It encourages the growth of the green grass and ripens the kindly fruits without which man and the lower animals would starve. In a very real sense a mutton chop is part of the bounty of the sun. The fallen trees of the forest, changed in form and substance, buried deep and released by the sweat of a vast army of coal miners, liberate sunshine absorbed

ONE OF EARTH'S SAFETY VALVES

Fear of the unknown has dogged the generality of humanity since the dawn of history. Our earliest ancestors believed that somebody, and not a mere something, fanned the crimson frightfulness of the volcano, hurled the hot stones and flung up the stinking, smouldering mass of molten lava that vomited from the mouth of the vent, spreading grey ruin in its wake. Here is the main crater of Vesuvius during an eruption. The column, consisting of water vapour, chlorine, carbon dioxide and other gases, together with dust and ashes. rose beacon-like several hundred feet into the air, a sight of terror at a distance of many miles.

long ago and stored up for future service. Oil, so essential to modern civilization, is probably of similar origin.

Wind and rain are among the gifts of the golden orb that many men once worshipped and a few still do. The discovery, or rather

COLUMNS OF VOLCANIC LAVA

The Giant's Causeway, in Ireland, consists of lava floes that have taken the shape of five- or six-sided columns.

the rediscovery, that the sun is a doctor with healing in its rays is comparatively recent. The ancient Greeks appreciated the fact. It has led to the healthful development of hiking, the advertising of "desirable" and other houses as veritable sun-traps, and the invention of divers devices for counterfeiting sunlight.

The temperature of the great gaseous mass of the sun at its surface is 6,000 deg. centigrade; at its centre it is believed to be in the neighbourhood of 40 million deg. centigrade. Its diameter is 864,000 miles; its mass 329,000 times that of the earth. The lord of the solar system is expending

energy at the rate of 250 million tons a minute, or 75,000 horse-power for every square yard of its surface. It is well that the rays are filtered and partially absorbed before they reach us, otherwise humanity and all things living would be annihilated.

The sun is not without blemish; it has spots on its face. They are "holes" by means of which the ultra-violet radiation of its interior finds an outlet. Many of them are much larger than the earth. Two spots which made their appearance in 1936 each covered an area of some 1,600 million square miles. By observing the position of sunspots Galileo (1564–1642) came to the conclusion that the sun revolved on an axis in the same way as the earth.

Influence of Sunspots

About every eleven years, for a reason at present unknown, these spots become more numerous, and apparently have a very definite influence on terrestrial affairs. They affect the growth of trees and crops, interfere with radio, telegraphic and telephonic communications, increase the frequency of magnetic storms and the northern lights, and cause the population of wild life to increase or decrease.

It is found that when there are more sunspots there are fewer small woodland animals, such as fox, lynx and rabbit, and that when these phenomena are decreased, breeding is greatly speeded up. Pines in California and Germany make more rapid growth when sunspots are most numerous.

Tongues of Flaming Gas

Sunspots are centres of vast whirlpools in the solar atmosphere. These tongues of flaming gas, or prominences, vary a good deal in measurement. They would seem to average about 150,000 miles in height, although one is recorded as having shot up a towering eminence of 620,000 miles; another reached 1,550,000 miles.

Sixty of the ninety-two elements found on the earth, including oxygen, hydrogen, nitrogen, carbon and iron, are present in the sun. How were they discovered?

Chandeliers ornamented with pendants of cut-glass were indispensable accessories of the Victorian drawing-room. They were among the "correct" things of a correct period. The hanging lustres threw bands of colour on the immediate surroundings. With a triangular prism not dissimilar, Sir Isaac Newton (1642–1727) found that a beam of sunlight, to all intents and

EXPLORERS OF THE REALMS OF SPACE

Sighting the big telescope at Greenwich Observatory. Inset from middle left are four famous astronomers: Nicolaus Copernicus, 1473–1543; (below) Galileo Galilei, 1564–1642; (top right) Edmund Halley, 1656–1742, and (bottom right) John Flamsteed, 1646–1719, the first Astronomer Royal. His salary was £100 a year. Flamsteed devoted most of his time to the compilation of a catalogue of the fixed stars, on which he was still at work when he died. He listed nearly three thousand; modern telescopes make hundreds of millions visible to man. Sir Christopher Wren, famous architect of St. Paul's Cathedral, designed the observatory.

purposes colourless, when passed through a prism was split up into a band, or spectrum, of coloured light. By passing the coloured light through another prism it became colourless sunlight once more.

What he failed to discover was, to quote Sir William Huggins (1824–1910), a pioneer in spectroscopic astronomy, "the narrow gaps wanting in light, which, as dark lines, cross the colours of the spectrum and constitute the code of signals that give information of the chemical nature of the celestial gases by which the different light rays have been blotted out, or by which they have been enhanced."

Spectral Lines and Their Meaning

Sir William H. Wollaston (1766–1828) was the first to notice these dark lines, which were subsequently studied in great detail, but not explained, by Joseph von Fraunhofer (1787–1826), after whom they are named. Finally, Robert Bunsen (1811–99) and Gustav Kirchhoff (1824–87), following almost innumerable experiments, found that the light of any incandescent element produced in the spectrum bright or dark rays exclusively characteristic of that particular element. The yellow lines of sodium, for example, are not duplicated by any other substance. The spectra of earthly elements correspond with those in the stars.

Sir William Huggins tells us what happened during the course of his own initial research, when "an astronomical observatory began, for the first time, to take on the appearance of a laboratory. Primary batteries, giving forth noxious gases, were arranged outside one of the windows; a large induction coil stood mounted on a stand on wheels so as to follow the positions of the eye-end of the telescope, together with a battery of several Leyden jars; shelves with Bunsen burners, vacuum tubes, and bottles of chemicals, especially of specimens of pure metals, lined its walls.

"The observatory became a meeting-place where terrestrial chemistry was brought into direct touch with celestial chemistry. The characteristic light-rays from earthly hydrogen shone side by side with the corresponding radiations from starry hydrogen, or else fell upon the dark lines due to the absorption of the hydrogen in Sirius or in Vega. Iron from our mines was line-matched, light for dark, with stellar iron from opposite parts of the celestial sphere. Sodium, which upon the earth is always present with us, was found

to be widely diffused through the celestial spaces."

Sometimes the process has worked in a reverse way, and an element unknown on the earth has been discovered in the realms of space. In 1868 P. J. C. Janssen (1824–1907), a French investigator, and Sir Norman Lockyer (1836–1920), working independently, noticed a bright yellow line in the solar spectrum not associated with any known element. The latter called it helium—"sun substance"—a name derived from *helios*, the Greek word for sun.

Nearly thirty years later Sir William Ramsay (1852–1916) found that the mineral cleveite when heated gave off a gas hitherto unidentified, which he designated krypton. A tube of the new gas was dispatched to Sir William Crookes (1832–1919), who reported: "Krypton is helium."

Helium, according to Lord Rutherford (1871–1937), was formed from hydrogen under some as yet unknown conditions in the stellar system. Although heavier than hydrogen, helium is non-inflammable, and therefore specially suitable for use in airships. Radium ejects atoms of helium, which may be seen with the aid of an instrument called the spinthariscope.

If you have not skipped the dates given in brackets you will have noticed that whereas a century passed between the deaths of Newton and of Wollaston, a succession of discoveries in astrophysics followed within the next 110 years. Physical science had ceased to be the Cinderella of knowledge.

The Sun's Planetary Family

There are nine members of the sun's planetary family. Mercury is nearest to the parent body, followed by Venus, Earth, Mars, Jupiter, Saturn, Uranus, Neptune and Pluto. Some of them have attendants called moons, or satellites, which rotate on their own axes and revolve around the major body, as the latter revolves round the sun, in orbits, or paths.

Mercury is a mere 36 million miles away from the sun, and the smallest of the planets. The brightest of them is Venus, which is about the same size as the earth. No oxygen can be detected in its atmosphere, but there is carbon dioxide and probably nitrogen.

The poets are fond of referring to the "music of the spheres." In 1932 the "voice" of Venus was picked up by means of a telescope and a photo-electric cell. The beam set up a small electric current, which was amplified and broadcast by radio.

HOME OF THE WORLD'S MOST FAMOUS METEORITE

The Kaaba, the Holy of Holies of Islam, at Mecca. A fragment of a meteorite, which according to tradition was given to Abraham by the angel Gabriel, is built into one of the corners. No Mohammedan pilgrim, thousands of whom visit the holy city every year, leaves without kissing the stone. The veil is a black brocade with a golden border.

The distance of Mars from the earth varies from about 35 million to 63 million miles. Its diameter is only about half that of the earth. Of all the planets of the solar system, except perhaps Venus, it is the one most like our own, though the physical conditions are different.

The blue-green areas referred to as seas on maps of the planet are regarded by some scientists as indicating vegetation, while the brick-red tint of other parts may indicate extensive deserts of pulverized ironstone. What water exists pours from the snow-capped polar regions during summer, and it has been suggested that the network of lines that sears the surface may consist of artificial irrigation canals.

This was not the theory propounded by Giovanni Schiaparelli (1835–1910), who discovered them in 1877 at Milan. He merely put forward the notion that they were *canali*, that is, "channels." The suggestion that they owed their existence to other than natural causes was emphatically and enthusiastically championed by Professor Percival Lowell (1855–1916) and Dr. W. H. Pickering. According to Professor Svante Arrhenius, the Swedish Nobel prizewinner, the so-called canals are cracks which have become filled with sand or dust.

TO CATCH THE HEALTH-GIVING RAYS OF THE SUN

A modern secondary school near London which affords maximum light, predominant features being the glass tower which surrounds the main staircase and the extensive number of large windows on every side.

Jupiter is a great disappointment to astronomers because a belt of clouds surrounds it, but a red spot in the planet's southern hemisphere has attracted considerable attention since it was first systematically observed in the latter part of the nineteenth century. Its atmosphere is so dense that the pressure is about one million tons per square inch.

Saturn is unique on account of its rings. They are probably miniature moons, the remains of a satellite that approached too near and was shattered. Uranus, originally mistaken for a comet, was discovered by Sir William Herschel in 1781, and Neptune by J. C. Adams in 1845.

Not until 1930 was Pluto added to the list, as the result of a twenty-five years' search by a band of enthusiasts at the Lowell Observatory at Flagstaff, Arizona. Dr. Percival Lowell noted certain irregularities in the movements of Neptune and rightly deduced that they were due to a body beyond that planet. It is at a distance of 4,185 million miles from the earth.

Sir George Darwin (1845–1912) put forward the interesting theory that the moon is a piece of the earth which flew off owing to the terrific speed at which the globe was then rotating. That it will ultimately return and form a ring system similar to that of Saturn is suggested by Dr. Harlow Shapley.

It is a mirror that reflects a little sunlight on the earth, but whether it is cold and dead, as is generally believed, is a matter of controversy. The moon is supposed to have neither atmosphere nor water, to be roasting by day and freezing by night, but Professor W. H. Pickering holds that it supports a low form of life and that the many volcanoes on its surface are still active.

Another suggestion is that the craters are splashes made long ago by intensely hot meteors crashing into the moon's surface strata. The result of a drop falling into water is the erection of a central cone of liquid; those who support the bombardment theory believe that the craters on the moon mark the spots where the explosions occurred.

Reference has been made to the "music of the spheres." Now for a word about the power of moonbeams. In 1933 the observatory of Arcetri, in Tuscany, picked up, transformed and transmitted rays of moonlight by radio to Chicago, where they were used for lighting lamps at the exhibition then being held there. The action, or pull, of the moon raises tides both in the oceans and in the earth's crust.

Does intelligent life exist outside the earth? There might be forms of life on the moon, according to Professor H. H. Turner, but they would be different from those we know. Camille Flammarion declared that nothing prevents the supposition of the existence of individuals with bodies lighter than our own and endowed with different and perhaps more numerous senses.

H. J. Gramatzki, working in association with Professor Julius Franz, is of the opinion that some form of life is possible on Uranus, Neptune and Jupiter. Plant organisms, he says, cannot thrive in the deep twilight of Venus, "but when we consider that there is upon our own earth a bacillus which without sunlight and chlorophyll (which makes leaves green) can live in the darkness of mud, where it releases carbon dioxide, then this life problem is already settled in principle."

Speaking at the University of Chicago in 1932, Dr. W. MacMillan suggested that "Out in the heavens, perhaps, are civilizations

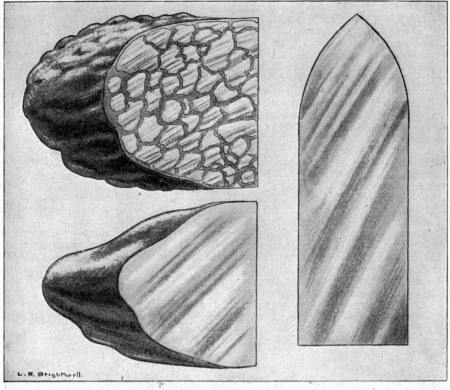

STEEL FROM THE LABORATORY OF THE SKY

Iron, nickel and phosphorus are among the elements met with in metallic meteorites. Two halves of iron meteorites with cut surfaces compared with a sectional view of a naval armour-piercing shell. The shell is actually four times the size of either half meteorite.

as far above us as we are above the single cell, since they are so much older than ours. Magnificent forms of life have grown up over magnificent stretches of time, only to perish in some cataclysm. Magnificent forms of life will always grow up if this theory be true, that the universe is continually being rebuilt at some unknown sub-electronic level."

The Martians as Thought-Forms

Dr. E. W. Barnes, Bishop of Birmingham, feels that there is good reason to believe that the planets on which life has appeared are in the aggregate numerous, though they may be relatively sparse in any particular region of the cosmos. "It is surely beyond the limits of probability," he says, "that a cosmos so vast should have in it but one planet, otherwise in no way exceptional, on which life had appeared."

"Though we do see on Mars possibilities of some sort of life," asserts Dr. H. Spencer Jones, the Astronomer Royal, "it is more probable that we are looking at a world that is the home of spent life. Life probably flourished there millions of years ago, but has been dried up by the atmosphere, and has probably by now become almost impossible." Dr. A. M. Low makes the point that "Martians might be so advanced as to exist simply as thought forms."

This is on the lines of Professor Forest Ray Moulton's suggestion. "If there is life on the planet Mars," he writes, "the higher forms at least are quite different physically from the higher forms on the earth, for they are, and must be, more or less adapted to their widely different environments. Likewise if Mars is the abode of highly intelligent life, the stage of development of this life may correspond more nearly to that of our predecessors millions of years ago than to our own, or it may correspond more closely to that at which our successors will have arrived millions of years in the future.

"When one thinks what revolutions in living science has wrought," he adds, "and what changes in political institutions and social and economic relationships have taken place in the last few centuries, man pauses in awe before the possibilities of millions of years. Yet on Mars, or perhaps on other worlds, such stages of development may already have been reached. Although these thoughts are speculations, they are not useless if one does not fail to remember they are speculations, for such mental exercises help man to consider more objectively the varied problems of his own life."

Planets and stars—which are really suns numbering hundreds of millions—are not the only bodies in space. Thousands of asteroids, or planetoids as they are sometimes termed, exist between Mars and Jupiter, and are probably fragments of an exploded planet. The so-called double, or binary, stars are not double, although they appear to be. They are two stars revolving round a common centre or each other. Meteors, popularly but incorrectly termed shooting stars, blaze up out of the void and disappear, or succeed in reaching the earth as meteorites.

In the laboratory of outer space steel is being produced similar to that made by man in his blast furnaces. Iron, nickel and phosphorus are among the elements met with in metallic meteorites, which have revealed no substance unknown on our planet. Stony meteorites contain similar materials to our rocks. Lord Kelvin made the daring suggestion that life may have been brought to the earth by this means; Professor Svante Arrhenius thinks it may have come from other planets or suns.

Showers of Dust

Not until meteors enter the earth's atmosphere do they become luminous. As they travel at a speed that often exceeds sixty miles a second, the friction set up causes them to become white hot. Some 40,000 tons of their dust is showered on the earth every year.

The path of a group of meteors known as the Perseids crosses that of the earth each year in August. It is believed that they are the remains of a comet which broke up in 1862, but in whose orbit they continue to keep. They are called the Perseids because they radiate from a point in the constellation

CASTING STEEL IN A BRITISH MILL FOR BRITISH SHIPS

Rolling and casting steel in a British mill where plates for the giant luxury liners the "Queen Mary" and the "Queen Elizabeth" were made. As many as 6,500 tons of slabs have been rolled out in one week. The laboratory of outer space is producing similar steel.

THE GREAT NEBULA IN ANDROMEDA AND A PASSING METEOR

The brilliant path of a meteor photographed by accident when the camera was focused on the great nebula in Andromeda, which is seen in the centre. Meteors travel at a speed that often exceeds sixty miles a second. The friction set up causes them to become white hot. Some 40,000 tons of their dust shower the earth every year.

Perseus. In a less scientific age they were referred to as the tears of St. Lawrence.

The bluish-green trails of the Leonids appear once in thirty-three years, though stragglers from the main body are usually in evidence in November. In the year 902, notes an old record, "there were seen, as it were lances, an infinite number of stars, which scattered themselves like rain to right and left, and that year was called the Year of the Stars." Since then, and perhaps long before, the Leonids have been moving through space, bringing dismay to some observers and delight to others.

When the earth was younger, a colossal meteorite, estimated to weigh over a million tons, crashed in the Arizona Desert, U.S.A. It displaced 200 million tons of rock and formed an immense crater four-fifths of a mile wide and 570 feet deep. Attempts to find it have failed despite several determined and costly ventures. On one occasion only iron-stained sand rewarded the efforts of the drillers; on another the tool was lost. At a depth of 1,300 feet nickel-iron was disclosed. Seventy-six feet lower material was struck that did no more than blunt the drill. Dynamite was then tried, but without success, and the project had to be abandoned. Meteoric iron is scattered in the vicinity over a fairly wide radius, and about twenty tons of meteorites have been picked up in the neighbourhood.

A Sacred Meteorite

A meteorite is built into one of the corners of the Kaaba, the Mohammedan Holy of Holies, at Mecca. One fell at Crumlin, near Belfast, in 1902. It turned the scales at 9 lb. 5½ oz., over a pound in excess of a specimen which had ploughed into a field at Rowton, Shropshire, twenty-six years before. These are small compared to the 36-ton specimen brought from Greenland in 1879 by Rear-Admiral R. E. Peary, the Polar explorer.

In 1938 Russian airmen were surveying a wild part of Siberia when they discovered an area which had been devastated by a meteorite in 1908. The tremendous displacement of air caused by its passage had felled many square miles of forest in the region watered by a tributary of the Yenisei.

The brilliant glow of the monster, which probably weighed several hundred tons, was visible an immense distance. Thousands of peasants, scattered over a wide area, were almost scared out of their wits,

for the gleaming flash was regarded as the end of all things. A month or two later another visitor from the sky buried itself in Tajikistan. At Bacubirito, in Mexico, there is a meteor weighing fifty tons.

"Comets appear as signals for the removal of the old and the diffusion of the new," avowed an Eastern philosopher 600 years before Christ. Plague, pestilence, floods and famine were attributed to the sinister influence of the celestial wanderers.

What Comets are Made Of

They are, according to most authorities, clusters of meteors and a vast volume of glowing gas. The spectroscope reveals carbon monoxide, well known to motorists and a constituent of the gas which sometimes plays havoc in coal mines; cyanogen, a deadly poison; hydrogen, nitrogen and oxygen. The movements of comets are controlled by solar gravity.

The most famous, or perhaps one ought to write infamous by reason of the hysteria it has developed in humanity, is Halley's Comet. It appears regularly every seventy-five years, and so far as is known has caused no physical harm to anybody. The last time it was seen was in 1910, when it terrorized multitudes of people in India, China, Iran (Persia) and Russia.

The history of Halley's comet has been traced back to 373, for in that year the Chinese recorded a comet which is believed to be identical with the one which the astronomer whose name it bears studied in 1682, over thirteen hundred years later. Sir Isaac Newton thought that eventually it would fall into the sun, with the sequel that the solar heat would be increased to so marked an extent "that our globe will be burned, and all animal life will perish."

Earliest Picture of a Comet

Halley's comet is depicted in the Bayeux tapestry, where King Harold and his court are represented pointing to the harbinger of fate from the top of a tower. This is the earliest known picture of a comet. It is also shown in the Canterbury Psalter, written in the twelfth century by Eadwine, a monk of Christ Church Priory, Canterbury.

The earth has more than once passed through the tail of a comet. That it has been hit by the head of one is open to doubt, though the suggestion has been put forward that certain bays in the Atlantic coastal plain area of the United States of

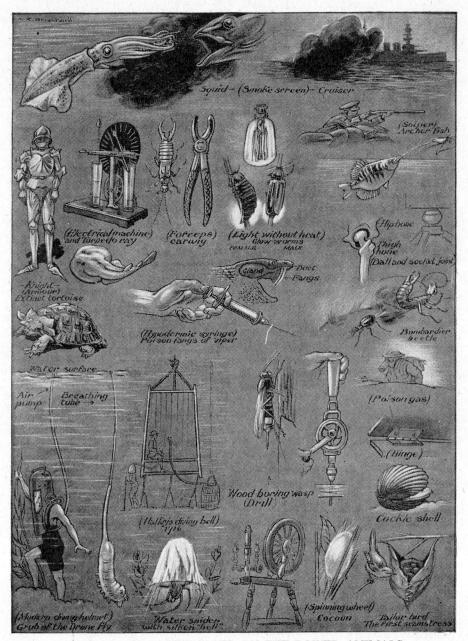

INVENTIONS FORESTALLED BY THE LOWER ANIMALS

Many of the lower animals possess organs which man has perfected as devices for his own use only after repeated experiments, sometimes extending over a long period of time. Some of Nature's apparatus paralleled by inventors are pictured above. A study of the boring methods of the teredo, or ship-worm, gave Sir Marc Isambard Brunel his idea for constructing the Thames Tunnel, and even poison gas and smoke screens have their counterparts in nature.

America were gouged out by the meteoric material that constituted the nucleus of a giant comet.

The infinitely great is built up from the infinitely small. This now obvious fact, suspected in the days of ancient Greece, has been confirmed by the scientific discoveries of the twentieth century. Then, as Field-Marshal J. C. Smuts has so well said, "Matter itself, the time-honoured mother of all, practically disappeared into electrical energy."

Movement in Everything

There is movement in everything, including the hardest minerals. Solids, liquids and gases are now conceived as made up of tiny invisible particles called molecules. These consist of atoms made up of electrons of negative electricity and protons of positive electricity, the latter being about 1,840 times as heavy as the former. They resemble a miniature solar system in that the electrons revolve like planets round a central proton nucleus, or "sun." Nature has not varied her model; the gigantic and the tiny follow the same laws.

"The discovery was quite recent," notes Sir Oliver Lodge, "that the same system of law and order that reigned through the heavens held equally in the interior of the atom, so that there was an atomic astronomy growing up before our eyes, leading us to wonder if there was any limit to smallness any more than there was any limit to bigness."

Hydrogen is at once the simplest and the lightest substance known. Its atom has one proton as its nucleus, around which a solitary electron revolves. At the opposite end of the series is uranium, one of the heaviest metals, whose atom has ninety-two satellite electrons. The place of an element round the nucleus in a list arranged according to the number of revolving electrons is called its atomic number; thus the atomic number of hydrogen is one and uranium ninety-two.

When atoms of different elements are combined, the elemental substances do not just mix and retain their individual properties; they change into something else. For example, one atom of oxygen and two atoms of hydrogen make a molecule of water. The difference between one substance and another is merely a difference in the combinations of the units.

The behaviour of the atom is to some extent indeterminate, and it is now held that light and radiation are disseminated in parcels, or quanta, rather than continuously. This suggestion was put forward by Professor Max Planck, of Berlin, in 1901, and is known as the quantum theory.

The atom-building processes may be taking place in what is erroneously called empty space, whence may issue the cosmic rays discovered by Professor R. A. Millikan, which he calls "messengers of creation." It was to get data regarding them that Dr. Auguste Piccard, a Belgian physicist, made sensational ascents in an aluminium gondola attached to a balloon in 1931 and 1932. Two United States officers made a similar exploration in 1935.

At the moment the evidence is inconclusive because followers of another school of thought are equally emphatic that atom-building takes place much nearer home. A terrestrial rather than a celestial source of origin is surmised.

"All the substances that we know, living bodies and plants, as well as the non-living materials of the earth, and, indeed, of the universe, are structures formed by putting together various groups of atoms in various ways." So says Sir William Bragg, who adds: "The forces that we see in action everywhere and those that we exert ourselves, all processes animate and inanimate, are based on the forces that atoms and molecules exert on each other."

Island Universes

The word *nebula* is a Latin word meaning a little cloud. In a sense it is entirely suited to certain luminous patches in outer space which are often referred to as island universes. In another sense the term is grossly inadequate, because the size of many of them is immense. There are dark nebulæ, nebulæ that give out light and are therefore called emission nebulæ, and nebulæ that shine by reflected light. The most remote—some of them are over 100 million light years away—are the spiral nebulæ, whirling gaseous masses which astronomers believe to be worlds in the making.

It may be that in the unplumbed abyss of time similar clouds of negative and positive particles came together, we know not how, and after a process of evolution, in which evaporation and gravitation doubtless played important parts, formed the sun and the stars. And from the sun the solar system, of which the earth we live on is a member, was eventually born.

LAKE IN THE CRATER OF A VOLCANO

Crater Lake, on the top of Mt. Mazama, Oregon, U.S.A. The cliffs of lava and ashes reach from 500 to 2,000 feet above the surface of the water, the depth of which is nearly 2,000 feet in parts. Wizard Island was doubtless built up after the disappearance of the volcanic peaks.

CHAPTER 2

EARTH'S BIRTHDAY BOOK

Earth's parentage. The age of the earth. Nebulas and meteorites. The elements in the earth's crust. Drifting continents. The succession of rocks. Britain under water. Submerged forests. The rise and fall of land and sea. The story of Atlantis. Lost lands and bird migrations. The shape of the earth. Geology and industry.

MOTHER EARTH's parentage is unknown and her age uncertain. She is not a blue-blooded aristocrat. Far from it; the materials of which she was made are rarely found in a pure state.

The old lady has kept a diary of sorts, but the venerable are apt to be hazy as to exact time, and the crumpled pages of her record, preserved in the fastnesses of the rocks, are undated. These negative facts have not prevented the Paul Prys of learning from trying to piece together a family tree and filling in the missing figures of the years.

In the seventeenth century Archbishop James Usher worked out Mother Earth's birthday to his own complete satisfaction. You will find 4004 B.C. printed in the margin of the first page of the Book of Genesis in many editions of the Bible.

Modern geologists are less certain. They hesitate to follow where Usher did not fear to tread. According to him the earth came into existence on Friday, October 28, 4004 B.C. The Rev. John Lightfoot, who in 1655 was chosen vice-chancellor of Cambridge University, calculated the hour as nine o'clock in the morning. The Flood, according to William Whiston, occurred on November 18, 2349 B.C., when the tail of a comet passed over the equator and caused a deluge of rain.

Lord Kelvin, endeavouring to work out the age of the earth by ascertaining how long it had taken to cool since it was in a molten state, announced in 1862 that the maximum was 400 million years and the minimum 20 million years. In 1897 he issued a revised version and assessed the maximum at 40 million years.

It is only fair to add that the famous

inventor was ignorant of the radio-active minerals, the discovery of which was afterwards brought to bear on the subject by a calculation from the rate of the breaking down of uranium. The result put Kelvin's figures entirely in the shade. According to this method of reading the geological calendar, the oldest rocks, called the Pre-Cambrian, alone took some 1,000 million years to form. Probably 500 million years have passed since then.

Salt Measures Ocean's Age

Other researchers, computing the accumulation of salt in the seas by means of elaborate estimates of the amount of material carried away from the land in a given time, have arrived at a figure of 330 million years for the formation of the 1,178,000 million million tons of ocean. Experts who base their statistics on geological evidence as well as the proportion of salt in the sea place their estimate at 900 million years. Professor Arthur Holmes asserts with confidence that "the age of the earth is not likely to be less than 1,600 million years." Einstein suggests 10,000 million.

In 1796 Pierre Simon Laplace, often referred to as the Newton of France, fathered what is called the nebular hypothesis. This suggests that the earth and other members of the solar system were formed by the condensation of rings of matter thrown off by the rapid rotation of a cloud of hot gas. The moons associated with some of them were detached in a similar manner from the new-born worlds.

How the Earth was Formed

The explanation most acceptable to later scientists is that an enormous star, passing near the sun, caused such an intense tidal action that the earth and the planets were torn off. Planetesimals, either solid or in the form of molecules of gas, added to the mass of the earth, as meteorites are adding to it now, though in much diminished quantities.

Laplace conceived that the outer crust of the molten earth cooled slowly and became rocks, in some of which metals were formed. The gradual but relentless process went on until at long last the condensation of the atmosphere filled in the gaps of the rugged surface and became seas, lakes and rivers.

The planetesimal theory has it otherwise. The earth, when probably no more than one-tenth of its present mass, cooled quickly and grew in size by the constant bombardment and accumulation of the planetesimals. Gases escaping from the falling meteorites, from the earth itself, and from volcanoes created an atmosphere. When the vapour condensed it showered down as water. Heat was generated by the increasing pressure of the interior and the decomposition of radio-active substances.

The core of the earth is believed to have the same composition as iron meteorites. On analysing 360 of the latter, the average contents showed 90·65 per cent of iron and 8·49 per cent of nickel—almost the same proportions as in armour-piercing shells.

About 99 per cent by weight of the skin of Mother Earth is made up of eight of the ninety-two known elements. Of them oxygen is by far the most common, with 47 per cent, followed by silicon, aluminium, iron, calcium, magnesium, sodium and potassium (with only 2½ per cent). Many of the most important materials essential to civilized man, such as carbon, copper, tin, gold, silver, lead and phosphorus, are squeezed into the remaining 1 per cent.

Earth's Internal Heat Store

That terrific heat exists in the interior is proved by volcanoes, geysers and hot springs. It is calculated that the heat stored in the rocks of the interior is at least 30 million times that available in the coal reserves that still lie buried.

According to a recent suggestion put forward by Dr. I. A. Nadai, of the University of Pittsburgh, the surface of the earth rests on a seething liquid sea sixty miles below. This is in keeping with what is termed the theory of continental drift, which has it that all the various parts of the earth were originally joined in one primitive mass.

A glance at a map of the world will suffice to show that the west coast of Africa and the east coast of South America would nearly fit if placed together. The mass apparently split and the two halves drifted away in opposite directions.

This interesting proposition was put forward in 1910 by Dr. F. B. Taylor, of Yale University, and subsequently developed by Professor Alfred Wegener. The suggestion that the Atlantic Ocean was due to the drifting to the west of North and South America had been mooted over half a century earlier, but it was no more than a hazy idea.

It is certain that ages ago Greenland, now in the grip of ice thousands of feet thick in places and variously estimated at from 512,000 to 825,000 square miles in area,

ICE CAP THAT COVERED 4,000,000 SQUARE MILES

A glacier is Nature's chisel. This magnificent specimen is on Mt. Robson, the highest mountain in Canada, which reaches 12,972 feet. The northern part of North America was formerly covered by an ice cap extending some 4,000,000 square miles. Today Greenland has an ice cap of approximately the same size. Recent observations showed that, out of one hundred Swiss glaciers, seventy-one were retreating and twenty-two were advancing.

WHY THE EARTH IS UNSTABLE

Glaciers have scraped, torrents have gouged, the chemical elements of the air have corroded, wind and sand have blasted, and avalanches have crushed. Other causes are also illustrated in this diagram. While the coast of Scandinavia is rising, that of Greenland is sinking.

was the home of luxuriant vegetation. Ferns that lived there are now to be found in Central and South America, Africa and the Malay Archipelago. Coal is worked in Spitsbergen and has been discovered in the Antarctic, which is evidence that trees once flourished in both territories. It is even possible that Britain was near the equator, and South Africa and India in the South Polar circle.

The theory of continental drift has it that the earth's substance is made up of three main strata or layers. That on which we live is believed by some scientists to be about thirty miles thick. Beneath it is a viscous fluid called magma, somewhat of the nature of pitch, 1,800 miles deep. On this float the massive continental rafts. Immediately below, dense and compact, is the earth's iron heart.

To simplify matters and make reference as easy as possible, the succession of rocks is divided into periods. We will follow the arrangement and details given on the ingenious illuminated column exhibited in the Geological Museum, London. The figures in brackets represent the approximate number of millions of years covered by each period.

The oldest and lowest of all are the Pre-Cambrian (1,000). Immediately above are the Cambrian (90), followed by the Ordovician (60), the Silurian (25), the Devonian (40), the Carboniferous (75), the Permian (40), the Triassic (25), the Jurassic (25), the Cretaceous (60), the Eocene and Oligocene (35), the Miocene and Pliocene (24), and the Pleistocene (1). This last is the period during which modern man made his appearance, and in which we live.

Now let us look into the meaning of the names. Each classification reveals a whole chapter of valuable information. "Pre-" stands for "before," and Pre-Cambrian

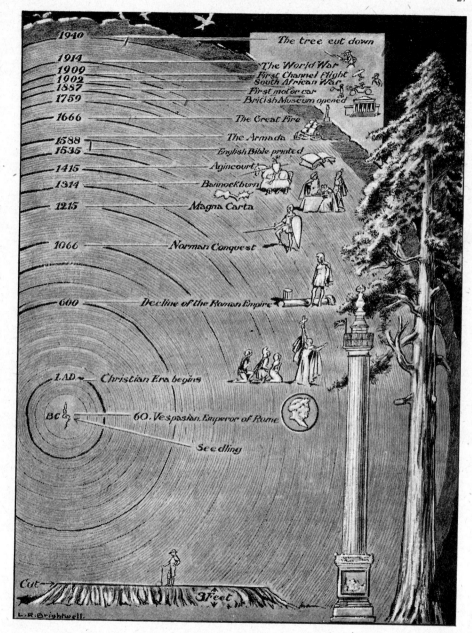

1940   The tree cut down

1914
1909   The World War
1902   First Channel Flight
1887   South African War
1759   First motor car
    British Museum opened

1666   The Great Fire

1588   The Armada
1535   English Bible printed

1415   Agincourt
1314   Bannockburn

1215   Magna Carta

1066   Norman Conquest

600   Decline of the Roman Empire

1 A.D.   Christian Era begins

BC   60. Vespasian Emperor of Rome

    Seedling

Cut   3 feet

L. R. Brightwell

THE AMAZING LIFETIME OF A TREE

This Californian pine was planted in 60 B.C. when Vespasian was Emperor of Rome. Outstanding events which happened before it was cut down in 1940, and their relation to its stages of growth, are indicated. At the right its height is compared with that of the London Monument. The tree was 340 feet high, and its diameter 3 feet from the ground shown (bottom left) compared with the proportions of an average man, was 35 feet.

therefore explains itself. The Cambrian is so called because the rocks of the period are highly developed in Wales, as are those of the Devonian system in Devon. Ordovician is named from the Ordovices, a British tribe that inhabited north Wales, and Silurian from an ancient British people who inhabited south Wales.

Carboniferous means coal-bearing. Permian rocks occur typically at Perm, in Russia. The rocks of the Triassic, from "triad," a set or group of three, are divided into three series, the Keuper, Muschelkalk and Bunter; hence the name. Jurassic takes its designation from the Jura Mountains, between France and Switzerland. Cretaceous is from the Latin word for chalky.

How Rocks are Classified

Eocene, from the Greek for "dawn," was chosen by Sir Charles Lyell because it marked the dawn of the present order of animals. The prefix "Oligo" stands for "few" and indicates that remains of modern animals are scarce in the Oligocene rocks. Miocene means middle recent, Pliocene more recent, Pleistocene most recent.

About the Pre-Cambrian rocks we know little. In the Cambrian period life may have made its first feeble struggle. The Devonian, Carboniferous, Jurassic, Eocene and Oligocene periods are notable for rocks produced by the action of volcanoes or great heat. Mountain building characterized the Devonian, Permian, Eocene and Oligocene periods. During the last two, the Himalayas, Andes, Alps and other mountain systems raised their heads.

On the time scale of the years Mount Everest, Chimborazo and Mont Blanc are almost in the first blush of youth. The hills of Charnwood Forest, low-lying enough now but once of no mean elevation, boast a longer and older pedigree, for they go back to the Jurassic. In the Permian and the Cretaceous the land and the sea respectively reached their maximum extension.

Order or Jumble?

It must not be thought that every inch of the earth has its succession of rocks, or that they are necessarily in chronological order. On the contrary, no country has a complete collection; the records have been found in a great variety of places.

Order may be heaven's first law, as Pope avowed, but there is certainly a good deal of confusion in the rocks. They have been tilted and twisted, bent and broken, pushed up and forced down by titanic forces. The land has changed shape, been added to and diminished, and plunged beneath the waters of a devouring sea. What is now Great Britain was once firmly joined to the continent of Europe, which extended beyond Ireland and Iceland. The Thames was a tributary of the Rhine.

The British Isles have been submerged entirely, drowned in parts, become almost all desert and nearly covered by ice. Some of the hills of the Pennine Range, which stretches from the Tyne to Derbyshire, were once sands of the seashore. On some the marks of ripples are clearly evident.

The drowned forests of Great Britain are numerous. Remains of trees are buried in the estuary of the Thames and in the Humber, beneath which there is believed to be an untapped coalfield of 25,000 million tons. At low tide old stumps may be seen off the coast of Lincolnshire and on the beach at Milandreath, in Cornwall.

Forests Beneath the Sea

The familiar trees of today, oak, beech, elm, elder, hazel and willow, flourished in the now drowned forests. Lumps of peat, tusks of mammoths, and the bones of the woolly rhinoceros, bear, bison and other animals have been brought from the depths in the trawls of fishermen seeking their finny harvest in the North Sea, where ages ago there was dry land.

London, that proud capital, is sinking again, slowly but surely. It has dropped eight feet since Henry VII came to the throne. The loss has been made up artificially, for man is ever digging and dumping. When excavators delve for the foundations of modern buildings on the Thames Embankment it is by no means rare for them to come across the remains of wharves far below the present river level.

Strange enough, you may think, yet geology reveals something stranger. Lower still, unaffected by the rumble and tremor of traffic and the strivings of a teeming populace, is part of a range which begins in southern Ireland and ends at the Harz Mountains in Germany, where the dome-shaped Brocken reaches a height of 3,733 feet. From it miners win treasures of gold, silver, lead, copper, iron and sulphur.

Other places have risen. Sweden, for example, is still adding to its stature today.

There is little doubt that a land-bridge once existed where now is Bering Strait. Across it trudged the Asiatic adventurers

WHEN EUROPE JOINED AMERICA

The bridge once connecting Asia with America. Left to right: wild sheep, mastodon, mammoth, bear, musk ox, reindeer, wild horse, wolf, fox, wolverine, bison and primitive nomadic man.

who became the original settlers of America, as before them many an animal now extinct had passed. Gibraltar is the tiny but important relic of the neck that joined Europe to Africa.

Plato, one of the greatest of Greek philosophers, writing some four centuries before the birth of Christ, states that certain Egyptian priests told Solon, the famous law-giver, that 9,000 years before his time a land existed beyond the Pillars of Hercules, now known as Apes' Hill, on the African coast near Ceuta, and at Gibraltar. The territory was larger than the whole of North Africa, and Asia Minor, and its armies conquered all the lands of the Mediterranean save Athens. Then a terrible catastrophe happened. Atlantis was engulfed, disappearing "in a day and a night."

Fact or fiction, tradition of a lost continent has persisted, and a number of eminent geologists believe that there was such a land-mass. The bed of the Atlantic has undergone many changes at various epochs, and is still unstable.

Atlantis may have included Madeira and the Azores before they became islands. Between the latter and Portugal soundings have located sand and gravel, indicating a sunken shore line.

Was Atlantis in the North Sea? Professor Arvid Holgbom, of Upsala University, locates the lost territory as the Dogger Bank when it was high and dry. According to him the people who inhabited the place had a Bronze Age culture, and through them the Celts of Britain had marked influence on the culture of the Swedes. News of the disaster was spread far and wide by merchants from the Mediterranean.

An even more daring notion is that Cro-Magnon man, about whom we shall read later, emigrated from Atlantis, of which the Antilles, Azores, Canaries and Caribbees

WORK OF WEATHER AND WATER

Building up and pulling down, construction and destruction, such is the universal law governing Nature's handiwork. Two lonely fragments of a sea-eroded cliff washed by Georgian Bay, Ontario. On the left other pieces of rock are seen in process of breaking down.

are the remaining peaks, when their land began to break up. This was some 25,000 years ago. The sorely stricken refugees sought shelter and safety in the region of the Bay of Biscay. Perhaps they exploited the mines of Andalusia and built the lake village which is said to have existed before Seville was built.

The extinction of the civilization of Crete has been suggested as the origin of the legend, though Crete does not happen to be near the Straits of Gibraltar. Great Britain has been dubbed the lost Atlantis by an Italian investigator; Georgia, in the Russian Caucasus, has also been mentioned in this connexion. Arabian geographers considered the Welsh Avalon, the Irish St. Brendan's Island, the Greek Isles of the Blest and the Portuguese Antilha (the Antilles) as possibilities. Indeed, there is almost no end to the list of identifications, which include countries as wide apart as America and Palestine, Scandinavia and Libya.

One more suggestion, and that not the least valuable. It is stated that every year a great many birds fly to a part of the Atlantic where no land is visible and perish as a consequence, just as the little lemmings of Norway attempt to swim to an unknown destination and are drowned. Are they the unwilling and unfortunate victims of an ages-long instinct implanted in them by a long succession of generations? Do they attempt to find the homes and haunts of ancestors who made their homes in vanished Atlantis?

The Sahara, which now extends over nearly 3,500,000 square miles, was once a fertile region, with well-watered areas inhabited by a race which hunted and tilled the soil. Professor James H. Breasted was of the opinion that the original occupants of the Nile Valley were migrants from the great plateau, where a decreasing rainfall robbed them of their means of living.

The Arabs have a tradition that the northern part of the desert was well wooded and had a sufficient supply of water when their forebears entered it, and that it did not dry up until the thirteenth century of the present era.

Our primitive ancestors doubtless regarded the earth as flat, as did the early star-gazers of Babylonia and China. Thales of Miletus, who died about 546 B.C., held a similar opinion, as did his contemporary Anaximander, though some authorities are a little doubtful and think that he believed in a spherical earth. Plato (about 427–347 B.C.) conceived the earth as a stationary globe in the centre of the universe and the seat of the World Soul.

The curvature of the earth has been shown in many ways, including the familiar and much-quoted gradual disappearance of a ship below the horizon, first the hull, followed by the upper works, and then the tops of the masts. The shadow of the earth on the moon, when the earth comes between the sun and the moon during an eclipse, is another proof, which Aristotle (384–322 B.C.) duly noted.

In 1930 Captain A. W. Stevens, of the United States Army, furnished additional evidence. During a flight in an aeroplane he took a number of photographs that definitely pictured the roundness. Although the Andes were invisible to him, his camera picked them out at a distance of over 300 miles and showed the bent horizon of the Pampas. This is believed to be the first record of its kind.

Geology is of immense practical value to industry. Large sums of money have been lost through lack of knowledge of it. Basing its faith on the advice of a tin miner who asserted that a raised beach of dead shells indicated the presence of oil, a syndicate set about boring and promptly lost nearly £20,000.

We shall see in due course how man has built up several types of civilization on the basis of the materials he has discovered and drawn from the earth. He has brought almost every kind of rock into service. Metals have made rich contributions to his material comfort—and to his discomfort, be it added. Truth compels the admission that many of the good things of life have evil implications and can be put to fell use.

SEEKING THE WHITE MAN'S GOLD IN AFRICA

Natives of Uganda using a drill when prospecting for gold. Man has brought almost every kind of rock into his service. Several types of civilization have been built up on the basis of the materials he has discovered and drawn from the inmost recesses of the earth.

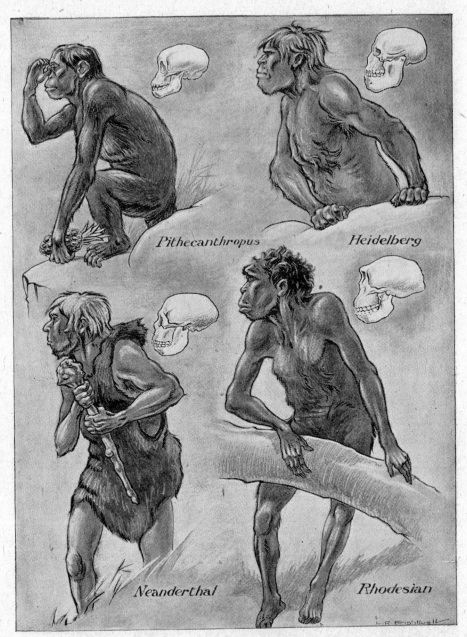

Pithecanthropus

Heidelberg

Neanderthal

Rhodesian

L. R. Brightwell

NATURE'S EARLY EXPERIMENTS IN THE MAKING OF MAN

A reconstruction of four near-men and their skulls, fragments only of which have been found. The oldest semi-human relics are those of Pithecanthropus, the Ape-man of Java, which were unearthed in 1891–92. Torrid heat, frigid cold, fearsome beasts, famine and disease doubtless aided and abetted the extinction of near-man. His brain was unequal to the strain of conditions that had become too exacting, and he made way for our direct ancestors.

EARLY INHABITANTS OF A SWISS LAKE VILLAGE

The first houses, as distinct from affairs of leaves and branches, were constructed of wattle and daub and were built on wooden piles driven into the banks or beds of lakes or rivers.

CHAPTER 3

THE COMING OF MAN

What is life? Simple plants and animals. How living things developed. Giant reptiles of the past. Forerunners of modern man. How primitive man lived. Relics of our ancestors. Beginnings of art. Where did man originate? Stone Age flint factories. Domesticated plants and animals. Forecasts of civilization. Lake-dwellers and their life. Is war natural to man? Cannibalism, ancient and modern. Primitive customs of today.

WITH a sense of humour not always noticeable in scientists, the first Lord Rayleigh said on one occasion that as it seems to be agreed that no one can say what life is, it is rather premature to discuss how it began. Which is closely paralleled by a remark made by Sir Frederick Gowland Hopkins at a meeting of the British Association for the Advancement of Science: "All that we yet know about it (life) is that we know nothing." Such a pronouncement is a sensible way of shelving a bothersome subject. Unfortunately it does not dispose of it.

A number of scientists have come to the conclusion that life is a property which all matter may possess, given the right conditions for its development. Sir E. Ray Lankester held that living matter evolved, by intermediate steps, from inanimate matter, which would seem to be much

the same notion though expressed differently. Aristotle taught that it was self-starting, but Pasteur proved that it could not originate from nothing. The medieval notion that a dead horse breeds wasps was not mere foolishness but only short-sightedness. Students in the Middle Ages saw the insects crawling about carrion and inferred that the wasps had suddenly sprung into existence. They did not observe the eggs of the insects laid in the dead body. The French chemist excluded all living matter from a container and nothing living appeared.

Sir Oliver Lodge postulated "an ether of space that has a substance far more continuous than that of matter. It pulsates with life, but we cannot perceive it. Life is revealed to us when it enters organs that for one reason or another are sufficiently receptive. The material body in which life is

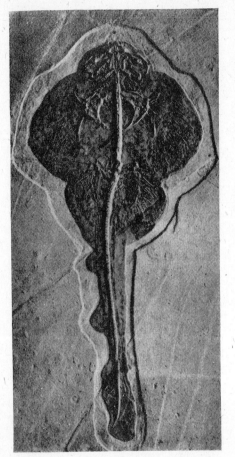

FOSSIL OF AN ANGEL FISH

This creature, while resembling the sharks in the position of the gill clefts, had a depressed body like that of the existing rays.

displayed to us may take many forms. Life is so eager to proclaim itself that it may just as easily assert itself in a flower struggling on a refuse heap as in the person of genius." To this Sir Oliver's opponents respond that ether does not exist.

All living things grow and multiply. So do some things not generally conceived as being endowed with life. Crystals grow and multiply, yet life is not associated with them. We must proceed a little warily here, however. Viruses, the active cause of many diseases, increase indefinitely, but only in living tissue. Whether they belong to the animal, the plant or the mineral kingdom has been the subject of interminable wrangles.

When seen under a microscope the virus which destroys the leaves of tobacco plants resembles a collection of crystals. It therefore has the characteristics of both living and dead matter. For all we know a re-arrangement of the atoms which compose it might endow the material with life. Dr. Charles Devonport has suggested the possibility of a change arising in one of the viruses, such as that of influenza, that might work the destruction of mankind.

Chemicals in the Body

That the human body contains quite a collection of minerals, including iron, sulphur, carbon, phosphorus, magnesium and lime, has been known for many years. Silver, manganese, tin and copper have recently been added to the list. Most of these substances are present only in minute quantities, but if any of them are absent or deficient the body suffers. For example, if hæmoglobin, which is the red colouring matter of blood, lacks sufficient copper, an anæmic condition asserts itself. There is thus a definite connexion between the so-called dead and the living.

Knowing this, gifted men in the laboratory, armed with test tube and retort, have striven to create the type of vital energy which we call life. They have succeeded in manufacturing some of the substances found in living organisms. That is all. Life itself has not been added to the list of artificially made products obtainable at the nearest drug store. It has even eluded identification. Nobody can point to any "thing" or "process" and say: "This is life."

Simplest Forms of Life

The cell is the unit of living matter, as one is the unit of mathematics. The cortex or covering of the human brain alone contains 10,000 million cells. The first living creature was probably no more than a tiny one-celled jelly-like organism, a minute mass of protoplasm, or "first substance," which flourished in primeval mud. Primitive organisms, so indeterminate that they are called plant-animals because they cannot be distinguished as either plant or animal, abound today.

They are closely related to the simplest plants and the simplest animals. Some of them possess chlorophyll, which is the green pigment of plants that enables them to break up carbon dioxide and build up such carbon compounds as sugar and starch. Sugar has been artificially produced from

DICTATOR OF THE AGE OF REPTILES

The thunder lizard, or brontosaurus, one of the dinosaurs. This heavy-limbed reptile with a tiny head and bulky tail was a vegetarian. Remains that have been discovered suggest that when fully grown it weighed over thirty tons and had a length of some sixty-six feet.

FORMER DENIZEN OF A CANADIAN RIVER

The head and body of palæoscincus were protected by hard bosses of bone and spines of horn. Remains of this reptile, which resembled a vaster version of the turtle of more recent times, have been found on the banks of the Red Deer River, Alberta.

water and carbon dioxide when exposed to light. Perhaps in some such way the oceans of the world were provided with food ready for life at its coming. The lowest creatures that are definitely animals are known as Protozoa. There are some 8,500 species, or kinds, including the amoeba, which assimilates food by absorbing it and which multiplies by the most elementary process of all, namely, by splitting in two.

Man's Humble Ancestry

From such ancestors as these, denizens of the slums of the seas, branching off in divers directions and assuming many forms, have come all plants and animals, including man, though he did not arrive for millions of centuries, when the scene had greatly changed. "Blue blood" does not seem so very blue in the light of such proletarian beginnings, but perhaps the miracle of man is all the greater by reason of his humble start. It was a long and wearisome climb to the top of the tree. St. Francis, the rich poor man of Assisi, spoke better than he knew when he called all creatures his brothers. All are near or distant relations. "The chemical and other physiological processes of living organisms, no less than their anatomical structures or geological history, point to a relationship of various species which is intelligible only upon the inference that such species have sprung from a common ancestry." Thus Dr. Michael F. Guyer, while Professor William Patten adds that: "The universal reign of law and order, which it has been the special privilege of science to reveal, is nothing more or less than the revelation that Nature is a unified co-operative system, and that better results are only achieved through better mutual service."

Evolution and Progress

We must not necessarily associate evolution, or development by means of a gradual process, with progress as it is usually understood. In the Victorian period, when Charles Darwin and others amplified a theory put forward by Darwin's eccentric old grandfather, Dr. Erasmus Darwin, in 1794, and by Jean de Lamarck in 1809, the year of Charles Darwin's birth, many people held that evolution was entirely in the direction of "one far-off divine event."

Evolution may work both ways, upward and downward, ascent or descent. A species may develop, remain stationary, or disappear. Faculties come as the result of needs; if they do not stand the strain imposed by existing conditions, they disappear. Some animals have overcome an unfavourable environment; others have thrown up the struggle and gone under.

The sedentary barnacle, that remains anchored all its life, comes of a family that swims. It has degenerated, as has the sea squirt, which begins existence in a way that suggests the joy of life but speedily loses its initial activity and ends by settling down minus some of its organs.

The horse is the posterity of the four-toed eohippus that stood no more than a foot high; it has progressed. The king-crab has remained as it was for millions of years. The gigantic dinosaurs have become extinct.

Much of the evidence regarding the development of life is necessarily missing. Many animals came and went, leaving not a trace behind. Their bodies were soft and decayed rapidly. In some cases, however, the remains were hard enough to make an impression on the earth; in others chemical action preserved the animal or plant as a fossil. There are many missing chapters in the story of life's evolution.

The Sea, Life's First Home

For millions of years the sea was the only home of life. Its first inhabitants were mere swimming specks of animation. Such were the animalcula. Later, more complex forms, like the sponges and the corals, gave up a free and active existence and anchored themselves. They settled down to the humdrum. Sea lilies or stalked starfishes made a veritable animal forest of the ocean bed.

The pioneers of a blood system and a more complex internal machinery were the round worms, humble forerunners of all the bulky, individual forms of animal life we know today. Blood makes it possible for oxygen to be conveyed to a creature's innermost recesses, and so enables it to increase in size, within mechanical limitations imposed by environment, in three dimensions.

When, after long preparation, the land was "to let," vegetation doubtless staked the first claim. Algæ invaded the low-lying flats, and became the forerunners of mosses and horsetails. The first animal adventurers, pioneers with amazing potentialities, were probably worms and crustaceous creatures that looked rather like scorpions. They did not take up permanent residence, but came and went, for the transition from sea to land was a daring experiment that wanted getting used to, as a diver has to become

FORMIDABLE CONTEMPORARY OF EARLY MAN

The woolly rhinoceros flourished with early man and the mammoth. Bodies of this bulky animal have been discovered in excellent preservation in Siberia. It was a favourite subject of the cave-man artist, whose "canvas" was the rocky wall of a cave or a piece of bone.

accustomed to his rubber suit and unusual means of getting air.

Perhaps the lancelet, a little leaf-shaped creature from one to three inches in length, with slightly iridescent sides and nearly transparent, is a prototype of the first back-boned animal, though the skeleton is mere gristle, without vertebræ, ribs or jaws. Some of the early fishes were heavily armoured with large bony plates on the head and body; others had fearsome teeth.

The sharks arrived. One of their predecessors was the dinichthys, or giant fish, which had a six-foot head and a total length of twenty or thirty feet. On the land insects made their appearance and gave the world its earliest essay in music.

How Lungs Developed

In the mud fishes the swim-bladder, which is a sac filled with gas that makes floating easy, is modified and becomes a rudimentary lung. This was later amplified by the amphibians—the newts and their allies—which can live both on land and in water. Whilst some fishes can make tolerable progress out of water by means of their paired fins, it remained for the amphibians to develop fin rays into fingers and toes. Even so they were by their construction largely bound to a moist environment, as provided by the vast water-logged forests which later formed the coal measures now vital to almost every human activity.

The Age of Reptiles

The reptiles came like a conquering army. They were so numerous and devastating that the period of from 100 million to 200 million years during which they were the dictators of the world is called the Age of Reptiles. Because they have had a "good Press," mainly on account of the huge size of the fossil remains that have been discovered, it is the dinosaurs—the name means terrible lizard—that are chiefly associated with this great space of time. Actually they developed late, and were preceded in the seemingly endless procession by the lizards, tortoises and turtles.

The dwarf dinosaur flourished with the giants. Several thousand species have been enumerated, and they ring every conceivable change upon the accepted reptile plan. Some were of elephantine build, others caricatured the existing ostrich-like birds

The giant herbivores developed heavy and extravagant armature to counter the attacks of giant predacious species. But one and all were characterized by grotesquely small and feebly developed brains.

Side by side with the dinosaurs there lived many of the more recognizable reptile forms, the true lizards, snakes and tortoises, which, perhaps, by demanding less food, have contrived to live on to the present time.

There must have been many contributing causes for the dramatic disappearance of the dinosaurs, with their often gigantic frames but very limited intelligence. It has been suggested that a cutting off of the sun's ultra-violet rays by volcanic dust, resulting in a cooling of the earth, may have been

in America with a wing span of twenty-five feet. The archæopteryx, which appeared towards the close of the Cretaceous epoch, was Nature's pioneer attempt towards a feathered fowl. The first mammals made their appearance about the same time. They combined accepted mammalian with reptilian features, and possibly produced their young from eggs. Mammals that lay eggs are still found in Australia. The echidna, or spiny ant-eater, is one of them, and the platypus, which has fur, a bill like a duck and webbed feet, is another.

Whales are not fishes but mammals that bear relics of their terrestrial origin in shrunken hind limbs, while the fore limbs have been converted into paddles, or flippers.

PROTECTED BY BONY PLATES AND SPINES

As its protection stegosaurus, which was a dinosaur, had two rows of bony plates on its back and eight spines towards the end of its tail. Like many other giant lizards of the past, it lived on the luscious vegetation that flourished in the Mesozoic geological age.

in part responsible for their extinction.

It may be that the fearsome dragon which St. George slew, and about which so many stories are told, was a monster of some sort, though the dinosaurs vanished utterly millions of centuries before the dawn of man. Lord Wyfold maintained that the famous white horse carved in the hillside at Uffington, on the Berkshire Downs, is a dinosaur, though it seems more likely to have association with the badge of Hengist, a name which means horse; that animal was displayed on the Saxon's standard.

The Age of Reptiles saw the first vertebrate essays towards a conquest of the air. Remains of pterodactyls have been found

The biggest mammal lives in the sea. It is the sulphur-bottom whale, which sometimes attains a length of eighty-seven feet or over. If it were hollow it would accommodate a full-grown African elephant standing up. Even then the cargo would not touch the "ceiling" of the cabin. The largest extinct mammal is the baluchitherium, which was an exaggerated rhinoceros. It owes its strange name to the fact that the first fossil remains were found in Baluchistan. A full-grown specimen stood fifteen feet at the shoulder, and must daily have consumed food enough for several elephants.

Changes in the climate that led to starvation, the warfare of the strong against the

GIANT OF THE FLESH-EATING DINOSAURS

Tyrannosaurus in search of prey, represented by two dinosaurs known as triceratops. The bony frill protecting the neck, and a single horn on the nose and two horns over the eyes made triceratops, although itself a vegetarian, a formidable opponent.

weak—in which bulk was often at grave disadvantage—and other factors helped to wipe out many species. They came and went, some to bestride the earth and others to eke out a furtive existence on sufferance.

Many got trapped in swamps and asphalt lakes, as happened at La Brea, in California, and near Baku, in Russia. Anxious to slake their thirst, the beasts unknowingly plunged into the morass. Millions of years later the bones of elephants, ground sloths, sabre-toothed tigers, wolves, jackals, hyenas, bears, bison, deer, horses and vultures were discovered and now enrich our museums.

Our long-extinct relation near-man was apparently not in the direct line of descent of modern man. There would have been a bend sinister on his escutcheon, had he possessed one. He came, it is generally conceded, from ape stock, but how he diverged, when and why he descended from the trees—if, indeed, he ever lived in them— are open questions. The name given by scientists to the earliest near-man who left a trace behind is *Pithecanthropus*, which is as unattractive as its more easily remembered form, the Ape-man of Java.

"It seems certain that man has indeed arisen from an ancestral great ape," said Professor D. M. S. Watson in the course of a

REPTILE OVER THIRTY-FOUR FEET IN LENGTH

The flesh-eating allosaurus finishing the remains of a meal of brontosaurus. When on the prowl this dinosaur, like many other species of the giant extinct reptiles, walked on its hind feet. The fore limbs were only used for fighting or tearing purposes. A skeleton brought to light in Wyoming, U.S.A., measured over thirty-four feet in length.

Romanes lecture at Oxford. "The human stock, like that of many other mammals, gave rise to short-lived side branches, whose members exhibited an unbalanced evolution, some of their organs developing more rapidly than in the main stem, whilst others paralleled the giant apes in their evolution and produced structures which have never existed in our own ancestors. The brain of man is constructed on exactly the same plan as that of a gorilla. No structure visible to the naked eye or discoverable by the most refined microscopical technique in the one is absent in the other. In the brain, as in the animal's whole structure, the differences are of size and proportion and not of kind." Some years ago Professor G. H. F. Nuttall discovered a means by which the blood relationships of animals could be established. He found that human and ape blood gave almost the same reaction.

To this usual belief there is an eminent dissentient in Dr. H. F. Osborn, formerly Curator of the American Museum of Natural History, New York. "Man," in his judgment, "came along a path of his own, and never passed through the ape stage. The human stock was separated from other animals when the first great plateaux appeared."

Links With Our Past

One or two links of many that survive to show our very obvious cousinship with the lower animals may be mentioned. A child in the womb, no more than one-third of an inch long, has a tail one-sixth the length of its body. In due course the tail shrinks and disappears internally, but the tail-wagging muscles remain, purposeless but persistent. This means not that man ever had a tail, but that his ancestors had. It vanished when they stood upright; an erect pose rendered such an attachment unnecessary.

The lanugo, or pre-birth hair, which occurs principally on the back, is probably a survival of the stiffer hair on the same part of the body of dogs, monkeys and other animals. Hair may literally stand on end in human beings under peculiar emotional stress, just as the hair on a dog's back bristles up when it scents danger.

Survivals of the reptilian jaw in man are the hammer, anvil and stirrup bones of the middle ear. The human jaw, according to Professor D. M. S. Watson, originated in the acanthodian, a shark-like creature of the Silurian period, long extinct. The gill furrows of the fish are in evidence in the human embryo five weeks after fertilization. In the higher animals that live on land the proportion of salt in the blood is nearly the same as in creatures which live in water.

Horses and many other animals can wriggle their ears when insects annoy them. Some human beings can do the same, though less violently because the muscles have not been so highly developed.

Ears that Betray Evolution

Another vestige of the past is the projecting point more noticeable in some ears than others. This is a relic of a time when they more closely resembled the pointed ears of lower types. Many of the lower animals have a third eyelid. There is a fold of skin in the inner corner of human eyes which still remains as a trace of this.

As Professor D. L. Mackinnon notes, the doctrine of evolution holds out a great and inspiring hope for the human race: "For if it be true that the apes are our relations, still they are very poor relations, whom mentally we have incredibly transcended in what, geologically speaking, is a very short space of time. And we are only at the beginning. There are millions of years before us wherein our race may still have time and opportunity to work out its great destiny. May it not be that man, as we see him now, is but a shadow of the god-like image into which he may yet be fashioned?"

Time was of no consequence in the faraway days of near-man. It came and went, a perpetual mystery, and none took notice of its passing. Night succeeded day, season followed season without his recording it. Experts have sought to fix a date for the appearance of near-man, and have merely agreed to disagree. Perhaps a million years ago would not be far wrong. The figure is open to contradiction, but not by fact, at least on the basis of present knowledge.

How Old is Mankind?

"The date at which human and anthropoid (ape) lines of descent began to diverge," says Sir Arthur Keith, "lies near the middle of the Miocene period. On our modest scale of reckoning, that gives man the respectable antiquity of about one million years."

He had everything to learn. No rich fruits of experience were to be had for the picking. He was ruled by his stomach. Hunger made him a hunter, and if he succeeded in finding a meal his only ambition was satisfied. He had a single need and no wants. The wants came later, and in due course developed into necessities. The result is an exceedingly complex civilization in which simplicity plays but a minor part and shows a general tendency to disappear.

Early Men and their Food

We have no means of knowing what the earliest man-like being ate. Urged on by curiosity he doubtless made preliminary experiments with the fruits, nuts, leaves and roots that a bountiful Nature provided in the dense forests in which he existed. Many of the monkeys, lemurs, and so on, are mixed feeders, and the man-like apes, though normally fruit eaters, acquire a taste for meat dishes under man's influence.

He was the hunted as well as the hunter. Sabre-toothed tigers, mammoths, bears, hippopotami, bisons and rhinoceroses were not easy beasts to tackle. Foes in a very literal sense, the animals were also friends in a way that near-man was quite unable to appreciate. They helped him in his task of developing his brain.

It was a case of the survival of the fittest. A lump of stone dropped at the right moment by the climber perched on a rock, or the bough of a tree, might kill an unsuspecting and moderate-sized wolf. Bigger beasts could not be tackled in that way. Various earthworks scattered up and down Great Britain are perhaps crude attempts at pitfalls. The weapons of the almost-humans would not have much effect on the tough skin, but once caught, the animal would gradually starve, become weaker and weaker, and more readily surrender to an attack of boulders. It must have been more than a one-man job, and suggests the start of co-operation, if not of corporate life. Whistles and carved staves, the former for signalling to fellow-hunters and the latter as insignia of rank, hint at this.

The Beginnings of Tools

So far as we can ascertain the first tool devised by near-man, apart from a lump of wood used as a club, was the fist-hatchet or hammer stone, which he gripped in the palm of his hand to make his pioneer mechanical experiment 200,000 years or more ago. Specimens have been found in Southern Europe, Africa, India, Japan and North America. It must have been a simple thing that led man to value the usefulness of a pointed weapon. The complex had not yet disturbed the world. Possibly a thorn that

ADAM

According to the Scriptures Adam was the first man. This is Jacob Epstein's representation of him carved in alabaster.

pierced his finger or a sharp pebble that cut his foot gave him the idea.

However this may be, he chipped flints to a point, clumsily enough at first but with increasing skill as he became expert, and fixed them in some way to a handle. There are plenty of these worked flints, but no holder has survived the test of time.

Life experimented with several species and found them wanting. They failed and disappeared, leaving no more than a few

WORLD'S FIRST ENGRAVERS

They operated on bits of mammoth tusks, reindeer antlers and the like. Painters worked in the innermost recesses of caves.

bones, and odds and ends of roughly chipped flints which testify that they tried with fumbling fingers to make something. The inventor's path has never been an easy one. It was not then; it is not now. Edison made many failures before he found a satisfactory filament for his electric light bulb; near-man must have been even more patient when, in his blundering way, he attempted to fashion the world's first implement.

Torrid heat, frigid cold, fearsome beasts and famine doubtless aided and abetted the extinction of near-man. The brain was unequal to the strain of conditions that had become too exacting. Much the same is true of individuals of the present Speed Age, but neurasthenia does not ravage and destroy whole peoples. Even modern war, the most terrible and exhausting of conflicts, fails to do that. The Ape-man of Java, Heidelberg man, Peking man, the Dawn-man of Piltdown, Rhodesian man, Neanderthal man and the rest came and went, as had the ponderous baluchitherium and the long-necked but likewise feeble-witted dinosaur.

The odd bits and pieces that the near-men left behind them have given inquisitive scientists of the far distant twentieth century so much food for thought as to furnish a veritable mental banquet. Some were within more measurable distance of the human branch than others. A fragment found in South Africa and known as the Taungs skull was regarded by its discoverer as the missing link that is supposed by some to connect man with ape. Other authorities disagreed, and held it to be no more than a border-line case of low development.

The Oldest Near-Man

The oldest semi-human relics are those of the Ape-man of Java, discovered by Dr. E. Dubois at Trinil, on the Solo river, in 1891–92. The treasures were not much to look at, but were regarded by anthropologists as more precious than much fine gold. The fossil skull cap, two teeth and the thigh bone aroused immense interest, controversy and perplexity. They were not found together, in a neat little heap, ready for inspection like a soldier's kit, but lying some distance apart, the thigh bone about forty feet away from the other remains.

The shape of the Ape-man's teeth showed that they were primarily for breaking nuts and hard-skinned fruits. The skull cap had the projecting ridge over the eye sockets and the receding forehead characteristic of the apes. These features suggested that the original owner was intermediate between the lowest type of man and the highest ape.

In this connexion it may be of interest to mention that after the execution in 1892 of Frederick Bailey Deeming, who murdered two women and four children, his skull was carefully examined by Professor Sir Colin Mackenzie, who declared that it was "typical of prehistoric man of the most primitive type known to science." It may not be too gross a libel on the Ape-man of Java to suggest that in mentality he was a Deeming of perhaps half a million years ago, though he may not have possessed similar criminal inclinations.

Heidelberg man, so called because his chinless but massive jaw-bone was first encountered at Mauer, near Heidelberg, Germany, stalked about in a very different part of the world from the Java Ape-man. Both his range and his numbers were probably limited. It is scarcely likely that any of these near-men lived to the proverbial ripe old age. Nature was an enemy rather than an ally. They were experiments that failed.

A contributing cause may have been an epidemic such as the scourge of the Middle Ages popularly called the Black Death, actually bubonic plague. This terrible epidemic began in 1347, and before it had run its course had robbed the world of 42 million inhabitants. A child born today may expect a life of sixty years, thirty-nine more than a boy or girl could anticipate in the sixteenth century. Near-man's life must have been more hazardous.

When excavating for gravel at Piltdown, Sussex, workmen came across parts of a fossilized skull. It meant nothing to them other than the pathetic interest associated with human—or in this case near-human—remains. It aroused intense enthusiasm on the part of Mr. Charles Dawson, who secured the relic and afterwards found a canine tooth, half of a lower jaw-bone and a number of flint instruments.

An Early Sussex Man

The skull seemed to have a human affinity, though the projecting canine teeth were of the kind usually associated with apes. The chin was still absent, as in Heidelberg man, but the heavy overhanging ridge above the eye sockets had gone, giving the brow an almost if not entirely human appearance.

It is thought that these three entities flourished between the first and second glacial invasions, when the weather was warm and what we should term congenial. With the coming of a third icy period Neanderthal, or Mousterian, man appeared on the scene. Once again Germany is in evidence, for the first skull of this type was picked up in a cave near the Neander River, though remains have since been discovered in places far distant, including Gibraltar, Malta, Jersey, Croatia and Palestine.

Discovery of Fire

Man sought the shelter of caves, and cloaked himself with the skins of the beasts he had killed. Hitherto his own shaggy hair had provided sufficient protection. How, when and where he made the first fire is unrecorded. Perhaps as he sat patiently tapping stone against flint to fashion a weapon the tiny sparks kindled some nearby tinder, and the secret was revealed. It may be that a volcano, or a forest set ablaze by lightning, gave him the revelation. At a sufficient distance it afforded him kindly warmth, despite its devastating effects when not under control. He may have preserved a few embers and tended them for present and future service. Somehow he learned the virtues of flame, and captured it for his own dire need.

Anatomists tell us that the Neanderthalers, thick set and massive jawed, probably slouched along with unwieldy gait, their heads bent forward like sleuth hounds in popular fiction. They learned how to

A MAMMOTH AS A CAVE MAN SAW IT

An engraving of a mammoth on a piece of ivory that probably formed part of the animal's tusk. It was picked up in the cave of La Madeleine, in France. The self-taught artist succeeded, despite his poor tools, in executing a most life-like representation of the animal.

fashion flints into more practical shapes for killing and skinning animals.

The dead were buried with their stone implements ready for service, together with a supply of food. With the gradual development of intelligence there dawned the hope that life did not end at death, but continued. Although he had many characteristics of the ape, Neanderthal man had a larger brain than the average European of today. What he had in quantity he lacked in quality.

Woman Plays Her Part

Only a little over a century and a half ago the aboriginals of Tasmania were less advanced than the Neanderthalers. The Tasmanians were naked and houseless, kept no domesticated animals, and had no idea of agriculture. Their weapons were wooden spears, but they did not fish; they could kindle a fire but had no knowledge of making utensils other than of fibre. They cut their food with a knife made by chipping one side of a flat stone. The language of the Tasmanians was merely sufficient for them to name ordinary objects of everyday life.

"Woman's work is never done," though it started long before the dawn of written history. At some remote period she first began to ply the needle. Some ingenious individual discovered that a splinter of the ivory of a mammoth's tusk, with a hole drilled in it by a flint and threaded with a tendon, was a very useful instrument for roughly sewing skin clothing. The ordinary steel needle used by our own womenfolk therefore remains true to type.

With their flint instruments the men began to scrape out bones and fashion them into spoons. Thus "manners" first came to table, or rather to a meal. Bows and arrows were evolved, the bow perhaps by noticing how a twig sprang back after having been pushed aside. Man was becoming increasingly observant. He now appreciated both the little and the big. He used his opposable thumb more and more.

Neanderthal Man's Successors

After occupying the stage for a period that probably exceeded ten times the Christian era, the Neanderthalers made way for, or were perhaps exterminated by, Cro-Magnon or Aurignacian man, a much finer type who fashioned better tools, hunted with better weapons in what is known as the Reindeer Age, and gave to the world its first artists, engravers and sculptors.

Stone continued to be used, but other materials were also employed. Bone, ivory, wood and the teeth of animals proved useful. The Cro-Magnons made arrows or darts of wood, harpoons, pins and needles of bone, in which sinew was used as thread, and necklaces of perforated teeth. Thus personal adornment made a beginning. Animals have paid a heavy price for it ever since. Ivory was carved into rings and statuettes.

Remains of this people were first found in a cave at Cro-Magnon, France. At Solutré, in the department of the Côte-d'Or, skeletons have come to light which show the fine physique that the earliest representatives of modern man in Europe could attain. Three skeletons of our direct ancestors unearthed in 1923 belonged to men who stood over six feet in height.

They must have been veritable Sandows, but they cannot be regarded as typical of their race as a whole, because other specimens have shown only moderate build. Yet all emphasize the difference between the bully-like Neanderthaler and the upright Cro-Magnon. The skeletons of Solutré were buried with their faces to the east, thus disproving the oft-repeated statement that Christians were the first to inter their dead in that position.

Britain's First Artists

These early men flourished when Britain and Ireland were part of the continent of Europe, and the North Sea and Irish Sea were dry land. It is therefore somewhat remarkable that none of the artistic efforts of the Cro-Magnons has come to light in England, although it has been suggested that a drawing of a horse's head found in Robin Hood's Cave in Derbyshire is the work of one of their artists.

The first representation of a human figure to be discovered in Britain was picked up in the same happy hunting ground. It is masked and apparently in an attitude of ceremonial dancing. Skulls found at Cheddar are considered as belonging to a tribe allied to the Cro-Magnons.

The engravers operated on bits of mammoth tusks, reindeer antlers and the like; the painters worked in the innermost recesses of caves. The passage leading to them is never a matter of a few yards. The "studio" of the Pyrenean cave of Niaux, in the Ariége, France, is nearly a mile from the entrance, and as cold as was the sub-Arctic weather of the days in which the bison, reindeer, and wild horse were pictured. On some of the bison assagais point at the heart.

THE PIONEER MINER BEGINS HIS LABORIOUS TASK

Early Neolithic man in a flint mine thirty feet within a chalk hill-side. (Bottom, right) chalk lamps burning oil or fat. (Bottom, left) flint knife, axe head and flint tools. With the deer-horn pick the miner is bringing down a mass of chalk and unworked flints.

The cave of Altamira, near Santander, Spain, is a kind of national gallery of pre-historic art, although the word "national" is none too happy because many a millennium was to come and go before the first nation came into existence. It may be that the pictures were associated with the idea of magic, of the wooing by pictured wishes of the real animals that were hunted. The present-day Bushmen of South Africa picture animals in out-of-the-way spots on rocks and in caves.

Sometimes the Altamira paintings are superimposed over an earlier effort, it may be because the latter did not please the artist or had lost its potency as a luck-bringer. Nobody knows. In many cases the technique amounts to genius. There is, for instance, a running boar that gives an impression of speed that would not disgrace the Royal Academy, and a bison in the attitude of lowing that is a truly amazing example of realistic portraiture.

The cavern of Les Combarelles, with its 400 or more designs, "tangled and inter-laced," was explored by the indefatigable Abbé Henri Breuil, who spent twelve years in the investigation. Some of the drawings could not be deciphered, but those which were included 116 horses, asses or kiangs, thirty-seven bison, nineteen bears, fourteen reindeer, thirteen mammoths, nine ibexes, five stags, three does, one Dama deer, five lions, four wolves, one fox and one woolly rhinoceros—a pictorial zoological gardens! Among representations the learned Abbé was uncertain about were figures resembling a fish and a snake. A silhouetted hand, tent-like huts—perhaps for spirits—javelins and sexual symbols were included.

It seems to have been forbidden to depict man in a normal way, for the drawings are crude in the extreme, and ceremonial masks or hunters' disguises are almost invariably worn. It was as though the artists of 20,000 or 30,000 years ago had heard of the commandment: "Thou shalt not make unto thee any graven image, or any likeness of any thing that is in heaven above, or that is in the earth beneath, or that is in the waters under the earth," and compromised.

Paintings similar in character, and perhaps executed at more or less the same time, have been revealed in South Australia, the Sahara Desert and in Colorado, U.S.A. The not unreasonable suggestion has been made that artists migrated to various parts of the world from a common centre.

Primitive Palettes and Colours

The pictures at Altamira are more colourful than those at Les Combarelles. Granite pestles with which the artists ground their colours have been found. These were mixed with bone marrow. For paint tubes the hollow leg bones of deer were used. The chewed end of a stick or a bundle of feathers constituted the brush. Red, yellow, brown and black were employed, obtained from natural oxides. Some of the paintings are in such awkward positions that the artist must have worked lying on his back, as did Michelangelo when adorning the Sistine Chapel in Rome. Crude lamps fashioned of chalk afforded a glimmer of light.

A delightful human touch is associated with the finding of the great art gallery of the cave men at Altamira. In 1878 the Marquis Marcelino de Sautuola was digging in the floor of the cave, searching for buried relics of the past, in the company of his little five-year-old daughter, when the child suddenly shouted: "Toro! Toro!" and pointed to the roof.

Her father looked up and found that the bull was anything but imaginary. He announced the discovery, which was promptly pooh-poohed. The critics laughed at his assertion that the pictures were the work of Stone Age artists. Over a quarter of a century passed before the tables were turned and the authenticity of the paintings was officially recognized.

The Oldest Extant Sculpture

As though not to be outdone, boys discovered the oldest sculpture in the world. A small subterranean stream meanders from a tree-clad hill in Montesquieu-Avantes, France. The rivulet had always been associated with evil. At long last and greatly

daring, in the autumn of 1912 a youthful band of adventurers built a raft, armed themselves with torches and set out to beard whatever spirits haunted the dark passage to the underworld.

They were not a little disconcerted by what they found. Engravings on the living rock, a heap of bones, the marks of animal claws and human heel prints, and clay models of a male and female bison awaited their daring; of bogles and ogres there was not a trace. The evil spirits had fled, but they had left their marks!

Experimental Men

Other experiments in the human line were made in life's laboratory. They include the nomadic Solutreans from the east, whose favourite food seems to have been ponies; mammoth hunters and eaters who flourished in the vicinity of the Danube and dumped the remains of their feasts near Piedmost, Capsians who arrived in Spain from Africa, and the apparently hybrid Azilians of Spain, France, and elsewhere.

At Kanam and Kanjera, Kenya, remains were found by Dr. L. S. B. Leakey which are held to be in direct ancestral relationship to modern man, although of an earlier period than remains uncovered in 1913 at Oldoway, Tanganyika (then German East Africa), by Professor Hans Reck, of Berlin, about which a wordy warfare was indulged in for twenty odd years. Previous to the later finds, Oldoway man had been regarded as the oldest known representative of *homo sapiens*, as our species is called.

Early Man in Africa

While Kanam man did not have a chin so prominent as ourselves, it was certainly well developed, and he is held to be the oldest authenticated representative of modern man. From him Kanjera man, whom Sir Arthur Keith regards as the earliest stage known in the evolution of the negro, was probably descended.

Skulls of Kanjera man showed an advance, as did the type of instrument found with them. Whereas the Kanam culture was very crude and the pebbles used in the making of the implements were only roughly chipped, Kanjera man used a hand axe, sometimes called a *coup-de-poing*, specimens of which have been found in England, France, Spain and parts of Africa.

The question is sometimes asked, and it is not an unnatural one, whether women are occasionally raped by anthropoid apes.

OLDEST INDUSTRY IN THE WORLD

(Top left) A Brandon flint knapper about to "quarter" a nodule of flint. (Top right) A quarter which has been struck off. (Bottom left) Striking a flake from a quarter with a flake hammer. (Bottom right) Working a flint with a knapping hammer. These modern exponents of an ancient craft use metal tools in place of the stone implements of their ancestors.

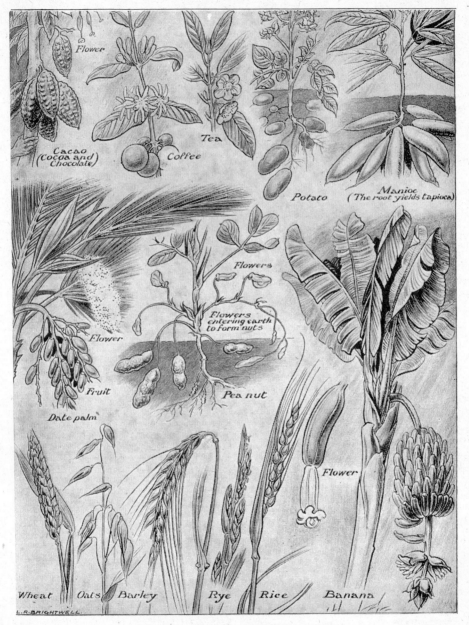

KINDLY FRUITS OF THE EARTH

The most patient and learned investigators have failed to trace the origin of agriculture. We have no means of knowing what the earliest man-like being ate. It is not likely that he was wholly vegetarian: indeed, traces of his meals of animal flesh are frequently found even today on the sites of his camps. Many of his kind must have been killed by poisonous berries or roots before he learnt to discriminate, for, urged on by curiosity, he doubtless made preliminary experiments with the fruits, nuts, leaves and roots that a bountiful Nature provided.

FARMING THROUGH THE AGES

Ploughing and sowing in Babylonia. Hand sowing. Ploughing in medieval England. Threshing in Persia. Crushing grain with sleigh in ancient Egypt. Thirteenth-century labourer. Threshing in France. Oxen treading corn in Bengal. Threshing with oxen. Typical thresher elevator. Ploughing with horses. A petrol-driven "deep tiller." It is believed that the people of the Old Stone Age were hunters and no more. Millet may have been the first grain cultivated. The bread wheats probably developed from two wild varieties, einkorn and emmer.

LINKING THE PAST WITH THE PRESENT

The little bridge that connected a lake dwelling with the bank was the modest predecessor of such mammoth structures as those that span Sydney Harbour in Australia and the Golden Gate in America. This primitive bridge crosses a stream on Dartmoor.

Dr. Leakey, who was born and bred in Kenya, asserts that in the Congo it is not uncommon to hear that a Bantu or Pigmy woman has been seized by a gorilla. He therefore warns us that we must keep in mind "the possibility of a cross between one species and another, although such a cross would not probably be a fertile one."

To this Sir Arthur Keith retorts that he has endeavoured for nearly half a century to get authentic details on the subject, and has not succeeded in securing evidence of any case of rape of a human being by a male gorilla or chimpanzee.

That apes are descended from ancient man is the suggestion put forward by Professor Max Westenhofer. His contention is that apes developed their arms at the expense of their brains, the blood supply going mainly to the limbs at the expense of the development of the mental organs.

Early Man in Ancient China

A number of interesting discoveries have been made in a cave at Chow-kow-tien, near Peiping (Peking), China. They consist of remains of near-man types probably living at about the same time as the creatures of Java and Piltdown. In brain capacity Peking man was perhaps below the Neanderthalers. He fashioned implements of stone, bone and deer's antlers, and knew the use of fire, which was one of the most important discoveries ever made. We have it on the authority of Sir G. Elliot Smith that Peking man could speak, and that his brain case reveals a closer co-operation of hand and eye than was found in previous representatives of the sub-human.

At Taungs, near the Vaal River, Bechuanaland, in a limestone cave chock full of stalagmites, quarrymen blasted a strange-looking skull out of the rock. Professor Raymond A. Dart, of the Witwatersrand University, examined it and declared it to be "a creature well advanced beyond modern anthropoids in just those characters, facial and cerebral, which are to be anticipated in an extinct link between man and his simian ancestor."

Taungs Man or Taungs Ape?

Some members of the scientific fraternity did not agree with this verdict. These included Sir Arthur Keith, who declared the skull to be that of a very young anthropoid ape showing kinship to gorilla and chimpanzee, yet having certain human characteristics that had not been met with previously. Sir G. Elliot Smith added that it revealed signs of much nearer affinity to primitive man than to any other ape, fossil or living. This agrees with the finding of Dr. R. Broom, who placed the Taungs skull in man's family tree at some point just before the human branched off from the apes.

Rhodesian man made a fossilized reappearance at Broken Hill in 1921. As he was found with the bones of animals still living in Africa, experts were somewhat diffident in expressing an opinion as to his age. The skull had large brow-ridges and a receding forehead, somewhat resembling that of Neanderthal man.

"There would be grave difficulties," according to one authority, "in imagining this stooping, slant-jawed, low-browed creature as standing in the direct line of man's ancestry. A more plausible explanation, scientists are now virtually agreed, is that this creature was one of Nature's unsuccessful tries; undoubtedly related to man, but representing a failure that led nowhere. There were ages in the earth's history, it now seems probable, when many of these abortive part-men lived on earth."

The expenditure of much patience and many dollars has not enabled scientists to solve the riddle of the first appearance of man in America. Though several promising trails have been followed up, they have proved to be no more than blind alleys. Professor E. Ameghino, who spent a great part of his life investigating the matter, concluded that man evolved in Argentina, but nothing has come to light to substantiate so bold a claim. Over half a century ago gold miners dug up what came to be known as the Calaveras skull. At first regarded as of considerable antiquity, it proved to be the remains of an American Indian of a less remote date than was originally supposed.

Dr. Ales Hrdlicka, during the course of an extensive journey of investigation, saw American Indian types in Tibet, and concluded that they were of the stock from which the pioneer explorers and settlers had sprung. The Punin skull discovered in 1923 in the Andes of Ecuador would seem to be of early origin. In this particular instance the invasion was probably made by way of Australia rather than via the northern land bridge that once connected Asia with America across the Bering Strait.

M. P. Rivet, the French scholar, summing up the evidence, concludes that the original homes of the founders of American civilization were Asia, Australia, and Malaya-Polynesia. Darwin advanced the theory that Africa is the cradle of the human race. Mongolia, believed to be the original home of many animals now extinct, has its advocates. Eastern Asia, Central Asia, the Sahara, Egypt, Australia, Polynesia, Malaya, and Western Europe have been suggested. The fact that all the present peoples

PRIMITIVE SWING BRIDGES OF ROPE

Deep chasms above swift streams in the Jhelum Valley, India, are crossed by rope bridges or the even simpler method of hauling travellers across on a single cable.

of the world are divided into four groups leads Professor J. B. S. Haldane to believe that humanity made its start in four different places, which seems far more probable than that man originated in a common centre, although much of his culture may none the less have done so.

Mankind's First Industry

Mining was the world's first industry. Upon it our present civilization is based, although many a long day passed before our primitive forefathers stumbled upon a means of using metals and changed the course of history. Their first essay was flint mining. It must have been extremely arduous work digging with a pick that was no more than the antler of a deer, and shovelling with the shoulder-blade of an ox. A grass rope was of service—when it held. The tale of mining disasters is not modern.

The shaft of a mine on a hill known as Blackpatch, near Worthing, Sussex, is twelve feet deep and sixteen feet in diameter. Seven galleries radiate from the base.

Industry, of whatever character, suggests some manner of exchange. Those who worked in the chalk and fashioned flints could not take part in the chase, and vice versa. How the primitives assessed the relative value of their flints and foods for purposes of trade we do not know.

In France one of the largest supplies of flint was at Grand-Pressigny, Indre-et-Loire, and it is evident from the various degrees of completion in which specimens have been discovered together that mass production was in vogue. Mr. Henry Ford and other introducers of this method are thereby absolved from original sin in the matter. A certain number of men performed one process and others another. Flints not required for home consumption were taken to Belgium and Switzerland.

Flint Knappers of Today

Brandon, Suffolk, is the last refuge of the flint knapper in England. Here a few part-time workers continue the oldest industry, but whereas early man used stone tools their successors employ metal. The flint is mined at Lingheath, South Brandon, and brought to the surface as large nodules. The nodule is first "quartered" by resting it on a thick leather knee-pad and splitting with a square section iron head. The flake hammer, a lighter edition of the latter, is then brought into use and a number of flint flakes obtained from the "quarters."

The flake is transferred to a heavy wooden block in which is set an upright steel stake insulated by leather packings. It is held in loose contact with the front edge of the stake and struck lightly with a hammer having a head rather like a chisel. The flake is fractured by the resulting upward blow on the under side due to the rebound of the leather-packed stake. Both ends are thus removed, leaving the centre portion, which after trimming becomes the finished gun flint, ready for service in some remote and out-of-the-way territory.

Until 1835 nearly all the flints for the British army were supplied by the craftsmen of Brandon, who, until the advent of the percussion cap, were some 200 strong. The industry had quite a boom in 1935 when war, never officially declared, broke out between Ethiopia and Italy, for many of the Abyssinians were armed with old-fashioned weapons of the flint-lock type.

Fire-sticks, Flint and Steel

For centuries the only means of obtaining fire, other than by twirling a stick between the hands on a piece of wood until the friction caused it to break into flame, was by the use of flint, reference to which is made by such classical writers as Pliny, Vergil and Claudian. At the beginning of the nineteenth century the method generally in use was the striking together of a flint and steel so that the sparks generated fell on tinder, which caught alight.

The most patient and learned investigator has failed to trace the origin of agriculture. It is believed that the people of the Old Stone Age were hunters and no more. Probably millet was the first grain to be cultivated. That known as *Panicum colonum* was certainly used by the early Egyptians, but whether wild or cultivated is unknown. *Panicum miliaceum* has been discovered in a Swiss lake-dwelling and also in an early settlement in South Russia, though it has never been found growing in a wild state in either of these parts.

Wheat is the earliest type of cereal that has come to light in Mesopotamia (Iraq), though barley was common there 2,000 years before Christ, and it grows wild in North Africa and some parts of Asia. Probably oats were originally cultivated in Northern Europe. The small wheat known as einkorn is to be found today in a wild state in Asia Minor, and emmer, another kind of wheat, was grown in Egypt, the Mediterranean region and Mesopotamia.

PILE DWELLINGS IN THE PHILIPPINES

A village on Mindanao, the second largest island in the Philippines, which was a centre of conflict during the Second World War. Houses of this kind afford protection from the attacks of wild animals and give immediate access to the open highway of river and sea.

It has been suggested that the bread wheats are the offspring of these two wild varieties. In ancient times, Professor J. L. Myres tells us, the alluvial region between the Tigris and Euphrates "raised two, or even three, crops of wheat a year, with a yield of 200 or 300 grains from one seed."

In 1926, when conducting excavations at Jamdet Nasr, some seventeen miles north-east of Kish, Dr. S. Langdon discovered in a jar in a Sumerian house a quantity of charred wheat which dated from about 3500 B.C. It was *Triticum turgidum*, rivet, or cone wheat. The discovery, suggests Dr. Langdon, confirms the theory, long accepted by historical botanists, that Mesopotamia, the well-watered region between the rivers Tigris and Euphrates, is the original home of the bread-making wheats.

The wild ancestor of maize has not been traced. The plant was being cultivated by the American Indians when Columbus reached the New World. The grass which the Aztecs of Mexico termed teosinte, "grain of the gods," has been discovered wild, but never maize. According to Dr. T.

Gann it must have taken many centuries before the latter was evolved from the former. Corn is not native to America.

The story goes that when Hernando de Cortes was in Mexico, rice was sent from Spain for his army. Some of it was given to the monastery of Coriba, and while discharging the sacks the monks came across a few grains of corn. These they placed with some mould in an earthenware pot. The corn bore several ears, and the seed from them was sown in the open, where it continued to flourish, thus proving that the cereal was suited to both soil and climate. In Babylonia the date palm is a native tree; rice was introduced by the Arabs.

Dogs of Our Ancestors

The dog would appear to be the first domesticated animal. The fantastic creature sacred to Set-Typhon, spirit of evil, pictured on Egyptian monuments, is believed by M. P. Hippolyte Boussac to represent it. According to this authority a painting at Beni-Hassan shows the Red Sea dog in full liberty in the desert, its freedom being indicated by the absence of the collar usually shown. The prototype of this ancient species still haunts the coasts of the Red Sea, a link with the polished stone civilization.

The dog's wild ancestors may have been wolves or jackals. There is much disputation on the matter. The Alsatian, Eskimo and Scandinavian elkhound have certain characteristics which closely resemble those of the wolf. A common originator has been suggested in the extinct Cynodictis, fossil bones of which have been found in western North America. Cynodictis, it is thought, crossed to Asia via the Bering bridge, as the dingo of Australia is believed to have come from Asia when the island continent was neither an island nor a continent, but connected with the Far Eastern mainland.

The First Tame Cattle

We are lamentably ignorant about the domestication of cattle, though Turkestan and South Russia have been suggested as the homes of the people who first learned the art. In all these matters, as in the shaping of implements, it is quite likely that independent discoveries were made, in much the same way as Charles Darwin and Alfred Russel Wallace hit upon the idea of evolution in biology without consultation and at the same time.

In what is known as the Late or New Stone Age hand-made pottery and weaving made a beginning. Wooden shelters were erected, doubtless copied from the natural architecture of the forest. Cattle, goats, pigs, sheep and dogs were gradually domesticated. The primitive farmyard, fenced off from the forest by sticks and stones, made its appearance.

The first houses, as distinct from affairs of leaves and branches, were of wattle and daub erected on piles driven into the banks or beds of lakes and rivers, and connected by a little bridge, the modest predecessors of such mammoth structures as those which span Sydney Harbour in Australia and the Golden Gate in America. Many centuries later the architects of Venice and Rotterdam used piles in the building of their cities. Imperial Chemical House, Westminster, rests on piles. The total weight of this immense structure facing Lambeth Palace on the Middlesex bank of the Thames is estimated at not less than 150,000 tons.

Swiss Pile-dwellings

During an exceptional winter in Switzerland in 1853 vast numbers of piles on which a lake village had stood were left high and dry. Among the objects that came to light after ages of darkness were dug-out boats and fishermen's nets, barley, wheat and woven flax, and the remains of furniture and wooden wheels. The tools recovered were of stone and bronze, and as those of the latter were found above the former, the dwellings must have been occupied during the transition stage from stone to metal, though not necessarily by the same generation. Lakes Morat, Neuchâtel and Geneva revealed similar relics during a drought in 1921.

Man had become to some extent a social animal living in communities, though not always peaceably. Lake villages were not unique to Switzerland. They are also known to have existed in England at the Vale of Pickering, Yorkshire; Meare and Glastonbury, Somersetshire; in Scotland, Ireland, Denmark, Sweden, France, Belgium, Italy and Asia Minor, just as they are to be found in New Guinea today. The flesh food of their inhabitants included bison, deer, foxes and wild boar. Possibly the grain and flax were obtained from Egypt, where exactly the same varieties were grown.

Great intervals of time occurred between the happenings narrated in this chapter. Various races, sub-races and varieties of man played a part in them. It is easy to dispose of long periods in a paragraph.

OUSTING FLOOD WATER IN CHINA BY FOOT-POWER

"War," says Sir Arthur Keith, "is Nature's pruning-hook." She has other pruning-hooks in flood, pestilence and famine. Millions of lives have been lost in China owing to the overflowing of rivers. Here workmen are draining a cellar by means of a simple water-wheel.

Unfortunately in much ancient history, time is very unreal because we have no certain means of ascertaining its length in any way approximating to accuracy. The period when the lake-dwellers lived in Europe was perhaps about 10,000 years ago.

Reference to such divisions as the Stone Age, the Bronze Age and so on, does not mean that all men in Europe and elsewhere were Stone Age men or Bronze Age men at one and the same moment. Far from it. Some arrived at the various cultural phases earlier or later than others, and some tribes stopped short in their development and never outlived the most primitive.

There is no uniform civilization now

there was not then, and perhaps there never will be. Egypt was using copper tools 2,000 years before Britain and Northern Europe had abandoned those of stone. In the middle of the eighteenth century one-third of the habitable globe had not advanced beyond the conditions that prevailed in the Stone Age.

War is regarded by some authorities as a biological necessity; they would have it that the urge to fight is ingrained, an essential part of the make-up of all animals, human and otherwise. Sir G. Elliot Smith pleads that "man is by nature peaceful and well behaved." He holds that primitive man was non-aggressive, honest and truthful; a

IMITATING THE WILD BEAST

After killing an enemy the leopard men of the Belgian Congo make cuts on the body with an iron instrument to give the impression that the victim was mauled by a leopard.

creature of almost Arcadian perfection. According to him, since the great humanitarian movement of the eighteenth century, the knowledge collected by hundreds of travellers "establishes as a fact of observation the genial qualities of natural man wherever he is found."

Dr. W. J. Perry is at one with Sir G. Elliot Smith in this matter. He holds that the belief in a former Golden Age of peace and happiness is not a fairy tale but a reality, and that war is a relatively late phenomenon. "The story of warfare," he adds, "is that of the increasingly violent behaviour of ruling groups, doubtless stimulated by a variety of causes once it became organized."

Sir Arthur Keith contests this ruling. "Nature keeps her human orchard healthy by pruning; war is her pruning-hook," he avows. "Our human world has never had peace—not even for a year. What would our world have looked like at the end of five centuries of peace? Much, I suspect, as an orchard that has not known the pruning hook for many an autumn and has rioted in unchecked overgrowth for years."

Professor P. A. Sorokin and Mr. N. N. Golovin declare that in Europe alone over 900 definite wars took place during the period 500 B.C.–A.D. 1925. Dr. E. E. Free emphasizes his belief in three terse sentences that suggest the firing of a machine gun: "In the beginning, man hunted and fought. Each man lived for himself. Every other man was his enemy."

Nature's Pruning-hooks

Perhaps it may be suggested that Nature has other pruning-hooks in flood, pestilence and famine, without resorting to human warfare. The pruning-hook of the two world wars cut down flowers as well as weeds. Bullets do not pick and choose, carefully eliminating the undesirable. Bombs fail to appreciate the doctrine of the survival of the fittest.

"So far is war from being a biological necessity," says Dr. John Baker, "that it is practically biologically unknown except among human beings." Sir William Osler states this side of the case even more emphatically. "Let us remember," he writes, "that war is a human development, unknown to other animals. Though Nature is ruthless 'in tooth and claw,' collective war between members of the same species is not one of her weapons; and in this sense Hobbes's dictum that 'war is a state of Nature' is not true."

Warfare Among Animals

Man is apparently the only case of "dog eating dog" on the grand scale. Many monkeys that go in tribes make war on others of closely similar species, but they do not concentrate in vast hordes for the purpose. Baboons and various macaques fight, the usual cause of the quarrel being territorial rights in the matter of feeding grounds. The common blood-red ant of English woods habitually makes slave raids on the nests of negro ants. Being apparently too lazy to nurse its own young, it takes this drastic way of solving the problem.

So far as is known, man is the only animal that habitually, and as a matter of economics, makes war on its own kind. Economics as we understand them were non-existent in the remote times with which we are dealing. That there were forays and quarrels we cannot but believe; it is difficult to feel that the creatures of Java, Piltdown and Neanderthal were altogether gentlemen. We can do no other than give the Scottish verdict of "Not proven." The Greenlander has no word for war.

That cannibalism was indulged in on occasion is scarcely open to doubt. In a cave near Auch, in the south of France, human bones showing marks of human teeth clearly indicate that fact. Other remains split open or charred suggested a similar story when they were found at Krapina, Yugoslavia.

There must have been occasions when sheer necessity drove primitive man to so desperate a measure, but when an enemy was killed and eaten the idea seems to have been to preclude any possibility of vengeance on the part of the victim. Any virtues he may have possessed were passed on; any evil inclinations were got rid of.

In the court of last resort hunger is not a determined moralist. A few years ago a liner picked up a Japanese fishing smack containing two dead men and a pile of human bones. Doctors who examined the remains came to the conclusion that the last survivors had adopted desperate measures that had failed in their purpose.

Modern Cannibals

A French army officer, exploring a remote part of the Amazon in 1923, came across a tribe known as the Matanzas, or Assassins, which indulged in this practice with the idea of gaining added strength and prowess. In the same year there was an outbreak of cannibalism among certain tribes on the Ivory Coast, West Africa. While journeying through the Dutch East Indies, Sarawak and various islands to the north of Australia, Mrs. Charlotte Cameron came across natives who openly avowed that they were cannibals.

Near Lake Murray, in New Guinea, Capt. Frank Hurley made his way up a narrow path and found arrows stuck in the ground and a skull impaled on a pole. Then he came across a huge wooden building 300 feet long, fifty feet wide and thirty-five feet high. A human thigh bone was stuck on the ridge pole, and skulls grinned from the rafters. It was the communal house of headhunters. Killing for the sake of securing heads is supposed in some remote way to benefit the souls of the slayers' ancestors.

These customs are rapidly declining. An explorer who visited the island of Nias, off the coast of Sumatra, reports that while head-hunting is sometimes indulged in, the victims are often ransomed. The whole performance is gone through, prisoners are captured and their heads are placed on the block. Then release is granted, although the individual is kept in suspense until the last moment. A wooden effigy is placed on a beam to represent what, in earlier times before contact with Europeans, would have been the genuine article.

According to several authorities the suppression of cannibalism in Central Africa led to considerable slaughter of the gorilla as "the next best thing," a development which necessitated drastic legislation on behalf of the largest of the man-like apes.

ARMED FOR WAR

Some authorities think that early man was non-aggressive. Many present-day primitives are not. Warriors of the Guere tribe believe that holding green leaves while engaged in combat prevents them from being wounded.

WITH EYES TO SPY OUT AND SCARE EVIL SPIRITS

Chinese junks have eyes painted on the bows to spy out and scare evil spirits. These vessels are often beautifully decorated, vermilion, blue and green being the colours most favoured. Strips of bamboo are sewn across the sails to keep them flat and to enable reefing to be done easily and with the minimum of effort. Big cargo and passenger junks work the coasts and some of the large rivers of China. Though they seldom venture far out to sea, nearly a century ago one of these flat-bottomed and rather unwieldy vessels completed the voyage from Canton to the Thames, taking no fewer than 477 days to do so.

VOTIVE RELIEF TO THE GODDESS OF WILD LIFE

The Greek goddess Artemis, called by the Romans Diana, was the protector of wild life, childbirth and very young things. She may be associated with the Asiatic goddess of fertility.

CHAPTER 4

GODS AND DEMONS

Man's natural and ghostly enemies. The beginnings of religion. Origins of priesthood and kingship. Animal gods and demons. Totem poles become military standards. Water and fire spirits. A wedding with the sea. Magic and witchcraft. Modern believers in evil spirits. Charms and amulets. Worshipping the sun. The origins of Sunday and Christmas Day. History of the swastika. Stone Age temples and how they were built. Worship and the dance. Unlucky numbers. Superstitions and their origins.

BLAZING a trail is never easy. It is often extremely painful. Our ancestors of remote generations had everything to find out. They had to start in the infant class of the school of experience. There was no garnered lore; no accumulated wisdom. Dread of the unknown never left them. Fear ruled.

Danger, real or imagined, stalked the beginners of the race by day and by night. Everything was alive; there was no difference between animate and inanimate nature. The flesh-eating animals were visible enemies. They could be seen, and perhaps avoided or otherwise dealt with. Not so the storm, which howled and shrieked, tore and destroyed, and could not be dodged in the open. Some potent power, invisible and intangible, must activate the fume and stress. Later this power was embodied in a person. He must be mollified by the offering of gift and sacrifice.

Thus, it would seem, the first idea of religion, hazy as northern mists, came into the world. When agriculture was practised the wonders of the seasons must have made a deep impression. The dead earth gave birth to life, died and brought forth again. The Egyptians named the spirit who performed this miracle of miracles Osiris. The cycle of death and resurrection suggested the possibility of a life beyond the grave.

59

In this matter of the earliest beliefs, of the vague beginnings of what has been termed other-worldliness, we are still in the nebulous realm of supposition, of "perhaps" and "may be." As there are no written records, we must necessarily base many of our conclusions on the behaviour of primitive man as it can be observed today.

Ancient Priests and Kings

We remember the experience of our own early years: the dread of darkness and the relief of dawn; the strange fantasies of dreams, at once so real and unreal. These experiences were necessarily more vivid to folk without any cultural background whatever. For them science did not exist. There was no explanation; perhaps little comprehension of the workings of the body. Even the ancient Greeks, the fount of so much wisdom, thought that the brain was a sponge to cool the blood.

We can appreciate how the individual with a mentality above the average gradually gained ascendancy. The man with the biggest club and the best developed muscles to wield it was the first aristocrat. From head of a family to chief of a tribe, from chief of a tribe to ruler of several tribes, and thence to king seem fairly obvious steps. A man who pondered over dreams, who sought to understand them and believed or pretended he perceived a way by which to keep the gods at bay or ensure their good graces, became a solver of mysteries, a soothsayer, a witch doctor, a prophet, a priest; call him what you will. Some of these individuals exercised immense power for evil, some for good. "Wise" women who could cast spells and work charms, generally maleficent, came on the scene.

Rulers Who Are Gods

The ruler became associated with the idea of deity. The early Pharaohs were a combination of god, priest and king. The Emperor of Japan is worshipped as a god to this day. His ancestors descended from Heaven. "The Emperor is sacred and inviolable," according to the Constitution; his subjects are the children of the gods. This is the reason why they believe themselves invincible and explains in part their predatory policy.

Charles I of England insisted on the divine right of kings and lost his head; William II, German Emperor, maintained the same idea and lost his throne; the Son of Heaven, last scion of the Immaculate Manchu dynasty of China, was relegated to obscurity, to emerge as puppet ruler of Manchukuo under Japanese protection.

The evolution of the idea of God is so fascinating a theme that it has occupied the attention of a multitude of writers, who have penned whole libraries on the subject. The gradual revelation of God to man, which is a different matter, is related in an even vaster literature. There are those who hold that this unveiling has not been vouchsafed solely by what is related in the Scriptures of the Hebrews and the Christians. Other means and other personages may have entered into it.

Animals were worshipped from remote times. In some of the world's oldest stories they act the part of heroes and heroines and talk like human beings. Balaam's ass is a case in point. Æsop's fables have been heard, read and enjoyed by millions. "To the ear of the savage," says Sir Everard im Thurn, the famous traveller, "animals certainly seem to talk."

Sacred Animals of Egypt

The Egyptians had a most extensive collection of beasts, birds, reptiles, fishes and even insects that were regarded as sacred. This diversified menagerie included the jackal, bull, cow, leopard, panther, hippopotamus, baboon, elephant, cat and mouse; falcon, ibis, hawk, vulture, goose and swallow; cobra, crocodile, tortoise and frog; bee, grasshopper and mantis. Mudbrick vaults containing sarcophagi of sandstone for the burial of sacred cows have been discovered. Millions in India, as well as the Dinkas of the Nile, regard the cow with veneration.

In Mesopotamia the first female statue of early date was picked up at Ur of the Chaldees; it represented the goddess Bau, patroness of the poultry-yard. In Assam and Fiji moths are regarded as the spirits of dead ancestors.

The Cretans had dove and snake goddesses, and a bull god of appalling wickedness. Captives were demanded for this terrible creature with a human body. Paintings depict young men and girls being gored or dodging the sacred beast with a dexterity that would serve a modern bull fighter in good stead.

The Assyrians had a fearsome deity called Enkida, part man and part beast, who had horns and a tail. In Assyria little figures of dogs were buried in holes under the houses to ward off the influence of evil spirits

Russia

Germany

Austria-Hungary

IMPERIAL STANDARDS

The bird of "Revelation" used as a church lectern.

Imperial eagle (Found throughout Northern hemisphere)

Assyrian priest in eagle dress

Totem pole (British Columbia)

Lion-headed eagle – emblem of the Babylonian god Ningirsu – about 3,000 B.C.

Medallion of Ptolemy VI 154 B.C.

Chieftain (British Columbia)

German Medal: Battle of the Falkland Islands. 1914

Symbol of the Royal Air Force

Roman standard

EAGLES OF POMP AND CIRCUMSTANCE

Birds have been used as symbols throughout the ages, an early emblem being the lion-headed eagle Im-Dugud, which represented the first dynasty of Ur, about 3000 B.C. It is pictured above with two deer in its claws, together with other representatives of the cult, including an Assyrian priest and an American chieftain wearing their eagle costumes. All the proud empires which had the double-headed eagle on their standards have vanished.

On the other side of the world the Mayas of Central America worshipped Kukulkan, known to their successors, the Aztecs, as Quetzalcoatl, the god of life, who is represented as a snake with feathers like the quetzal. The Yezidis, who occasionally give trouble on the frontier of Iraq and Syria, have a deity in the form of a black snake, and retain sacred peacocks. Although they believe in God, they also hold Satan in great respect, and have therefore been regarded as devil worshippers. This is a mistake, their attitude being that God is

WORSHIPPED AS A GOD
The early Pharaohs were a combination of god, priest and king. The Emperor of Japan is worshipped as a god to the present day.

entirely benevolent, but Satan is not, and therefore requires propitiating.

The death serpent is the supreme totem of all the tribes of the Australian aborigines. In the Belgian Congo natives regard the rainbow as a snake which eats storms. The same people hold that lightning is an animal in the sky which carries fire in its mouth. Beisan (the Biblical Beth-shan) was once the centre of a serpent cult.

The Alaskan Indians believed in a fierce thunder bird, which made lightning with its flashing eyes, thunder with its flapping wings, and wore a cloud hat. The eagle

feathers that form so picturesque a feature of the head-dress of the North American Indian signify the sun and denote honours of war. They are substitutes for medals.

Magpies, according to the lore of the English countryside, may bring good luck or misfortune. It depends on how many are seen at the same time. "One for sorrow, two for mirth; three for a wedding, four for a birth," goes the jingle, which suggests that the rhymester was more concerned with getting his lines to lilt than endeavouring to retail scientific accuracy.

The effigy of a cock on the weather-vane of a church steeple has nothing to do with St. Peter and his denial of Christ. It is a pagan symbol associated with the warding off of evil spirits, who are supposed to be scared by its movement and creaking.

The peacock is regarded as sacred in various parts of India, and was once a Christian emblem of the soul, but in many countries it is held in anything but esteem. Greek legend has it that the hundred-eyed Argus, a treacherous individual, was turned into a peacock by the gods; the circular spot on each feather of the bird's outspread tail represents one of his eyes.

Under the Mosaic law storks were deemed unfit for food. Later they were held to be of good omen, though their association with a "happy event" in the family is a comparatively modern fantasy. In Iran at the time of migration storks are regarded as pilgrims heading for Mecca, and therefore treated with reverence.

Birds of Good and Evil Omen
Mocking-birds and parrots must have caused consternation to the human listeners who first heard them. When ravens were more frequent in Cornwall the sight of one of them would make the miners dubious as to the advisability of proceeding to work. The Arabs have a great regard for the hoopoe, which they believe is able to detect hidden wells and springs of water.

A totem is the emblem of the primitive belief that men are descended from or related to certain animals and plants, and is therefore sacred. It is a protecting spirit and may be adopted as a tribal or individual badge. Totemism has a wide range, and occurs in Australia, New Zealand, Polynesia, Samoa, Asia, Africa and among the American Indians.

The totem pole is a kind of heraldic device, but in some cases it is much more than that. It is also a grave and a memorial, for some tribes place the cremated remains of the former owner in a hollowed cavity in the rear. The wearing of the eagle mask by the war-god and priests of Babylonia may be regarded as showing that the Sumerians were devoted to the totem. As a general rule members of the same totem are not allowed to intermarry with each other.

Totems and Regimental Colours

The tribes of early Egypt had their totems. One of them, according to Sir G. Elliot Smith, was a placenta (after-birth) and an umbilical cord. The eagle that accompanied the proud legionaries of Rome, and the standards that are still used for ceremonial purposes by British regiments, have developed from such insignia. They are links with a past that is only apparently remote.

The bird symbol, from which the idea of angels may have been derived, is almost invariably regarded as a sign of good omen. Natives of Borneo when on the warpath are confident of victory if they have the good fortune to see a white-crested hornbill when stalking the enemy. The upper half of the head of a hornbill worn in the hair of a native of New Guinea is the outward and visible sign that he has "killed his man."

Christian art, which has borrowed appreciably from pagan sources, has made use of animals as emblems. Christ is called the Lamb of God. His symbols are the lamb, the pelican and the unicorn, and John the Baptist is frequently depicted accompanied by a lamb or carrying one. The bird which supports the Bible on one type of lectern in churches represents the flying eagle mentioned in the Revelation. The lion of St. Mark is familiar. The phœnix is a symbol of the resurrection. To Satan have been allotted the serpent, dragon and swine.

The gods of the Greeks and Romans also had animals which were regarded as sacred to them. To Zeus, also known as Jupiter and Jove, the chief god, was allotted the eagle; to Apollo, the god of the sun and of music, the wolf, the fabulous griffon, and the crow; to Mars, the god of war, the vulture and the horse; to Mercury, the messenger, the cock; to Neptune, ruler of the ocean, the bull; to Vulcan, the divine blacksmith, the lion. Juno, wife of Jupiter and queen of heaven, had the peacock and the lamb; Diana, the huntress, the stag; Minerva, goddess of wisdom, the owl; Venus, who presided over love and beauty, the dove, the swan and the sparrow.

PROTECTING SPIRIT

A totem is the emblem of the primitive belief that men are descended from or related to certain animals and plants and therefore sacred. This totem-pole is in Canada.

BUCENTAUR IN WHICH A RULER WEDDED THE SEA

For many a long year the Doge of Venice "wedded the sea" in commemoration of the Republic's conquest of Dalmatia in 998. The rite culminated in the flinging into the sea of a gold ring by the head of the State. The last performance of the ceremony was in 1789.

Water spirits and river gods are legion. If primitive man, seeing his reflection in the water, thereby conceived the idea of a "double," it is more certain that its constant motion suggested that it was alive.

During a recent drought many villagers in Yugoslavia, Hungary and Rumania revived an old rite in order to appease the anger of the rain god. They cut twigs and branches from trees and flung them into the nearest river or stream as an offering.

For a similar reason a native chief in Rhodesia had his son burned alive to save the tribe from drought. During the subsequent trial, counsel for the defence cited parallels from Hebraic and Semitic history.

For many a long year the Doge of Venice "wedded the sea" in commemoration of the republic's conquest of Dalmatia in the year 998. Eventually it became a most elaborate ceremony in which the doge, patriarch and ambassadors took part, culminating in the flinging into the sea of a gold ring by the head of the state, who cried as he did so "We wed thee, O sea, in token of true and lasting domination." The waters of the River Neva were blessed annually in the presence of the Tsar until the war of 1914–18 put an end to both the observance and the Romanovs.

The Ganges and the Jumna are sacred rivers. At Tribeni Ghat, where the waters join, the number of bathers often reaches one million at the annual religious fair.

The mermaid, with a human head and the tail of a fish, probably originated in the dugong, which is a mammal. Seen at a distance the head is not unlike that of a human being, though the face is not like the faces usually bestowed on mermaids.

The creaking of furniture is still regarded as an omen of death by people who publicly eschew superstition, but inwardly think that there may be "something in it." It is a relic of the days when trees were regarded as sacred and the habitation of spirits.

Life itself, according to Norse myths, had its origin in two logs of oak and elm respectively. Odin and two other gods were wandering about the seashore when they came across the pieces of timber, which were fashioned in a crude sort of way to represent the human form. This gave them an idea. Why not endow the blocks of wood with life? They did so, Odin bestowing the soul, Lodur the blood, and Hœnir the senses. The tree of life was a huge ash called Yggdrasil.

In 1938 Dr. Heywood, Bishop of Ely, raised the question of the late frosts and the apparent destruction by Nature of her own handiwork. "Discarnate, rebellious spirits," he said, "may have some temporary and limited power to exercise evil influences in the realm of Nature as they apparently have in the realm of humanity."

Some brain specialists do not rule out the possibility that evil spirits are a factor in mental disorders. Many Christians at the present day maintain the belief of their forefathers in a personal devil.

Religion, magic and witchcraft are means to an end. In its purest form religion is beneficent. More often than not magic and witchcraft have been put to selfish, and often evil purposes. Among many primitive peoples magic practised by an enemy is believed to be the sole cause of death. Hence the supremacy of the wizard or witch-doctor, who, by means of incantations and curses, can perform "miracles" impossible to the ordinary individual.

The tribal sorcerer doubtless believes in his powers, and self-reliance is always a useful asset. When things do not develop in the way he wishes, a more or less reasonable explanation is usually forthcoming. The law of averages is an ally of great value.

BATHING IN INDIA'S SACRED RIVERS

The Ganges and the Jumna are sacred rivers. At Tribeni Ghat, near Allahabad, where their waters join, the number of bathers often reaches one million at the annual religious fair.

It has been said that the drug-store of to-day is the outgrowth of the witch kitchen of the past. There is some truth in this. The women who dabbled in such matters had knowledge of a number of remedies about which their clients were completely ignorant. For instance, they used mandragora (mandrake) which has a narcotic action. Henbane, a sedative, also employed by the witches, is still to be found on the pharmacist's shelf both in the East and in Europe.

Spells Against Witches

One of the oldest spells against witches of which we have record was uttered in Babylonia over 5,000 years ago. In that country witchcraft was so rife that the priests of one of the several classes devoted most of their time to allaying its direful influence.

The Egyptians and Assyrians were equally witch-ridden. The Assyrians, in order to break spells and bewitchments, went through an elaborate form of ritual in petitioning the fire god Nusku to deliver them from their sinister influence. Little images of fiends and devils, made of wax, wood, clay and various other substances, were burned while a petition praying for deliverance was made.

The witches of Europe were supposed to trail the sky on brooms. Long before they took to this means of transport there was a general belief that witches met in conferences presided over by the devil himself.

Witchcraft Tests and Penalties

The methods of dealing with witches sentenced to death were various. In France they were usually executed by the sword or strangled, although Joan of Arc was burned; in England they were hanged and the corpses burned; in Scotland they were occasionally burned alive but more usually strangled and then burned; in the Isle of Man the poor wretch was placed in a spiked barrel and rolled down Slieaw Whuellian or burned. The law against witchcraft in England was repealed in 1736.

No witch could overcome the good influence of cold iron, hence the belief in the efficacy of horse-shoes. There was a time when scarcely a house in the West End of London was without such a guardian. Probably the earliest literary reference to them is in the *Iliad*, where Homer mentions "brazen-hoofed steeds," but this may be merely picturesque phraseology. As time goes in the historical sense the superstition cannot therefore be regarded as particularly old.

The brasses that adorn the trappings of horses further emphasize the tenacious and enervating grip that signs and symbols have had on the human mind. They date back to the days of Baal and Moloch, when not only horses but camels and yaks dangled them as a means of warding off the evil eye, precluding the machinations of black magic, and other baneful influences. Peasants in the south of Italy wear ear-rings for the same purpose. Eyes are painted on the bows of Chinese junks to spy out and scare evil spirits. Figureheads were placed on ships to propitiate Neptune, god of the sea.

Teeth That Ward Off Fairies

Charms, amulets, talismans and mascots served a similar purpose, and are not unknown today. The natives of Madagascar wear a crocodile tooth to ward off attacks by the living reptile. Teeth supposed to have been taken out of toads' heads, or from those of wolves, were believed to protect a baby from the power of fairies.

A ring, having to all intents and purposes neither beginning nor end, is the symbol of eternity. It is also the sign of authority. We are told that "Pharaoh took off his ring from his hand and put it upon Joseph's hand." It is as much a part of the insignia of a bishop as is his crozier. There is an Arabic tradition that Solomon's ring was the secret of his wisdom. Prince Albert, the husband of Queen Victoria, was the first to break the tradition that had obtained for many years that at a royal marriage the bridegroom should give the bride a ring that had been used on similar occasions.

The Sun Becomes a God

It is impossible to say what object was first worshipped by early man. Probably the sun, which seemed to be so very much alive, gave light and heat, and made what appeared to be a stately procession from one side of the earth to the other. It changed its garments, rising in gold and going to bed in crimson, and seemed to have something to do with the ripening of the kindly fruits. Never could one gaze on its face at high noon unless it was veiled, for its full strength was blinding. Today, almost within a stone's throw of one of the world's greatest observatories, American Indians may be seen standing motionless waiting, as did their ancestors, for the dawn.

The Egyptians worshipped the sun under

various designations from the earliest times. Their supreme god, and they had many, was Re, the righteous sun-god. The name, which is often compounded with others, is easy to remember, for not inappropriately it is pronounced *ray*. The Pharaoh was the embodiment of Re and high priest of all the deities. His consort was high priestess of Hathor, the sun-god's wife.

For a time On, later to be called Heliopolis by the Greeks, near the modern Cairo,

The almost sacred character of water is in evidence, for the sun-god was the offspring of water and bathed in a celestial lake every morning before he appeared above the horizon. There was nothing dismal about the ceremonies which took place. Purification in a pool within the precincts, the offering of food to the god, singing and instrumental music played their parts. Vestments were worn, incense filled the air, and there was an elaborate ritual.

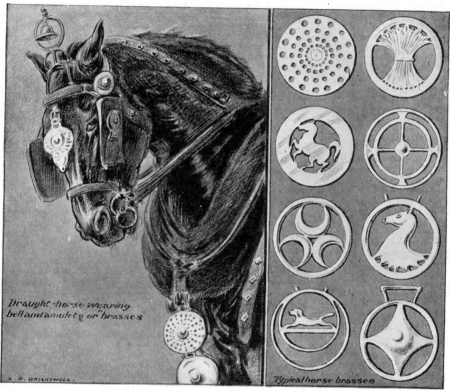

Draught-horse wearing bell and amulets or brasses

Typical horse brasses

TO WARD OFF HARMFUL INFLUENCES

The brasses that adorn the trappings of horses date back to the days of Baal and Moloch, when not only horses but camels and yaks dangled them as a means of warding off the evil eye and other baleful influences. Some common varieties are shown on the right.

was what Rome is to Catholics. It was the great centre of religious activity. There a many-columned temple was built that was to set the style in architecture for places of worship throughout Egypt. As it was manifestly impossible for the king and queen to be here, there and everywhere at once, statues of them were set up in each temple to signify their presence among their subjects and worshippers in spirit if not in body.

A stone altar stood in the forecourt, and there was a shrine which usually held a model of the boat in which Re made his voyage in the sky.

A little image of the god was in the cabin, veiled from sight. The periods of duty required of the priests were divided into watches, as are those of every seaman who sets sail from the ports of the world in the monster vessels of the twentieth century.

Akhenaten (Amenhetep IV), who lived about 1375 B.C., asserted that there was but one god and not a multiplicity of deities. So far as is known he was the first man to do so with anything approaching definiteness, although the idea had been mooted in his father's time, and even earlier. But Dr. Aylward M. Blackman points out that "the new religion was entirely materialistic in its conception of the Supreme Deity, in marked contrast to the—it must be confessed—much more spiritual conception of the old religion. It was the actual cosmic

DEDICATED TO NEPTUNE
A figurehead representing Nelson. These devices of earlier days were placed on ships to appease Neptune, the god of the sea.

body, the physical sun itself, not a mysterious power incorporated in it or working through it, which Akhenaten made his subjects worship." Nevertheless, his hymn to Aton, as the new god was called, compares not unfavourably with the Psalms.

On the death of Akhenaten his son-in-law and successor, Tut-ankh-amen, returned to the many gods of his fathers, and the late Pharaoh was damned by the priests and officials as a heretic and a criminal.

During the last few years there has been a revival of sun-worship in various parts of Europe, the idea being that civilization robs humanity of certain virile qualities that were conspicuous when pagan rites held sway:

in other words, an attempt to revert to type.

When the Huns overran part of Europe they were wont to cut scars on their cheeks to make them look even more terrifying than they were normally. This practice was revived in Hungary, the first victim being a baby. The rites took place on a hill, where the assembled men and women awaited the first glimpse of the sun. On its appearance bonfires were lighted in its honour, and hymns sung in its praise. Then the senseless and cruel half-moon scars were made and the child given the name of Arpad, after the conquering Magyar who became the first king of Hungary early in the tenth century.

Sunday, Day of the Sun
In early times Sunday was set apart for the worship of the sun. It did not definitely become a Christian institution until towards the end of the first century, when it was usually referred to as the Lord's Day.

The most appealing of the solar deities was Mithra, the sun-god of Persia. He was not worshipped in the light of day but in caves or cellars. The reason for this is not so strange as it seems, because it was believed that he was miraculously born of a rock.

Mithra was the giver of life, protector of the weak, champion of the poor, conqueror of death, and fought the hosts of darkness led by Ahriman. His principal festival was held on December 25, and when Christianity superseded what might have become its greatest rival its followers saw no reason why they should not celebrate the birthday of Christ, which was unknown, on that date associated with the worship of the sun.

In Mithraism the idea of sacrifice, found in so many great religions, was conveyed by the slaying of a bull, whose death resulted in the coming of life. The cult made rapid headway among the Romans, and for the first three centuries of the present era held considerable sway in Britain. Apparently women were excluded from this religion, which may account in part for its gradual decline and decay in favour of Christianity.

Origins of the Swastika
The swastika, now so familiar as the emblem of Germany, is one of the earliest symbols known. It has made its way round half the world. Originating, it may be, in Mesopotamia, where it has been found on Elamite pottery, it has been discovered in India, China, Tibet, Iran, Asia Minor, Etruria, Sweden, Mexico, Peru and Britain

In America it is thought to represent north, south, east and west and to symbolize the ruler of the winds and rains. It has been used on tombs, rock carvings, Celtic stones and coins. Associated from early times with Buddhism, it has been used for centuries in Japan as an heraldic cognizance both in its left-hand and right-hand forms.

In Northern Europe it was known as the fylfot, or hammer of Thor, the Scandinavian god of thunder. This suggests a reason why some church bells in England bear the symbol, for in ancient days it was believed that the ringing of church bells afforded protection from tempests. The vestments of the sculptural figures of Bishop Edington of Winchester and of Abbot Jean de Tot of Notre Dame de Jumièges, Normandy, bear swastikas, as does the dress of a grave digger represented in the catacomb of San Callisto, Rome.

Sir George Birdwood, an eminent authority on all matters relating to early India, held the opinion that the right-handed swastika is the symbol of Ganesa, or Ganupati, master and protector of all auspicious ceremonies, and also of the sun of the upper world in its daily course. The left-handed or sinister swastika is the symbol of Kali, and also of the sun of the underground world in its nightly course west to east.

Vishnu's Sacred Lotus

The question whether the latter is unlucky, representing as it does everything associated with darkness, has led to much controversy. It is this form that was chosen by Herr Hitler and his associates to represent the Third Reich, and it appeared on the coat of arms of Bihar and Orissa.

Another suggestion is that the swastika represents the eight-leaved lotus that sprang from the navel of Vishnu, the All-Pervading. The sacred lotus of Egypt is not an Egyptian but an Indian flower, and this suggests that intercourse between the two countries must have taken place from remote times. The swastika is frequently introduced in the geometric designs characteristic of Caucasian rugs.

Perhaps we shall not be wrong if we call it a universalized symbol which, in its journey from land to land, has acquired various significances while still retaining something of its original shape. The arms of the Isle of Man are an allied form copied from a pillar cross near Maughold church.

The preservation of the body after death was a natural sequel to the belief that life

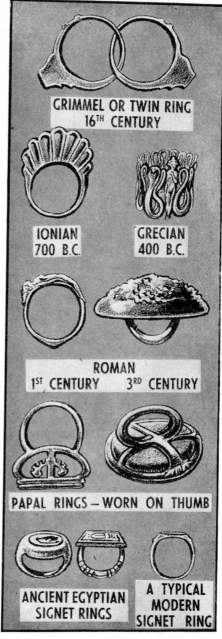

GRIMMEL OR TWIN RING
16TH CENTURY

IONIAN
700 B.C.

GRECIAN
400 B.C.

ROMAN
1ST CENTURY   3RD CENTURY

PAPAL RINGS — WORN ON THUMB

ANCIENT EGYPTIAN SIGNET RINGS

A TYPICAL MODERN SIGNET RING

RINGS OF MANY KINDS

A ring, having to all intents and purposes neither beginning nor end, is the symbol of eternity and the sign of authority. A bishop's ring still "weds" him to his see.

went on when the heart ceased to beat.
Probably before the dawn of this hope no
special attention was given to the disposal
of a corpse. The main thing was to get rid
of it. Perhaps it was left by the roadside,
where animals and birds carried on the
work of undertakers, as do the vultures in
the Towers of Silence of Bombay. The
Egyptians sought to preserve the remains
of an important personage by embalming
them. In the Old Stone Age dead notabilities
were placed in caves and the openings
sealed. If no cave were available an
artificial one was hewn in the rock.

Artificial Caves

With the coming of the New Stone Age
the wide open spaces were no longer
shunned. This may seem a violent break with
tradition, but it was not so in reality, for it
would never do to offend the gods, who are
nothing if not conservative. The cave idea
was still retained, but the cave was specially
built. Massive unhewn slabs were stood on
end or on edge to form the sides, and others
placed on top to make a roof. It thus
resembled, to all intents and purposes, the
earlier tomb.

The dolmen, as it was called, was usually
rectangular, though sometimes circular.
Dolmens are to be found in many parts of
the world. No doubt the idea was to commemorate the dead in a more fitting and
imposing way. The situation of a cave
might be forgotten, and "out of sight, out
of mind" was no less true then than it is
now. Trees and undergrowth soon ob-
scured the site. A stone erection, covered
with earth and forming an artificial hill, was
an ever-present reality. Within it squatted
the dead man, still in a sense a member of
the family. The giant pyramids of Egypt
and Mexico are architectural dolmens.

Dolmens and Barrows

Sometimes several dolmens were placed
together in the form of a tunnel and given
side compartments. These are known as
barrows. One called the West Kennet
barrow, at no great distance from Marl-
borough, Wiltshire, was originally over 330
feet long, seventy-five feet broad and eight
feet high. Seventy bodies were found in an
example at Borreby, in the Danish island of
Zeeland, and over a hundred in another
near Arles, France.

Long before Jacob raised a pillar to commemorate his dream of the heavenly ladder
and the promise that his seed should be as

the dust of the earth, men had erected
upright stones called menhirs, roughly
suggestive of the Egyptian obelisk. Some
of them were put up singly, of which the
most notable example is in Brittany. It now
lies broken in four places, a fallen giant
sixty-seven feet long and weighing some
350 tons. Other menhirs were placed in
imposing avenues. At Carnac, Brittany,
there are regiments of them numbering
nearly 1,700. Their alignment suggests a
definite connexion with sun worship.

At Avebury, Wiltshire, are the remains
of two double rings of stones that were
surrounded by a ditch and a vast rampart
on which stood a wider circle of menhirs.
Such formations are called cromlechs, and
this example is the largest of its kind. The
stones numbered hundreds; indeed, the
place is so extensive as to suggest that it
may once have been the capital of Britain.

Building of Stonehenge

Stonehenge, on Salisbury Plain, is a
similar construction, which may date from
about 2000 B.C. If this date is approximately
correct, the site of Maiden Castle, Dorset,
later to develop into a densely populated
town and stronghold that was to make a
valiant stand against the Romans, was
being occupied by its first inhabitants at the
same time. Bronze was being slowly introduced, but the tools used in the construction of Stonehenge were of stone. This was
long before the period of the Druids, with
whom the place has been somewhat too
closely identified. Stonehenge was probably
a colossal seasonal clock for telling the time
of planting and harvest by means of the
position of the sun.

Not the least of the tangle of mysteries
that cluster around Stonehenge is that of
the material of the monoliths. The larger
stones are of local rock and are usually
referred to as sarsens or greywethers. The
huge table rock called the altar stone is of
old red sandstone. The smaller stones of
the inner circle are a blue stone unknown
in the neighbourhood. The nearest material
of the kind is to be found in the Prescelly
Mountains, in Pembrokeshire, Wales, about
180 miles away. The method of transportation was probably by road, though roads
as such did not exist. Many of the stones
weigh several tons.

The building of Stonehenge has been
attributed to many peoples, including the
Danes, the Irish and the Egyptians. Merlin
is supposed to have brought the stones

from Kildare. As to the Druids, Sir W. Boyd Dawkins categorically asserts that the great monument has nothing to do with them. Some students would have it that the megaliths of Britain and the eastern hemisphere have an affinity with those of Guatemala, Yucatan and Peru.

The giant boulders were probably placed on rollers and hauled by an army of men who tugged at ropes made of strips of hide. One wonders which was the more tiring task: that of the men who placed the rollers in position and, as soon as the stone had passed, picked them up and put them ahead, or that of the hauliers.

The digging of the holes was hard work, but experience in the flint mines had taught the excavators a trick or two. Three sides would be perpendicular and the other sloping, so that the stone could slide down and be forced upright. Perhaps the lintels were levered up a temporary causeway preparatory to placing them in position.

The largest circular artificial mound in Europe is the tumulus of Silbury Hill, within a mile of Avebury.

There now seems to be grave doubt whether the American Indians entertained the idea of Heaven as a happy hunting-ground. Recent research tends to show that they were not primarily interested in what happened after death, but in the immediate present. All they asked of the deities were means whereby needs might be supplied and enemies overthrown. Moreover they had a kind of affinity with the animals they hunted, and apparently realized in a vague kind of way that creation was a whole, that the greater also included the less, long before modern science proved that such a notion was something more than mere fancy.

Incense and Tobacco

Incense was offered to Re by the ancient Egyptians, and its use continues in the services of the Christian Church. The burnt offering of the American Indian was tobacco smoke. On important occasions such as the making of a treaty, the ceremonial calumet, or peace pipe, was brought forth. The bowl was frequently of stone; the stem was the quill of an eagle or a reed, richly decorated. The tobacco was lighted from the fire around which the parties squatted, and passed from lip to lip till the fragrant weed was consumed.

The Sioux have it that on a certain occasion the Great Spirit called all the tribes in conference. When they were

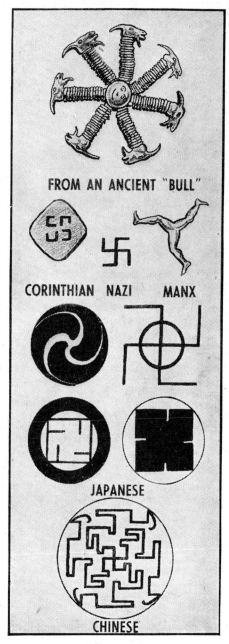

FROM AN ANCIENT "BULL"

CORINTHIAN   NAZI   MANX

JAPANESE

CHINESE

SWASTIKA IN MANY FORMS

The swastika is one of the earliest symbols known and has many forms. It may have originated in Mesopotamia and spread thence to ancient India and the Far East.

WELCOMING THE BIRTH OF A NEW DAY

*An early morning scene many centuries ago at Carnac, Brittany, where avenues of stones
numbering about 2,500 extend for miles. Their alignment suggests a definite connexion
with sun worship. The stones are known as menhirs, and are roughly suggestive of the
Egyptian obelisk. Some of the tallest of the stones are five feet or more in height.*

assembled he took a piece of red stone,
moulded it into a pipe, and began to smoke.
The puffs that issued covered the gathering
as with a cloud. "This stone is red," he said,
"it is your flesh and belongs to you all. Out
of it make no more tomahawks, war
hatchets, nor scalping knives. Use it only
to make the pipe of peace, and smoke therefrom when you would propitiate me and
do my will." Then he disappeared in the
cloud he had created.

Modern dancing has no religious significance; cynics go so far as to say that it has
almost ceased to be dancing. The first dances
were an essential part of worship. The
graceful little performance of children with
the clapping of hands goes back to about
3300 B.C., as an Egyptian tomb of that time
portrays.

Many references are to be found in the
Scriptures to dancing, which remains part
of the ritual of the Mohammedans, the
Bedos of India, and the American Indians.
Dancing was a rite in the Christian
Church for several centuries, and relics of
its religious use still exist in Spain. One of

Fra Angelico's most beautiful paintings is
of a dance of angels and saints at the
entrance to Heaven. Not all Greek dances
were of a religious character; some were no
more than orgies. Roman dances were at
first entirely connected with worship, but
they gradually became more and more
secular, although in southern Italy a solemn
dance took place at a funeral.

Dancing is excellent physical and mental
relaxation if not carried to excess, but its
psychological side is often overlooked. In
the Middle Ages plague, pestilence and
famine were all too frequent, and when they
abated the inevitable reaction followed.
People were in a state bordering on hysteria,
and gave themselves up with little restraint
to dancing as a means of forgetting.

It became a mania and men and women
danced until they dropped. The whole
population of a town would suddenly cease
work and take part in the craze. Bridges
crashed as a result of the sudden strains
put upon them.

A mild epidemic of what is known as
tarantulism, from the belief that the mania

was caused by the bite of the tarantula, raged in the United States as recently as 1923, again, it will be noted, following a time of intense strain.

The story of the Pied Piper of Hamelin is based on a legend connected with the dancing mania. It was discovered that following exhaustion the sufferers fell into a deep sleep, which usually cured them. The municipal authorities therefore secured the services of musicians to aid and abet them in an endeavour to bring the malady to a climax as quickly as possible. The Hamelin piper disputed the fee offered, hence his revenge described in Browning's poem.

If a chapel dedicated to St. Vitus were handy, patients were taken to it, the idea apparently being that "like cures like," for the saint had been seen dancing in his dungeon with several angels shortly before his execution. St. Vitus now has the doubtful honour of being associated with a nervous disorder otherwise called chorea.

In these days of enlightenment, in which many, though by no means all, of the nooks and crannies of the human mind have been explored to good purpose by specialists such as Dr. Sigmund Freud, Karl Jung, Alfred Adler and others, it is difficult not to suppress a smile at what we consider to be the strange beliefs of the children of the race. Yet many of the beliefs linger on. Apparently these race habits are invincible.

Why is Thirteen Unlucky?

The reason why the number thirteen is held to be unlucky is unknown. The belief existed long before the Last Supper, when thirteen persons were present and one of the company hanged himself. That historic occasion doubtless gave an immense fillip to the idea. Incidentally the most famous picture of that event, Leonardo da Vinci's wonderful painting on the wall of the refectory of the Dominican Convent of Santa Maria delle Grazie, Milan, perpetuates

TIDYING UP AN OLD BATTLEFIELD

Excavations conducted by Dr. R. E. Mortimer Wheeler at Maiden Castle, near Dorchester, revealed a number of skeletons of warriors who fell in a battle fought in the year 40.

the superstition that it is unlucky to spill salt. Judas Iscariot is shown in the act of doing so.

In the myths of the Hindus the sitting of thirteen at table is regarded as certain to bring misfortune to one of the party. Norse mythology has it that the twelve chief gods were at supper when Loki, the god of mischief, arrived and took his seat. Loki, jealous of praise given to one of the servants, slew him.

Time and again the Press play to the gallery when thirteen men are missing as a result of a disaster at sea, but it never mentions the vessels that return safely to port every day of the year with that number on board alive and well. At the outbreak of the War of 1914-18 there were thirteen houses in the village of Woolley, Somerset. Thirteen men went out to various fronts. Thirteen men came back, as is recorded on a brass tablet in the parish church.

So far no way has been discovered of warding off the evil implications of Friday. Long ago it was set apart for public executions. Thirteen pence was the sum paid to the hangman. Tradition has it that Adam and Eve were driven from Paradise on a Friday. The significance of Good Friday need not be stressed. As Columbus set out on a Friday on the voyage that led to the discovery of America, it is regarded as a lucky day, even to the present time, by Spanish sailors.

Walking under a ladder is alleged to be unlucky. It harks back to the Rome of the Cæsars, when criminals walked under a ladder on the way to execution.

The gap between cave man and his modern successors is bridged by these strange fancies, born of events that happened in the twilight of the race and apparently destined to haunt the dark recesses of the mind for many a long day yet.

STONEHENGE REMAINS AN UNSOLVED PROBLEM

Stonehenge, on Salisbury Plain, was probably a colossal seasonal clock for telling the time of planting and harvest by means of the position of the sun. Many of the stones weigh several tons. The largest of them are of local rock. The smaller stones of the inner circle may have been brought from southern Pembrokeshire, a distance of about 180 miles.

BUILDER OF THE SECOND PYRAMID
The head of the Sphinx is believed to be a portrait of Khafra (Khephren), builder of the Second Pyramid. In its original state the Sphinx was painted a brilliant red.

CHAPTER 5

THE DAWN OF CIVILIZATION

Had civilization one source or many? Early ships and seafaring. Egypt and Babylon.
Copper tools. Corn, wine and money. Stone replaces mud. Egyptian dams and canals.
Paper comes into use. The building of the pyramids. Farming by the Nile. Daily
life in ancient Egypt. Rameses II's mighty empire. Care of the dead.

OF LATE years increasing attention has been given to another puzzling problem, that of the distribution of culture. Formerly it was believed that civilizations gradually came into being as the result of independent experiments. Each little or big gathering of mankind found for itself how to hammer flints, to polish stone implements, to build, to sow and gather food and so on. No help came from outside sources. In a word, each group was self-taught.

Many scholars now hold an entirely different view. They believe, and can produce much evidence to support their view, that civilization spread by various routes and in devious ways from Egypt and Babylonia. Famous upholders of this theory were Dr. W. H. R. Rivers and Sir G. Elliot Smith,

after whose deaths Dr. W. J. Perry became its most eminent exponent. The school maintains that what is often called the Ancient East, which includes Egypt, Crete, Babylonia, Elam and Syria, was the original home of civilization. Elliot Smith was nothing if not dogmatic as to the pre-eminence of Egypt, whose people, he was convinced, invented agriculture, irrigation, government, the arts and crafts, shipbuilding, costume, furniture and musical instruments, the use of metals, first devised a calendar and the alphabet, and much else.

The earliest boat was not fashioned by man but by Nature. It was no more than a drifting log on which the pioneer navigator sat astride and perhaps paddled with his feet. Several logs formed a raft, a means of communication still widely used. The first serious attempt at shipbuilding, following the primitive dug-out, was the tying together of bundles of papyrus reeds, with a raised bow and stern. According to Elliot Smith the latter peculiarity set a standard, sometimes slightly modified, that is not obsolete after nearly sixty centuries of service. This is evident from its present-day use in Burma, Uganda and other parts of the world.

"Passing down the ages," he writes, "one can establish an unbroken chain of events to prove that the types of ships used at successive periods by Cretans, Phœnicians, Romans, Arabs, Indians, Malays, Chinese, Melanesians, Polynesians, the pre-Columbian people of Central and South America, and in medieval and modern times by the great European sailors, all exemplify the persistent influence of naval architects of ancient Egypt, who determined the form and the method of construction of the ships and developed the rudiments of seamanship."

How Egypt's Culture Spread

It is not suggested that the Egyptians dispatched travellers to the four corners of the earth to spread their culture. What is meant is that their arts and crafts, and not a little of their philosophy of life, were diffused from place to place, directly or indirectly, by various means of contact. Expeditions were sent to other lands for gold, spices, timber and other needs and wants, just as foreigners visited Egypt. There was no "splendid isolation" but a constant exchange of ideas. The intellectual infection spread with the development of trade.

Beehive huts have been found on Dartmoor of the same type as those used by Egyptian miners. Their presence would seem to prove that the gold, copper and tin of Cornwall were exploited by the subjects of the Pharaohs. Tombs hewn out of the living rock on the Malabar coast are similar to those of Egypt, while the Egyptian process of mummification has its counterpart in Melanesia, Peru, and elsewhere.

That the remarkable Minoan civilization of Crete owed its inception to Egyptian influence is the conclusion of Sir Arthur Evans, who excavated the Palace at Knossos and made other valuable contributions to archæology. The Israelites were not the only people who "borrowed of the Egyptians." The whole world, it would appear, gradually became indebted to them. Egypt's central position stood her in excellent stead. What she received she shared with others, not deliberately by means of intensified propaganda but through sheer force of circumstances. As Sir Leonard Woolley has pointed out, the Sumerian civilization of Babylonia was many centuries old when Upper and Lower Egypt were united by Menes.

Egypt's Stone Age

Whatever may be the eventual outcome of the discussions among the scholars, it is certain that Egypt, the early home of so many wonders, had its Stone Age, like all the rest of the world. The country looked very different from what it does today. A considerable portion of the now arid and useless desert was green as an oasis. The native name for Egypt was Kemet, the Black Land; the inhabitants called themselves Romitu, the people. Dr. J. H. Breasted suggests between 18,000 and 15,000 B.C. as the date of the appearance of man in Egypt; Sir Flinders Petrie makes its continuous civilization begin at about 8000 B.C.

Scrapers, planes and other articles testify that the native workers, who came of African stock, were skilful craftsmen when they set their minds to it. Their flint instruments may have been equalled but were never excelled.

It is probable that the first serious attempts to grow crops on a considerable scale were made in the country of the Nile. Miniature granaries were provided by digging holes and lining them with coiled straw rope. Although they were not big, and usually measured no more than three feet across, they were the ancestors of the giant grain elevators of today, some of which can store many millions of bushels of wheat.

First Western Civilizations

That the Babylonians and Egyptians were the earliest western civilized people is beyond question. They shared their knowledge to an appreciable extent, though perhaps Egypt took more than she gave, and improved on much that she borrowed. The wonderful river systems of the Nile in Egypt and of the Tigris and Euphrates in Babylonia made the land so prolific that there was no need to wander far for food.

This does not mean that famine was unknown. If the annual flooding of the Nile was inadequate, the rich fertilizing mud which it collected in its long passage from its source failed to reach the fields, and the people went hungry. Such a disaster happened about 3000 B.C., and for a time the

The first boat

Inflated skin rafts, used by Alexander the Great's soldiers, 360 B.C.

Basket raft, Euphrates

Amazon native raft

Congo dugout

Bark canoe

Outrigger

Chinese junk

Viking ship

Arab "dhow"

EARLY CHAPTERS IN THE STORY OF NAVIGATION

The earliest craft was fashioned not by man but by Nature. It was no more than a drifting log on which the pioneer navigator sat astride. Many of the craft shown have retained their peculiar characteristics down the centuries. The Viking ship, reduced in size and only slightly altered, may still be seen on Norwegian fjords. The raised bow and stern, in particular, link many small craft of today with those of the ancient Egyptians

country lived in the valley of the shadow of death. In Babylonia conditions were reversed. There the danger was too much water rather than too little.

The Egyptians had gold and silver very early. Recently excavators unearthed at Tell-el-Amarna a jar containing ingots of gold that weighed eight pounds and silver that scaled three pounds, doubtless the loot of a thief who had been forced to abandon his treasure and flee for his life. Many important expeditions were sent to the Sudan to discover or otherwise obtain gold. Not only men but women and children were employed in the workings.

From Cosmetics to Copper

The quick-witted Egyptians may have invented copper tools. At first the metal was used in its native state and hammered into shape, but later it was smelted from the ore malachite. The earliest graves contain articles made of the gleaming red metal, perhaps merely funerary objects.

Women painted their faces with malachite. "Irritated by the high cost of this item in the domestic budget," Lord Rutherford remarked, "it is suggested that a husband flung the pot of malachite into the fire, and thus discovered copper and bronze. Later, ladies became addicted to rouge, and we all know that if rouge (iron oxide) is flung into a charcoal fire we get iron."

Copper Uses, Old and New

Lord Rutherford was spicing his facts with humour, but his explanation is supported, in part at least, by Dr. W. J. Perry, who notes that green was regarded as a life-giving colour, and was used by the Egyptians "to give them more vital substance. In course of time they found that this green paint, when fused, produced copper, and of this metal they made beads and foil, then pins, and finally knives and chisels. Thus came about, by a series of steps, one of the most important events in the world's history, the invention of the copper chisel."

This is not the only theory that has been conceived to account for the discovery. It is suggested that a camp fire was lighted where copper ore happened to be present, and that when it died down the secret was discovered. Another supposition is that petroleum, seeping out of the earth, became accidentally ignited with the result that copper was revealed in metallic form. It is difficult to conceive of the present

age without this valuable accessory. The Egyptians used it in their architecture for sheathing and the capping of stone obelisks. Copper domes, while not general in Great Britain, are familiar throughout the continent of Europe. Copper and its alloys are indispensable to the engineer. In the transmission and distribution of electricity, and in the shipbuilding and transport industries, they play an increasingly important part. The propellers of the largest liners, the fire-boxes of locomotives, and essential parts of motor cars are included in the long list of articles for which copper is requisite.

Great Britain no longer supplies the metal to the world as she once did, but the British Empire has some of the richest deposits. The world's biggest artificial hole is the copper mine at Bingham Canyon, Utah, U.S.A. From it more material has been removed than was excavated during the construction of the Panama Canal, including over two million tons of copper.

By about 4000 B.C. the "land of Magan" —probably Sinai—is thought to have supplied both Egypt and Babylon with the coveted metal. A copper spearhead of that date has been found at Ur of the Chaldees. A thousand years later copper was also available in Asia Minor, Anau (Turkestan) and Cyprus—from which island the metal took its Latin name of *cyprium* or *cuprum*.

Chisel 5,000 Years Old

While examining a passage underneath the Great Pyramid, an archæologist discovered the point of a copper chisel embedded in the rock. This would seem to be proof positive that the Egyptians of between 2900 and 2750 B.C. had some method of hardening the metal, although chemical analysis failed to find any hardening substance in the ancient relic. To account for this it has been suggested that the material introduced was of a fugitive nature, or that the metal snapped when being used because it had become "tired," as sometimes happens with iron.

The means by which man found that the addition of tin enabled him to make stronger implements is one item in the long list of the historian's unsolved mysteries, but bronze was certainly used in Egypt as early as 2800 B.C. It was known in Crete earlier still, whence it may have spread to Spain, as it afterwards reached Italy and many other parts of Europe.

Hissarlik (Troy), close to the Hellespont

(Dardanelles), exported both copper and bronze to the Balkans, and long afterwards Hallstatt, on the Upper Danube, manufactured and exported leaf-shaped swords of bronze that became almost as famous as the Damascus blades of another day.

Granary of the Mediterranean

In normal times the chief export of Egypt was corn. What Australia and Canada are to Britain in the matter of grain supplies, Egypt was to the lands of the Mediterranean. Linen made from flax, some of it coarse but much of it of superior quality, was distributed far and wide. Gold was sent abroad, not to be taken out of one hole to be hidden in another, as is the modern custom, but to be used and distributed.

Egypt made wine, but not sufficient for her needs. Much of it was therefore imported, as were timber, spices, skins, cattle, silver, tin, copper, olives and olive oil. For many a long day goods were exchanged. Cash was unknown. Then barter gave place to ring money of gold, electrum and silver, the value being assigned by weight. Stamped coins did not come into general use before the time of Alexander the Great.

Money is still represented by strange articles in some of the world's out-of-the-way places. The natives of Benue Province, Northern Nigeria, use brass rods as currency; those of Yap, in the Caroline Archipelago, prefer stones, some as big as wagon wheels, for the purpose.

Barter in Modern Times

Barter, the earliest and most elementary form of exchange, of late years has been resorted to by many nations. In the thirties of this century Soviet Russia sent oil and various raw materials to France and took French goods to the same value, Poland received Yugoslavian tobacco for railway stock, Tyneside coal was transported to Finland, and Newcastle imported timber by way of payment. Many places in the United States reverted to barter during the disastrous financial blizzard of 1932.

The architecture that was to flower in Egypt in such colossal grandeur started humbly enough. It began with reeds gathered from the banks of Mother Nile and liberally daubed with mud. The materials were close at hand and the supply was plentiful. From such shelters to more permanent dwellings of mud bricks dried by the sun was the next step. None other has been taken by the fellahin, or peasants

UNSHAPELY BUT USEFUL

An Australian aboriginal manœuvring his dug-out canoe, crudely fashioned from the trunk of a tree. Primitive boats of a similar kind are often used on African rivers and lakes. Extreme care has to be exercised to prevent them from capsizing.

from those early days to the present time.

The first stone temple was an improved copy of these structures in a harder material. It was built at Saqqarah near the site of the Step Pyramid, so called because it is in the form of half a dozen steps. The temple and the pyramid are the oldest existing specimens of masonry, and were erected for an early king named Zoser about 3100 B.C.

The Step Pyramid

Imhotep, the architect, was afterwards deified as the patron of the arts and of learning. The height of the Step Pyramid is nearly 200 feet, the north and south bases measure 352 feet, the east and west 396 feet.

By 7000 B.C., centuries before the invention or use of the potter's wheel, red and white pottery was being made somewhat resembling that of the present Kabyle people who inhabit northern Africa. The use of silver, serpentine, hæmatite and lapis lazuli, together with marked changes in the form and substance of the earthenware vessels, suggest the invasion or immigration of a race from Asia.

Many-oared galleys with high bows and stern made their appearance as decorations on pottery. These early craft had cabins amidships connected by a gangway. The ships were sea-going, and not merely built for service on the Nile. Whether the standards on them indicated the port of origin or were emblems of gods remains a mystery.

The earliest taxes, paid in grain and flax, were levied by the local chieftains, who were responsible for the irrigation trenches that watered the fields. The water was raised by means of a shaduf, a long pole balanced on an upright post. From one end hung a bucket on a rope; to the other end was attached a heavy stone as a counterweight.

Cranes for Pyramid Building

Up and down, for hours on end, the bucket was dropped into the well or river, the precious contents tipped out, and the pail dipped again. It was a wearisome job, and it has not ceased through the intervening centuries. It is quite likely that a similar type of apparatus, which may be regarded as the prototype of the mammoth modern crane, was used in lifting the stones of the pyramids.

Thus, as in Babylonia, we have the beginning of civil engineering, simple enough when compared to the gigantic Sennar Dam that can irrigate millions of acres, and the Lloyd Barrage that has made barren Sind fertile, but a significant start on the highway of progress. Nor were the rulers content with making dry and thirsty land fit for agriculture; they reclaimed the marshy area of the Delta at an early period.

Senusret III, finding the First Cataract impassable for his ships, dug a canal to side-track this obstacle to navigation, thus setting a precedent for the future Suez Canal, which was opened in 1859 at a cost of about £17,000,000. Seti I cut a canal which joined the Red Sea and the Nile, and centuries later Necho widened it, as Hitler has enlarged the Kiel Canal connecting the North Sea and the Baltic.

The primitive inhabitants of Egypt, passing from the stage of making marks on clay, invented picture writing, manufactured paper from papyrus, cut for themselves pens from the stem of the same reed, and made ink with vegetable gum, soot and water.

Paper from Nile Reeds

The world's first paper was made by the wasp for nesting purposes. The Egyptians manufactured theirs by cutting strips from the stem of the papyrus plant, moistening them and laying them flat. Pieces of the desired length were then placed side by side, gummed, and overlaid by strips in the opposite direction.

After being dried and pressed any number of sheets could be joined, thus forming a roll that resembled in miniature the huge reels of paper which feed modern rotary presses. The longest papyrus in the world extends 135 feet and is seventeen inches wide; a roll of newsprint for the modern "national daily" is usually about five miles long.

The earliest columns in Egyptian architecture were imitations in granite of papyrus heads bound together. As we have seen, the first boats launched on the Nile were bundles of papyrus reeds bound together and tapering at both ends, in much the same way as the modern Venetian gondola. Shipwrights did not build boats, but wove them, until planks were substituted. They were made watertight with pitch, as was the little ark of bulrushes in which Moses was found by Pharaoh's daughter. Baskets were daubed in a similar way to hold liquids.

Receipts were sometimes given on pieces of broken pottery, while boards coated with lime and even the fine white limestone itself were also used for writing purposes.

By 4241 B.C. the Egyptians had worked out a calendar of 365 days, although it was

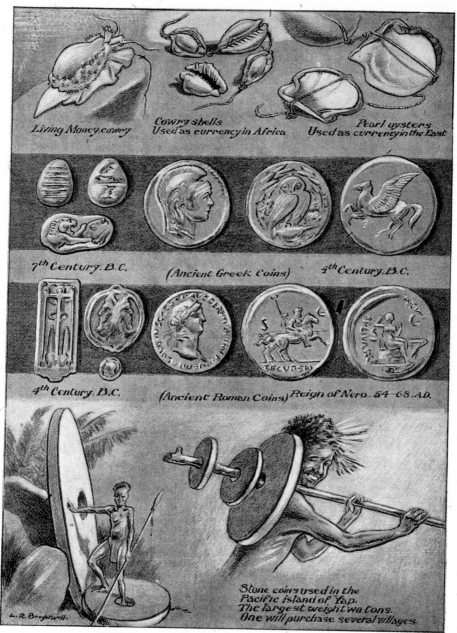

Living Money cowry

Cowry shells
Used as currency in Africa

Pearl oysters
Used as currency in the East

7th Century. B.C.

(Ancient Greek Coins)

4th Century. B.C.

4th Century. B.C.

(Ancient Roman Coins) Reign of Nero. 54-68 .A.D.

Stone coins used in the
Pacific island of Yap.
The largest weight wa tons.
One will purchase several villages.

L. R. Brightwell.

MONEY IN MANY SHAPES AND FORMS

Money is still represented by strange articles in some of the world's out-of-the-way places. Cowry shells are perhaps its oldest existing form. The natives of Benue Province, Northern Nigeria, use brass rods as currency: those of Yap, in the Caroline Archipelago, prefer stones, some as big as wagon wheels, for the purpose. Stamped coins did not come into general use before the time of Alexander the Great, King of Macedonia, from 336 to 323 B.C.

A POTTER AT HIS WHEEL

The potter's wheel has remained unchanged down the centuries, but by 7000 B.C., long before it was invented, red and white pottery was already being made by the Egyptians.

not until the Ptolemies (323–30 B.C.) that leap year was inaugurated by the allowance of an additional day every four years. Glazed pottery, glass moulded as a paste, and vessels of alabaster hollowed out by boring were made. It was many generations before the secret of casting and blowing glass was discovered. Carborundum, now extensively used in the making of emery wheels, was found useful for the purpose of drilling the hard stone.

The kingdoms of Upper and Lower Egypt were united under the rule of Menes (about 3400 B.C.), afterwards regarded as the representative of Horus, the sky god, who is said to have diverted the river seventy miles out of its course and built Memphis on its banks. Today the once mighty city is but a squalid village of mud hovels.

By 2800 B.C. the great blocks of the pyramid of Khufu (Cheops) at Gizeh, near the site of Memphis, were in position, a monumental mass of masonry weighing, it is computed, some six million tons. It could be accommodated in London if the whole of Lincoln's Inn Fields were given up to it. This and later erections were copies of the stepped pyramid cased in.

As the vast army of men toiled with their gleaming copper tools, hacking in the blazing sun at blocks that weighed anything from two to fifty tons, they must have wished that metal had not come into the world. According to Herodotus the pyramid took twenty years to build and 100,000 men were employed, including 4,000 masons. Half the time was occupied in preparing the site and building a great causeway, but work was possible only for three months in the year owing to the flooding of the Nile.

Robbing Pharaoh's Tomb

Long afterwards vandal Arabs, caring nothing for a dead Pharaoh buried in the heart of the structure, removed the facing of polished stone for building purposes, thereby robbing the tomb of some of its outer glory, as they robbed the interior of its treasure. Scant courtesy was paid to the remains of the poor. If they died in the neighbourhood of the desert they were interred in pits; if elsewhere, they were thrust unceremoniously into holes in rocks. Tubular drills fitted with hard stone points were used to smooth the granite. For some strange reason the method and the tools were lost or forgotten, and as Professor A. H. Sayce points out, the world had to wait until the era of the Mont Cenis tunnel before a similar instrument was employed again. This tunnel through the Alps was begun in 1857, say forty-six centuries later.

The head of the Sphinx is believed to be a portrait of Khafra (Khephren), builder of the Second Pyramid, and in its original state was painted a brilliant red. Of practical value was the subsequent construction in the Fayum of a vast reservoir to hold part of the overflow of the Nile at the time of inundation. This work is usually attributed to Amonemhet III.

It was from the Fayum that mortar and plaster were obtained for the pyramids, although it was not until 1927 that the big gypsum quarry which supplied the material came to light. About 2,500 unfinished alabaster vases were also uncovered, together with the flint tools used to shape them, thus furnishing proof of a subsidiary industry. Stone hut circles were excavated.

Some ten years later the quarries which supplied the greenstone diorite for the statues erected by Khafra, the builder of the Second Pyramid, were found in the Libyan Desert. One of the expeditions sent for the purpose of quarrying consisted of 1,200 soldiers, 1,000 men of the palace and 100 quarrymen. They took with them fifty oxen and 200 asses for haulage purposes.

So that there should be no likelihood of the men losing their way in the dunes, cairns were erected at intervals in much the same way as they are placed in Iceland and Norway today to mark the route when snow covers the roads. In one of these cairns was a recess which archæologists believe was used as a kind of letter-box.

Ships were sent to Phœnicia to be loaded with cedar logs obtained from Lebanon. Ebony was another highly prized wood, and parties were dispatched to the Sudan to obtain it and other supplies. Craft sailed westward and spread Egyptian culture along the shores of the Ægean and the Mediterranean, whence it reached the peoples of Europe, who were still busy fashioning flints. Quarrymen sweated in Sinai hewing stone for the houses of the gods while themselves sheltering in dwellings of dried mud.

Iron was known during the Bronze Age, but regarded as precious. References to it as "heavenly metal" suggest that it was first obtained from meteorites, those strange objects that fall from the sky and are perhaps the remains of planets overtaken by disaster. The idea is by no means fanciful, for in 1931 hundreds of fragments of meteoric iron were discovered in central Australia.

The native rulers of Egypt, as of Babylonia, were overthrown by Semites, who founded the Hyksos dynasty of Shepherd

FORERUNNER OF THE SUEZ CANAL

Senusret III (about 2000 B.C.), finding the First Cataract impassable for his ships, dug a canal to side-track this obstacle to navigation. He thus set a precedent for the future Suez Canal, constructed by de Lesseps, which was opened in 1859 and cost about £17,000,000.

IN THE TEMPLE OF KARNAK

On the left is Osiris holding the keys of life and death. Next to him is Tutmosis III, conqueror, and a prototype of Napoleon.

Kings in Egypt about 1800 or 1700 B.C., and introduced horses from Asia and chariots from Babylonia. These innovations had a marked influence on the development of the State. They gave further means of offence and defence and helped to make Egypt a military power and later an Empire.

In the earliest days the only animal used for carrying goods was the ass, evidently obtained from Africa. A crooked and pointed stick, the parent of the plough, was pulled by oxen. Branding irons were used for marking cattle. The Babylonians made a great advance by combining the operations of ploughing and sowing. A funnel, fed by a labourer, was attached to a pipe near the share and the seed slowly allowed to fall through its mouth to the ground.

Farmers agreed to differ about their agricultural methods, just as they continue to do in the twentieth century. Some farmers scattered the seed first and ploughed it in immediately afterwards; others ploughed first, scattered next and employed sheep and pigs to tread in the seed.

At harvest time the sheaves were carried to the threshing place by asses, which also trod the corn. Winnowing was carried out by tossing the grains into the air from wooden spades. To this day in Sind the Indian ryot tethers oxen to a pole, places his sheaves on the ground and lets the patient animals do the rest. Winnowing for many Indian peasants is no more than tossing from shovels fashioned of rice stalks.

Milling and Grinding

The Egyptians used earthenware jars for storage following their preliminary experiments in pits, but long before the coming of the Hyksos, granaries with divisions for different kinds of cereals were in use. A picture on a wall at Thebes shows millers at work. One man is pouring grain into a mortar, two other men are grinding with pestles, a fourth individual is emptying the mixture into a sieve, probably of papyrus, and a fifth is sifting the flour.

The first milling instruments were of wood, then stone was used, and finally metal. Grinding was done by means of two flat stones. The grain was probably dried or roasted before this operation, as was the method of Greece 2,000 years later. The Chinese, who cultivated wheat about 2700 B.C., used the pestle and mortar, as do many native races in Africa.

Models found in a rock chamber represent in a very life-like way a number of the many activities of the Egyptians some 4,000 years ago. In some strange manner these objects were believed to minister to the creature comforts of the deceased in the spirit world.

They show bakers grinding flour, mixing dough and shaping cakes; men brewing beer, which was regarded as a divine drink; a cattle pen with stock being fattened; the counting of cattle by a nobleman, attended by four clerks checking the herd on a papyrus roll; women engaged in spinning flax and weaving on horizontal looms attached to the floor; papyrus canoes; a sailing boat and the interior of a ship's cabin, complete with chair, couch and travelling trunks. By examining ancient containers it has been ascertained that the world's first brewers used excellent yeast but were careless of the purity of the water.

During their two centuries of power the Shepherd Kings did much to foster commerce between Egypt and Asia Minor. Expelled by a revolution, they gave place to the eighteenth Egyptian dynasty—the New Kingdom—which made Thebes, in Upper Egypt, its centre and inaugurated a period of conquest that led to the foundation of an empire. Tutmosis III, prototype of Napoleon I, undertook over a dozen campaigns, and with the spoils exacted made war pay for war. One of the obelisks which he set up now stands on the Thames Embankment, London, and is incorrectly known as Cleopatra's Needle. Another is in Central Park, New York. Ethiopia (Nubia) and Syria were overrun by imperial armies. The Sudan was conquered a second time.

Workers on the quays of Thebes, which extended on both sides of the Nile, were busy loading for overseas, notably Mycenæ, Cyprus and Crete, or removing cargoes from returned ships. Massive buildings of stone and humbler dwellings of the same material, as well as obelisks and temples, were erected in the boom period of Rameses II, the last of the great Pharaohs, though the third Rameses has some claim to fame by reason of his appreciation of the value of sea power.

Not content with advertising his own merits in these various ways Rameses II resorted to claim-jumping. He boldly erased the names of predecessors from their statues and inscribed his own. Propaganda is an ancient device, and its main characteristics do not seem to have altered to any marked extent through the ages.

Pharaoh's Sixty-foot Statue

Before the Ramesseum at Thebes the Pharaoh had a colossal statue of himself erected that was sixty feet high and weighed some 900 tons. It is believed to have crashed during an earthquake some twenty-seven years before the beginning of our era, and it has remained prone ever since. Rameses II did everything on a big scale. He is reputed to have lived to the respectable age of 100 years and to have begotten over 160 children.

The empire, attacked again and again, declined and disappeared, and by 1100 B.C. Egypt had shrunk to her former boundaries. Weakened rather than helped by the divided rule of the priest kings of Thebes and the kings of Tanis, victim of civil wars

and of invasion, she fell in turn to Assyria, the Persians and Alexander the Great. In 30 B.C. the country became a province of the Roman Empire, and prospered mightily.

So much for what we may regard as the material development of affairs. What of the human side, the methods of government, the interests of the ruled, the intimate home affairs of the people? Mankind in the neighbourhood of the Nile had made appreciable technical advance, but did this progress make for betterment in the sense of well-being? Did it conduce to what is ordinarily termed happiness?

In the early, but not the earliest, phase we may assume that the land was more or less divided between a number of chieftains,

WITH PESTLE AND MORTAR

The Chinese, who cultivated wheat about 2700 B.C., used pestle and mortar for milling, as do many native races in Africa today.

BUILT OF PAPYRUS REEDS

The first serious attempt at shipbuilding following the dug-out was the tying together of bundles of papyrus reeds, as shown at the top of this sculpture at Karnak, Egypt.

and that each chief was paramount in all that concerned his particular tribe. His authority was absolute. Totem standards were carried on ceremonial and warlike occasions, and painted poles and decorations erected similar to those we put up at coronations and other special events.

Like all primitive peoples, these rude forefathers of the mighty Pharaohs loved display. Although the scanty nature of their dress afforded little opportunity for elaboration, they wore kilts, and attached an animal's tail to the belt that held up the garment. The feather of a bird was stuck in the curly hair.

Of the early rulers of the land when it became two kingdoms, known as Upper and Lower Egypt, our information is of the scantiest. A picture in relief of King Semerkhet portrays him in two attitudes; in one he is wearing the crown of Upper Egypt, an affair of white linen shaped like an elongated cone, and in the other he has donned the more distinctive head-piece associated with Lower Egypt. These were afterwards combined in a double crown.

Queen with a False Beard

The same portraits also feature the false beard associated with the Pharaohs. Queen Hatshepsut, an early feminist who wore man's clothing, is represented on a statue with this sign of greatness. Another sculpture shows the Nile gods tying the stems of a lily and a papyrus plant together to symbolize the union of the two thrones.

For the purpose of administration the united kingdom was divided into districts or nomes. There were forty-two of these, each under the charge of an official called the nomarch, who was directly responsible to the Pharaoh. As was only to be expected, some of these nomarchs became extremely powerful, and their loyalty was sometimes in doubt. They had military and naval forces, and civil war was not unknown.

The king was compassed about by a multitude of officials—a bureaucracy, in fact. The most important of these powers behind the throne was the vizier, or chancellor, but the ranks included a treasurer, a controller of grain supplies, recorders, heralds, police officers, scribes, tax gatherers and petty officials. A person who had been presented at court and was known personally to the monarch was dubbed King's Acquaintance.

For a time the chief posts were regarded as strict prerogatives of members of the royal family, but this proved impracticable because heredity carries with it no guarantee of worthiness. A strong dynasty had little difficulty in coping with ambitious individuals; ambitious individuals had no difficulty in coping with a weak king. Rameses III called himself King of Mankind, and acted accordingly.

Pharaoh, the literal meaning of which is Great House, was the high priest, but the priests formed a powerful class. Whether they were able to attend efficiently to the worship of over 2,000 gods is open to doubt. The temples in which they ministered became enormously wealthy, thanks to the offerings of the faithful and of the monarchs, who devoted part of the spoils of conquest to religious purposes. There were also priestesses, who played, sang and danced.

Paradoxically, although the Egyptians seemed preoccupied with death and the hereafter, they did not shun the creature comforts of this life. They were a happy people who possessed a sense of humour, which some of their literature reflects. But the thought of death can never have been remote, for following the most sumptuous feast a model mummy was exhibited to the guests as a warning of the inevitable.

The principal musical instruments were the harp, nofre—a kind of long-necked guitar—lyre, trumpet, tambourine, sistrum —with metal staves or rings—and double and single flute. Dancing, both sacred and secular, was extremely popular. The cabaret was common when Britain was in the Stone Age. No festive occasion was complete without gymnastic displays and wrestling bouts.

Eleven Lions per Year

Sport was appreciated by the wealthy, who were fond of fishing and bringing down birds with a throw-stick, assisted by a cat. Wild bulls were caught with a lasso, and big-game hunting was indulged in. Amenhetep III killed 110 lions with bow and arrow in a matter of ten years.

Temple schools for boys of good or wealthy families were run by the scribes and priests. Special establishments were run for the education of future officials. When a schoolroom dating from about 3000 B.C. was unearthed it revealed a master's desk and troughs for holding writing materials. The daily allowance of food was three bread-cakes and two jugs of beer.

Nothing was attempted for ordinary folk, most of whom were illiterate. They were serfs, and only a little better off than the slaves that were imported or brought to Egypt as captives after a military victory.

Rejuvenation has been heralded as a new possibility in medicine. "How to change an old man into a young man of twenty" was dealt with by an Egyptian scribe in 1600 B.C. Amongst other things noted are facts of comparatively recent discovery, or rather rediscovery, such as that different parts of the body are controlled from centres in different parts of the brain.

One must not infer from this that the medical practitioners of ancient Egypt were only a few degrees removed from the specialists of Harley Street. For the most part their knowledge was negligible and associated with magic and demons. The possession or loan of a stone having some kind of resemblance to the part or organ of the body affected was regarded as likely to cure the trouble. A red stone held against the skin was supposed to offset anæmia.

The medicines were mainly of vegetable origin, although salt, magnesia, oxide of copper, antimony and other minerals figure in them. For some prescriptions to be efficacious it was necessary to repeat a magical formula when taking the dose. Castor oil, then as now, was a common but unpleasant remedy.

The dress of the so-called lower classes was simple enough. A linen loin-cloth

WARRIOR PHARAOH

Tutmosis III (1501–1447 B.C.) waged some sixteen campaigns. Realizing the value of sea power, he kept his armies supplied and reinforced by using the ships of his fleet.

HUNTERS IN EARLY EGYPT

The loin cloth worn by these Egyptian sportsmen suggests the kilt. A tail was worn and feathers in the hair. The first figure carries a mace and the symbol of the tribal god; that in the bottom left-hand corner is shooting an arrow with a flint tip from a bow.

sufficed the men, as it does today in many parts of the country. Children ran about naked; their mothers donned a shift. In the course of time the loin-cloth of the men gave place to a shirt, over which a flowing garment was worn.

After wearing their hair long, women took to plaiting it and using a wig, which was frequently stuffed to give it a very full appearance. The circlet round the head was often a thing of exquisite beauty. Gold wire might be employed for the purpose, and gold rosettes were attached to the wig. Vast quantities of pomade helped to keep the head cool. Scented oil was liberally used on the body. Footwear was made of papyrus fibre or skin.

Of jewellery there was plenty for those who could pay the price; that remains the rule. In addition to gold and silver, lapis lazuli, turquoise, carnelian, onyx, agate, amethyst, mother-of-pearl, chalcedony and many other precious or semi-precious stones were drilled, polished and set by craftsmen whose exquisite skill is testified by specimens of their work now displayed in the museums in various parts of the world.

How Mummies Were Made

The Egyptians embalmed their dead because they believed that the body would be needed in the life beyond the grave. The process was long and costly, and several methods were practised. The brains and various organs were first removed and preserved in jars. Spices were stuffed in the cavities, the abdomen was carefully sewn up and the body kept in a solution of soda or salt for ten weeks. It was then dried, anointed and tightly bandaged with linen, which was sometimes soaked in resin and painted to resemble the dead person. In some cases the corpse was given no more than the bath, and in others only the skin and bone were left intact. Animals regarded as sacred were embalmed in similar fashion.

Some of the early outer coffins were made to look like a house, but gradually they were shaped to resemble the human form. All manner of objects were placed in the casket, and occasionally many personal effects. The body of Tut-ankh-amen was enclosed in seven coffins, that which held the mummy being of solid gold.

The position of women in ancient Egypt was superior to that in the Turkish Empire which did not disappear until a republic was proclaimed in 1923. They had considerable freedom, and although men in the upper stratum of society often had several wives and mistresses, this was the exception rather than the rule. Sometimes a man married his sister or other near female relative, but the idea that the Pharaohs invariably contracted such marriages is now known to be an error.

Divorce was easy. No lengthy proceedings were involved. Apparently nothing further was required than for the husband to tell his wife that all was over between them and that she was at liberty to "Make for thyself a husband in any place to which thou shalt go." There the matter ended—provided she went.

We should know very little of the story of ancient Egypt but for the patient labours of the excavator, who brings the hidden things of many centuries to light. The work is anything but easy. Some 70,000 tons of rubble were moved during the progress of the search for Tut-ankh-amen's tomb.

Luxuries of the Tomb

When the tomb of Ra-Ouer, a prince and high priest who finished his earthly duties about 5000 B.C., was opened, statues of women wearing gowns that resembled the evening dress of a twentieth-century debutante were found, together with what appeared to be a chess piece.

It is comforting to know that dilatoriness in official quarters is not the invention of a nation notorious for muddling through. Some 4,500 years ago an officer lodged a complaint that the soldiers in his command had been sent to a depot to receive new uniforms and had been detained there for six days while they waited for supplies.

Maxims of Ancient Courtiers

Diplomacy was the usual mixture of oily words and worldly wisdom: "If thou art an underling in the following of a great lord who is in favour with the god (king), know nothing of his former insignificance. Raise not thy heart against him on account of what thou knowest of him aforetime, but rather hold him in awe on account of what has happened to him, for having cometh not of itself: it is the god (king) who maketh the great."

Such were sound hints for successful living in the distant days of the Pharaohs!

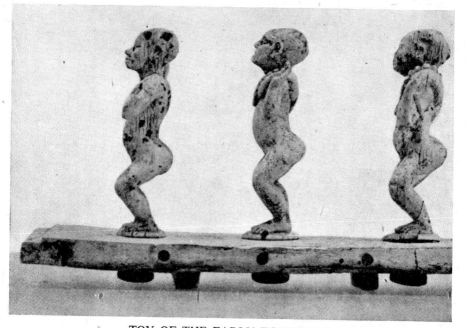

TOY OF THE EARLY EGYPTIANS

Ivory figures of dancing dwarfs, a mechanically operated toy of the early Egyptians. The hands and feet are as detailed as could be expected in figures of small size, and in the expression on the faces the primitive craftsman showed an exceptional degree of skill.

GREAT SEAL OF ENGLAND

In Babylonia a seal, the remote prototype of the Great Seal of England, took the place of a signature on letters and personal papers. The Seal for the reign of King George VI is of solid silver and impressions of it are attached to documents of first national importance.

CHAPTER 6

WONDERS OF THE OLDEST CITY

The "Fertile Crescent." Warriors of Babylonia. Mesopotamia as the Garden of Eden. How the Sumerians lived. Ur and its secrets. Beginnings of sculpture. Letters written on bricks. Links with the Bible. The Tower of Babel. How astrology arose. The story of the flood. Etana, the first aviator. Modern art in ancient Sumer.

PERCHED on the top of the wilderness of Arabia, crowning the desert, was a fertile crescent, to use a felicitous term coined by Dr. J. H. Breasted. On the west was the Mediterranean, on north and east great mountain barriers, on the southeast the Persian Gulf. The crescent included Palestine, Phœnicia, Syria, Assyria, Akkad and Sumer, the last two countries being usually grouped as Babylonia. Here races have met and mingled; East and West have repeatedly, for thousands of years, clashed and fought in deadly enmity.

The wandering Semites of Arabia discovered this territorial gift of the gods that stretched from the Mediterranean to the Persian Gulf, and began drifting to it with their flocks and herds across the sandy wastes. Tribe followed tribe over a period

that extended to centuries. The Canaanites found their way to Palestine, the Amorites eventually conquered Babylonia, and another group made the natural harbours of North Syria their stepping stones to an overseas commerce that led to the name of Phœnicia becoming known far and wide, even, probably, in distant Britain.

In Babylonia wheat grew almost as prolifically as ill weeds. "Of all the countries that we know there is no other so fruitful in grain," notes Herodotus, the shrewd old Greek traveller who wrôte the first Universal History. In the south of the country Hebrew tradition located the Garden of Eden. The rich alluvial soil, the kindly service of the twin rivers, the Tigris and the Euphrates, the ease with which crops were cultivated, the inexhaustible date palm, and

90

a ready supply of clay for building purposes made the country no mean resting place. Not, indeed, that there was a great deal of rest. The city-states into which the country became divided had their mutual jealousies which often led to war.

A sculpture shows a king leading his troops in battle, their long spears pointing horizontally, their bodies protected by immense shields that extended from neck to feet, and their heads, except for the face, encased in helmets that resemble the tight-fitting crash helmets of motor-cycle racers. They were probably of leather. This stone picture proved that the Greek phalanx "invented" by Alexander of Macedon—a body of men formed in close array—had been anticipated by the Sumerians.

This people, who took possession of the eastern part of the fertile crescent, did not come from the desert. It is suggested that they trekked from India and crossed the Zagros Mountains on the east, or made their way by boats along the shore of the Indian Ocean and the Persian Gulf.

Ur and Its People

They apparently arrived about 5000 B.C., and in course of time drained the marshes and irrigated the plains to provide water for the crops, dug canals, raised flocks and herds, and probably had carts before the Swiss lake-dwellers. They used caravans and boats, kept accounts and records in wedge-shaped cuneiform writing made with a stylus on clay, invented a calendar that frequently needed adjustment because a new month began with every appearance of a new moon, cast in copper, built houses and towers to their gods, employed slaves, and created a number of city states; an intelligent and gifted people.

Eridu, once on a lake that the Sumerians connected by canal with the Euphrates, and now far inland, was the chief port. Among the seats of kings were Kish, Erech, Babylon, Lagash and Ur. Nippur was the sacred city, the Jerusalem of the Sumerians, dedicated to Enlil, god of the air. Some of these places have completely disappeared. It may be that their civilization was as old as, if not older than, that of Egypt, and that their traders travelled to Britain, or at least to the Scilly Isles, to obtain tin for the making of their bronze.

Probably the world's first great city was built by Sumerians at Ur, the ancestral home of Abraham. Though it was assaulted, captured, sacked and rebuilt, its civilization

existed for thirty centuries. When the father of the Jewish people lived there it was already old and on the coast, but when its site was first investigated in 1854 it was a hundred miles inland owing to the silt deposited by the rivers. Beneath the huge and melancholy mound that the rain has washed and the sun baked with glowing intensity for over 2,000 years, excavators have found, and are continuing to find, the relics that constitute so much of the skeleton of history.

The earliest letter, dating from about

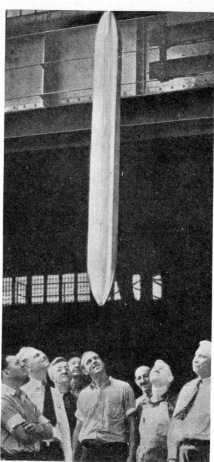

CONTINUING AN OLD TRADITION

The Sumerians buried documents in the foundations of temples, a custom still carried on in sacred and secular buildings. A cylinder containing messages was deposited in the World's Fair Grounds, New York, in 1938.

5000 B.C., was discovered at Tell-el-Obeid, four miles due west of Ur, and probably a suburb. It refers to a deed of purchase or hire of a field, and was enclosed in a clay envelope. It was buried in the foundation of a temple, a custom still carried on today in sacred and secular buildings. A cylinder containing messages was placed in the World's Fair Grounds, New York, in 1938, and various objects illustrating different aspects of the daily life of the twentieth century were sealed in the foundations of London's new Waterloo Bridge.

The earliest metal statues were unearthed at Tell-el-Obeid. The most ancient bronze stylus for making cuneiform inscriptions was discovered in the Babylonian area. Over 4,000 years ago a native trod on a clay brick soft from the maker's hands and left, in his footprint, a monument he never suspected. Amongst other treasure-trove that has rewarded much patient and devoted toil may be mentioned a fragment of sculpture depicting an angel, the earliest known, an inlaid gaming board, a statue of "a ram caught in a thicket," a clay model of a racing charioteer driving nine horses, "asses of the mountains" as they were called, a school exercise tablet and part of a dictionary of the Babylonian tongue.

GOVERNOR OF LAGASH

For a time a line of powerful governors ruled Lagash, afterwards the seat of kings. This unnamed worthy lived about 2300 B.C.

In the chapter of Genesis which traces the pedigree of Abraham, or Abram as it is spelt, particulars are given of the generations of Noah who pitched their tents on a plain in the land of Shinar, the Biblical name for Babylonia. "And they said one to another," according to the record, "Go to, let us make brick, and burn them thoroughly. And they had brick for stone, and slime had they for mortar. And they said, Go to, let us build us a city and a tower, whose top may reach unto heaven; and let us make us a name, lest we be scattered abroad upon the face of the whole earth."

The Tower of Babel

This structure, familiarly known as the Tower of Babel, remains of which have been uncovered although it was in ruins at the time of Alexander, was begun by King Ur-Nammu. He also built the Ziggurat at Ur, which was both temple and fortress, over fifty-three centuries ago. It was of solid brick, and in some respects resembled the Step Pyramid in Egypt, except that it had buttresses and steps which led to each of the three storeys. On the top was a shrine containing a statue of Nannar, the moon goddess and patron deity, who is represented on a great limestone slab holding a measuring rod and adze.

The Ziggurat was an artificial mountain of brick intended to imitate in a flat country the hilly nature of the land from which the inhabitants had originally come, and in which it was believed that the gods dwelt. This is an idea held in common by the adherents of many religions.

With great ingenuity the terraces were planted with trees and shrubs to make the illusion as complete as possible. Many centuries later the tower was encased with blue-glazed brick of great beauty. Compared to the pyramids of Egypt the Ziggurat is not overpowering; the base is 210 feet in length and 138 feet in breadth.

The tombs of the kings of the Third Dynasty of Ur, of which Ur-Nammu was the founder, were found in 1930 by that indefatigable excavator, Sir Leonard Woolley, the leader of the joint expedition of the British Museum and the Museum of the University of Pennsylvania. The king, who was known as the Merciful Lord who brought prosperity to Ur, created an extensive network of canals and vastly improved the irrigation system, which had been sadly neglected. He also erected massive walls to defend his capital. They were over seventy feet thick at the base.

It was an age of great prosperity, in which the temple shared. Produce was brought to the nearby storehouse, and while some of it was used by the staff for immediate purposes, the surplus was kept for service in time of shortage or war. Receipts were given and strict accounts kept. Loans were arranged, though the bank-rate was high. A seal, the remote prototype of the Great Seal of England, took the place of a signature. Priests practised the art of foretelling future events by means of a sheep's liver and gazing at the stars. Thus the pseudo-sciences of fortune-telling and astrology were born.

Houses uncovered twenty feet below the surface, and contemporary with Abraham, show that they were built of burnt brick and the interior walls of mud brick, which we may regard as representing the familiar breeze slabs and lath-and-plaster divisions familiar in our own homes.

The modern world is not nearly so modern in many of its ways as we are apt to think. Certain forms of recent architecture have reverted to the set-back style of the Ziggurat, which was also the progenitor of the church tower, and some sculptors have gone to the primitive for their proportions, or rather disproportions. While we do not make a cemetery of private houses by burying the dead underneath the ground floor, as was done at Ur, distinguished folk are still laid to rest in sacred buildings, Westminster Abbey and St. Paul's Cathedral for example.

The Flood—Babylonian Version

We have noted that all manner of objects were buried with the Pharaohs of Egypt; in Mesopotamia the early kings of Ur were sepultured with their entire court. It is not thought that those who were sacrificed were killed in a brutal way. They probably committed suicide by taking a deadly drug. Men and women, some wearing hair ribbons of gold, soldiers with spear heads of the same precious metal or of silver, grooms and drivers, oxen and asses have been found laid out in neat array. The cattle were yoked to chariots ready for immediate service in the future life.

The tradition of a universal flood is almost world-wide. That a disastrous inundation took place in the lower valley of the Tigris and Euphrates about 3200 B.C. is beyond doubt. Both the archæologist and

LIVER FORTUNE-TELLING
Model of a liver inscribed with omens and magical formulæ. It was used by the priests of Babylon for foretelling the future.

the geologist have proved it. An intensive study of the neighbourhood of Kish, some eight miles east of Babylon, and perhaps the Cush of Genesis, has disclosed various layers of deposits in which are fossilized remains of freshwater shells and fishes, victims of the fury of the rivers when they burst their banks. A similar layer of silt is collected at Ur.

Baked clay tablets give the Babylonian account of the Deluge, of which Uta-Napishtim is the hero. The likeness to the Hebrew version is remarkable. Warned by a god, the Babylonian Noah built a huge ship of seven decks, each of which contained nine cabins. When he, his family, animals and a pilot named Puzur-Amurru were safely on board the rain descended as never before, lightning tore across the sky, and the whole world became a wilderness of swirling waters. On the seventh day the craft came to rest on a high mountain top.

"I looked over the sea," says Gilgamesh, the narrator, "and a calm had come, and all mankind were turned into mud." A dove and a swallow were released. Both returned because they had "no place to alight on. I brought out a raven and let her go free. The raven flew away; she saw the sinking waters. She ate, she pecked in the ground, she croaked, she came not back."

Another myth of old Babylonia tells the story of the first aviator. He was a shepherd named Etana, whose flocks ceased to multiply. Hearing that there was a herb in the highest heaven that was a known cure for sterility, he persuaded an eagle to give him a lift. The gods became jealous of the earth mortal when within measurable distance of his goal, and he and his feathered friend were hurled to death.

A Greek fable runs on somewhat similar lines, except that in this case wings of feathers and wax were made by Dædalus, who with his son, Icarus, was imprisoned in Crete by King Minos. The inventor reached Sicily safely, but Icarus soared too near the sun, the wax melted, and he fell headlong into the sea.

History is constantly being revised. Until recently it was supposed that the people of Babylonia never used columns in their architecture prior to the Persian conquest of the country in the sixth century B.C. A colonnade cleared on one side of the court of a Ziggurat proved the existence of this valuable architectural feature at least a millennium before the coming of the invaders from the East.

There is every likelihood that brick architecture found its way from Babylonia to Egypt. At Kish it was shown that the Sumerians invented the panel decoration now being used so effectively in modern schemes. A series of slate panels inlaid with limestone figures came to light, in addition to one which portrayed the agricultural life of the people. Oxen pulled the plough and wheeled carts with leather tyres. Men milked the cows and sat behind them and not at the side, a practice still followed in Italy, and in Arabia with sheep and goats. There were free landowners but there were also slaves engaged in menial tasks.

A BABYLONIAN KING LEADING HIS TROOPS TO BATTLE

The famous Greek phalanx—a body of men formed in close array—generally ascribed to the military genius of the Kings of Macedon, was anticipated by the Sumerians. Holding their spears horizontally, their bodies protected by immense shields and their heads, except for the face, encased in leather helmets, a Sumerian army was a human fortress.

ART OF 2,500 YEARS AGO

A fine example of ancient art: a lion fashioned of enamelled tiles. In the days of Nebuchadnezzar (604-561 B.C.) this lion formed part of the decorative scheme of the sacred way of the city of Babylon. It is in an excellent state of preservation at the present day.

CHAPTER 7

EMPIRES AND CONQUERORS

Sargon and his campaigns. Hammurabi's code of laws. Trade regulations in Babylon. Substitutes for money. Assyria succeeds Babylon. Nineveh and its sculptures. Cotton. Fall of Nineveh. Nebuchadnezzar captures Jerusalem. Persia's rise to power.

By peaceful and warlike penetration the bearded Semites from Arabia gradually conquered Akkad, as northern Babylonia was called, and deposed the Sumerians. Moreover they established trade along the caravan route that ran between the Euphrates and the Mediterranean, and their wares reached Crete and perhaps India.

Sargon, who lived about 3000 B.C., a hero whom legend associates, like Moses, with having been discovered in an ark of reeds, and a rebel Semite, knit the territories together. He and his descendants, as Dr. W. J. Perry notes, "constitute the first known instance of a warlike military ruling group."

A Babylonian map of the world shows the earth surrounded by a great ocean, and above this early specimen of cartography is a narrative of Sargon's campaigns. In course of time his successors were to assume the comprehensive title of King of the Four Quarters of the Earth.

Sargon's son Naram-Sin, " the beloved of the moon-god," proved himself no less purposeful. A bas-relief shows him as a mighty conqueror sparing his enemies. In peaceful affairs he showed his wisdom by establishing a system of routes and ports, and he founded libraries of the clay slabs on which the literary men of the day engraved their records. His sense of the importance and practical value of metal was such that he secured the copper mines of Sinai from whence Egypt obtained her supplies.

After a period of rebellions and the conquest of the united kingdom of Sumer and Akkad by foreign invaders, an Amorite king named Hammurabi, following years of effort, made himself supreme in Babylonia. Under his rule extensive trade was developed.

95

canals were dug, and the oldest known legal code was given to the world.

The laws are engraved on a great shaft that also pictures the king receiving the code from Shamash the sun-god, who is seated on a throne resembling a Babylonian shrine, perched on a mountain. The laws, which number nearly 300, deal with such widely divergent matters as jerry-building and the keeping of vicious cattle, but many punishments for offences are harsh and cruel according to modern standards. While there are similarities, it is agreed that the rulings of Moses are superior ethically to those of Hammurabi.

The laws which concern trade include the death penalty for the theft of animals belonging to a temple or palace unless their value is forthcoming; for erecting a house that falls and kills the owner; for deception in the selling of beer. Fraud on an agent meant a penalty of six times the amount involved. Fees or wages were fixed for all occupations; women were permitted to carry on a profession or a trade.

In the selling of property a contract was drawn up on a clay tablet, the names of witnesses were added, and those who possessed seals stamped the document. Fields were rented, often on a profit-sharing basis, and houses leased.

Manas and shekels—weights and not coins—of silver were used for payment. Coined money, although invented in Lydia, in western Asia Minor, in the eighth century B.C., was not in use in Babylonia.

After Hammurabi's death the influence of Babylonia gradually declined. The

MAN-HEADED WINGED BULLS AS GUARDIANS

The stone for the colossal man-headed winged bulls that guarded the palace at Nineveh and prevented the entrance of evil spirits, was quarried in the hills of the northern lands, and floated down the river on rafts supported by sheep and goat skins blown up by slaves.

ASSYRIAN FORERUNNER OF THE TANK

The Assyrian Empire was founded on the conquests of an army that used spears and arrows of iron and armoured tanks that mounted battering rams protected by a cupola and a fighting tower. Inset, a modern tank. These weapons were introduced by the British in the war of 1914-18, their original appearance in action being on the Somme in September, 1916. There are several different types, including one which mounts guns firing 6-pounder shells.

STONE HORSES FOR SARGON'S PALACE

A tribute of horses for Sargon II (722-705 B.C.), founder of the last Assyrian dynasty. This bas-relief is from the great palace which he built at Khorsabad, near Mosul. Hitler's policy of removing some of the population of conquered countries resembled that of this king.

greater part of its trade fell into the hands of the Aramean kings of Damascus. An invasion from Eridu was followed by the coming of Hittites from Cappadocia and of Kassites from Mesopotamia almost contemporary with the Hyksos invasion of Egypt.

The Kassites stayed for nearly six centuries. But north of Babylon, situated not more than 250 miles away, on the west bank of the Tigris, was Ashur (Assur), the capital of Assyria, an energetic country that was gradually growing stronger. Babylonia fell before the onslaught of the Assyrians, whose symbol was the tree of life.

Eventually the whole of the fertile crescent was included in the Assyrian Empire, an empire founded on the conquests of an army that used spears and arrows of iron and armoured tanks that mounted battering rams protected by a cupola and a fighting tower, and which owed its culture to Babylonia, to which it had once belonged.

Nineveh became a city of great importance, with a palace the like of which had never before been seen. Water was brought from mountains thirty miles distant, and Sennacherib's civil engineers built what may have been the first aqueduct, a sub-stantial structure nearly 1,000 feet long. Cart tracks were transformed into substantial roads. Along them passed the king's messengers, who distributed his letters at various points and thus inaugurated a postal system. A magnificent library, running to many thousands of tablets, was formed by Assurbanipal.

The stone for the colossal man-headed winged bulls that guarded the palace and prevented the entrance of evil spirits was quarried in the hills, and floated down the river on rafts supported by sheep and goat skins blown up by slaves of proved lung capacity. The sculptors then got to work, and when the carving was completed the figures were placed on sledges, and by a process of dragging and levering drawn to their final destination and placed in position.

Success in the field eventually proved the undoing of the greatest congregation of states that civilization had so far produced. A fighting power has little or no reserve of men for the pursuits of peace. Industry necessitated the employment of aliens, who certainly introduced new knowledge, but when the kings found it incumbent to draw more and more upon the agricultural population for soldiers, and to utilize the services of foreign military adventurers, the policy led to internal decay as certainly as dry rot destroys timber.

In 606 B.C. the Assyrian Empire was an affair of yesterday. We owe to it one of the greatest necessities of the modern world, namely cotton. "The trees that bore wool," we are told, "were clipped and carded for garments." Examination by X-rays of cloth woven over 2,000 years ago proves that better cotton was being grown then than is available at the present time.

Not only did the Chaldeans from the south-east conquer Babylonia, but with the Medes from western Persia they annihilated Nineveh, the mighty capital of Assyria.

The last of the great Semitic empires was that of Chaldea, which began about 606 B.C. It included Babylonia, its possessors sharing with their allies what remained of the Assyrian Empire, taking the south and west, as well as dispossessing Egypt of Lydia and Palestine.

Under Nebuchadnezzar II and his successors both its internal culture and its commerce flourished. Agriculture must have contributed heavily to the vast sums necessary for the building of the wonderful temples and palaces of restored Babylon, the making of its luxurious hanging or roof gardens, the digging of the moat, the throwing-up of embankments, and the erection of massive walls and great gates.

Caravans of camels laden with merchandise ambled in, unloaded and set out again with their heavy burdens. Babylon was a clearing-house for the products of Syria, Arabia and Persia, and traders sent their wares, including excellent cloth, as far east as India and to the western extremity of the Mediterranean. Here the Hebrews, carried into exile after Nebuchadnezzar's capture of Jerusalem, sat down and wept, and early scientists mapped out the sky into the twelve signs of the zodiac.

It is to the Chaldeans that we are indebted for a seven-day week, with its day of rest. Their empire lasted until 539 B.C., when it fell before the onslaught of Cyrus, King of Persia, whose line came to an end a little over two centuries later with the conquest of proud and busy Babylon by the Greek armies of Alexander the Great.

REMAINS OF THE ONCE MIGHTY CITY OF BABYLON

Ruins of Babylon, the greatest city of antiquity. It was a clearing-house for the products of Syria, Arabia and Persia. Traders sent their wares, including excellent cloth, as far east as India and to the Spanish coasts at the western extremity of the Mediterranean Sea.

CHAPTER 8

CRETE AND PHŒNICIA

Guard-ship of the Ægean. Troy, the nine-times-rebuilt city. The palace at Knossos. The Iron Age begins. Levantine traders. Who were the Phœnicians? Tyre and Sidon. Solomon's navy. Was Zimbabwe Tarshish? Phœnician colonies in Africa. Tin from distant Britain. First voyage round Africa. Fall of Phœnician power. Its legacy.

CRETE lies like a derelict guard-ship watching the scattered islands of the Ægean Sea that form a broken bridge between Europe and the Near East. It was the stepping-stone by which the civilization of Egypt and of Babylonia reached Europe. Within a millennium (3000 to 2000 B.C.) the birthplace of Zeus, the mythical king of the gods, had risen from the Stone Age phase of development to a high stage of culture.

The earliest pottery of the Cretans was primitive and undecorated. Art was confined to crude modelling; the implements used were of stone and bone. With the dawn of the Bronze Age, perhaps a thousand years before that of Egypt, Crete awoke with the youthful energy of a child after a long and refreshing sleep. Grace is evident in the painted and patterned pottery. Egyptian influence is already at work, evidence of which is found in the shapes of the seals made of ivory obtained from Africa. Babylonia contributed the idea of using clay as writing material, though the hieroglyphs on the tablets that have been unearthed cannot be read.

Troy Nine Times Destroyed

What Crete gained or discovered of her own initiative was carried by traders and shared by many of the neighbouring islands. It spread to Troy, on the eastern mainland of Asia Minor and the watch-dog of the trade routes along the Danube—watch-dog, that is to say, when it was not being sacked and burnt; nine times it was left in ruins, and nine times it was rebuilt—and to Asia Minor, to Mycenæ, Argos, Tiryns and Orchomenos in Greece.

The sea kings in their cargo boats laden with oil and wine and other commodities crossed to Sicily, Italy and Spain. The northern islands of the Cyclades must also have exported minerals. Magnificent palaces, complete with what we consider to be modern comforts, including bathrooms and a drainage system, were built at Knossos (about 2100 B.C.) and Phæstus, on the north and south coasts respectively.

The palace at Knossos, so tortuous in its passages that it was termed the Labyrinth by the Greeks, was as big as Buckingham Palace. Magnificent frescoes covered the walls. One depicts a crowded theatre. Others show the costumes of the people, the women wearing dresses cut low in front, with flounced skirts like crinolines, and large shady hats. Men of no special social standing wore a loin cloth, kilt and high leather boots; officials a flowing cloak.

Knossos and Its Mysterious Fate

In Britain the lion is regarded as a symbol of power; in Crete the bull was held in similar respect. A picture shows athletes engaged in the dangerous sport of bull jumping, seizing the animal by its horns as it charged and throwing themselves in a somersault over its back.

In the magazines, stone jars, each big enough to form an air raid shelter, were used for storage purposes. At the height of its prosperity the population of Knossos was probably 100,000.

About 1600 B.C., earlier rather than later, there came a bolt from the blue. The palaces were razed to the ground, and the cities with them. Sir Arthur Evans, to whom we are indebted for so much valuable information about Minoan civilization, thinks that the disaster may have been caused by an earthquake. Or were the buildings put to the flame by an invader? We cannot tell, but we do know that the plucky Cretans did not abandon hope, despite the loss of so much treasure and doubtless of many lives. They rebuilt. Their artistic sense was revitalized by the disaster, and the Golden

Age of Crete began. Luxury and good taste were combined, which is unusual.

Extensive trade was carried on with Egypt, of which country Crete was a vassal for a time, and with the mainland of Greece. Olive oil, shell-fish for dyeing the rich purple that is still the colour of pomp and circumstance, and perhaps copper were exported. Potters, craftsmen in gold, silver, bronze and stone, and gem cutters produced beautiful work in a land that was not too prosperous to neglect artistic idealism and strove to make it reality. Again Knossos was destroyed. Crete waxed a little, then waned, and with the dawn of the Iron Age gradually faded into mediocrity.

Its place was taken by Mycenæ, on the mainland of Greece, referred to in the *Iliad* as "rich in gold," and probably a colony of Crete. There was commercial intercourse with the Baltic, either direct or otherwise, with Cyprus, Egypt, Asia Minor, Palestine, Phœnicia and perhaps Spain. Then Mycenæ and its settlements went the way of Knossos. Its buildings disappeared in smoke or remained as debris.

There again the Iron Age was beginning, as it was when mighty Troy was finally destroyed. The Iron Age, destined to bring about such marvellous developments after many centuries of retarded youth, came in the guise of a harbinger of ill luck. From the region of the Black Sea tribes armed with weapons of the new metal arrived. They were the ancestors of the Greeks, and among the towns they burnt, probably about 1050 B.C., was Mycenæ.

In a little strip of land some 700 miles to the east of Greece history was also being made. The Phœnicians were a highly

"THE MERCHANTS OF ZIDON, THAT PASS OVER THE SEA"

Phœnician sailors preparing for heavy weather. The main sheet has been hauled in before setting up a storm sail. Cables passed beneath the keel of the vessel and lashed to gunwales with grappling irons helped to relieve the strain and to hold the ship's timbers together.

efficient people thousands of years before the word "efficiency" was overworked.

They were the first to pursue the policy of peaceful penetration. While other countries of the ancient civilized world frequently quarrelled among themselves or with others, their general principle was to get on with their business as manufacturers and merchants, despite occasional jealousies that sometimes led to hostilities.

Had the Phœnicians sought to confine their existence to their narrow territory in North Syria it is extremely likely that they would have failed. Its area was inconsiderable—some 120 miles in length and varying from twelve to thirty miles in width—its soil limited, its water supply inadequate. Yet Nature was liberal in other ways. Palms flourished like the green bay tree and the wicked, hence the name Phœnicia, or the Land of Palms, given to it by the mariners of the Ægean Sea. Pomegranates, olives, figs and grapes were plentiful in the valleys; cedars crowned the summit of Lebanon; there were natural harbours.

It may be that the greatest benefactor of mankind is he who makes two blades of

FAMED ZIMBABWE

Some authorities hold that Zimbabwe is the site of Ophir, which furnished Solomon with gold. Other experts say that these ruins in Southern Rhodesia are not older than the fourteenth or fifteenth century of our era.

wheat grow in the place of one, but in the days of the Palm-tree People science and agriculture had not entered into alliance. The population expanded but the boundaries of the country remained immovable. The Mediterranean smiled and beckoned, and so this non-militant branch of the Semitic race took to the sea.

The Phœnicians were great shipbuilders, navigators, colonists and traders, but they were also great copyists. It is easier to improve than to invent. Like the Israelites, they borrowed of the Egyptians, and it is not unlikely that the Northmen profited by imitation of the Phœnicians.

Early Phœnician Ships

The earliest picture of a sea-going ship, a large Egyptian vessel with a double mast, dating from about 2800 B.C., shows a number of Phœnician prisoners on board. Even then the traffic in cedar-wood had been going on between the two countries for 200 years, perhaps longer; the inhabitants of Britain were living in the Stone Age in lake-dwellings.

In due course the Phœnicians set to work, improved on the design of the craft, and thenceforth became competitors as carriers. They copied other Egyptian products, such as metalwork, porcelain, glass and linen, which they dyed a rich purple or deep crimson with the help of a shell-fish called the murex, as did the Cretans, and entered into commercial rivalry. When they found that the Egyptians were writing on papyrus they imported the reed and gave up using clay tablets. They devised an alphabet which later formed the basis of Greek writing. Even in this there are traces of Egyptian influence.

What the tradesmen of the Levant took they passed on. There is reason to believe, for instance, that they introduced the Egyptian decimal coinage into Babylon, and the olive and the vine into Crete.

When Crete was a great sea power the Phœnicians were trading with Egypt, and probably by 1200 B.C. were busy in the Ægean. When Crete fell they had virtually no maritime competitors. They laid Africa under contribution for gold, ivory, and ostrich feathers, obtained spices, incense and perfumes from Arabia, various metals from Spain and Britain, and amber from the shores of the Baltic.

The immigrating Semitic tribes known collectively as the Phœnicians probably arrived before the middle of the third

THE ELLIPTICAL TEMPLE AT ZIMBABWE

Exterior of the elliptical temple at Zimbabwe, showing the conical towers. It is built of unmortised blocks of stone. Birds of soapstone or steatite that stood on monoliths have been represented as symbolizing the Assyrian and Phœnician goddess Astarte. One of them was over five feet in height. Similar ruins on a smaller scale exist in other parts of the country.

millennium B.C. "The Hyksos, the Phœnicians and the Hebrews," says Sir Charles Marston, "were as closely allied by race and language as the English and Scots." They settled down as independent city states: Aradus, Gebal (Byblos), Sidon and Tyre. The last two were the most important.

Tyre, the senior of the cities, was built on two rocky islands joined together and connected with the mainland by embankments built by Hiram I about 1000 B.C. Compared to a small modern town it was insignificant, for its wall enclosed only about 140 acres. The population it could not accommodate lived on the mainland, but the Eurychoros, where business was transacted, was within the walled area. There were two protected harbours connected by a canal. Sidon, some twenty miles away, was also on an island and had twin harbours.

Solomon, we are told, built a navy on the shores of the Red Sea, and his ally Hiram of Tyre "sent in the navy his servants, shipmen that had knowledge of the sea, with the servants of Solomon. And they came to Ophir, and fetched from thence gold, four hundred and twenty talents, and brought it to King Solomon." They also brought "algum trees and precious stones," and "the king's ships went to Tarshish with the servants of Hiram: every three years once came the ships of Tarshish bringing gold, and silver, ivory, and apes, and peacocks." Phœnician workmen and material were also employed in the building of the Jewish Temple.

The locality of Tarshish is uncertain, but is suggested as situated in the Malay Peninsula. Much speculation has also been indulged in as to the site of Ophir. Was it Zimbabwe, in Mashonaland, Southern Rhodesia? Old mining shafts over 100 feet deep have been found in the colony, but it is rather surprising that only a few crucibles have been unearthed in the ruins of the massive buildings of mortarless granite blocks, which certainly prove the existence of a civilization of no mean order, even if they never guarded treasure.

An age of several thousand years was assigned to them by Dr. Leo Frobenius, who was of the opinion that the main building was put up between 4000 and 2000 B.C., and that Zimbabwe was the centre of a great mining colony, the culture of which was Sumerian-Babylonian.

Phœnician Colony in Rhodesia?

Dr. David Randall-MacIver, the Oxford Egyptologist, reported after exploring the ruins that they were not older than the fourteenth or fifteenth century A.D., and that the so-called temple, 292 feet long and 220 feet wide, was a hill fort. Steatite or soapstone birds that stood on monoliths have been represented as symbolizing the Assyrian and Phœnician goddess Astarte.

That the Phœnicians had relations with South Africa was proved by the finding of a galley 180 feet long on the Woltemade flats near Cape Town. It was some six feet below the surface and three miles from the sea, which shows how the coastline has varied during the centuries.

Loaded with goods made in their own cities or brought to them by caravans from various interior countries, these early commercial travellers of the sea secured sufficient customers for their wares to warrant the establishment of trading centres, and eventually of colonies.

Phœnicia's Daughter City

Cyprus, by reason of its copper mines, early attracted them; they established settlements in Greece, Rhodes, Sardinia, Sicily and in North Africa. Gades (Cadiz), in Spain, was probably founded by them about 1000 B.C. Their first and longest-lived colony was Utica, signifying "Old Town," in North Africa; their most important was Carthage, on the Bay of Tunis, founded at the end of the ninth century B.C.

Carthage (the Roman form of Kathadisha, "the New City") eventually had some 700,000 inhabitants, far more than the mother city state, and it was her proud boast that "no Roman might even wash his hands in the Mediterranean." After fighting Rome in what are known as the Three Punic Wars, the city was destroyed by Scipio Africanus, rebuilt by Augustus, and finally razed to the ground by the Saracens in A.D. 698. Carthage not only had an extensive coastal traffic, but did important trade with Central Africa. She also carried on manufactures by secret processes with slave industry.

Spain and the Tin Islands, presumably Scilly, were apparently the main sources of supply for the tin used in the making of the bronze articles for which the Phœnicians were renowned. It has, however, been seriously doubted whether Phœnician boats actually called at the Scilly Isles. It is now more generally considered that the traders obtained the metal from some continental depot, although it is possible that they may have sailed direct from Cadiz, as stated by Strabo, the Greek geographer.

Posidonius, an early authority and a traveller in Britain in the first century B.C., relates that the inhabitants of Belerion (Land's End), after smelting and purifying the tin, beat it into masses, and carried it to an island off Britain called Ictis, which at low tide was accessible to wagons. Here the merchants bought the metal from the natives and carried it over to Gaul.

Tyre Seeks Tin in Britain

Whether Ictis is St. Michael's Mount or Vectis (Isle of Wight), which was once connected with the mainland, is a topographical bone of contention that yields a certain amount of nourishment to supporters of the two opposing schools. A block of tin weighing 159½ pounds, believed to be a relic of Phœnician trade, was dredged off Falmouth early in the nineteenth century.

The dangers and difficulties of a voyage from the western Mediterranean basin to Britain were considerably less than those which must have attended the circumnavigation of Africa, which Herodotus tells us was successfully accomplished by Phœnicians in 608 B.C. under the patronage of the Pharaoh Necho II. Nearly three years passed before the commander and his crew, sailing from the Gulf of Suez, reached home. At intervals the men landed, and sowed and gathered a harvest of wheat to eke out a scanty supply of provisions.

About 470 B.C. Hanno, a Carthaginian navigator, sailed with sixty ships and a cargo of emigrants to establish colonies on the west coast of Africa. After calling at various trading stations in Morocco, he proceeded to the Rio de Oro and beyond the Gambia to an island in a bay he named the Western Horn. The captain's log states that night was made hideous by strange music and piercing shrieks, and the mountains appeared to be on fire.

The vessels next proceeded to the Horn of the South—probably the peninsula of Sierra Leone. While on shore the crew discovered a lake surrounding an island that was the haunt of big hairy beasts with faces resembling those of very ugly old men. Three of the animals were captured, but on board they proved anything but amenable, and had to be killed.

Hanno much regretted this necessity, but he retained their skins as trophies and evidence. He called the animals *gorullai*, from which we get the name gorilla, the largest of the apes. This pioneer voyage to the west coast of Africa was the last to reach so far south for nearly 2,000 years.

In turn the Phœnicians of Asia Minor received the unwelcome attentions of the Egyptians, Assyrians, Babylonians and Persians, who either overran the country or exacted tribute. For long Tyre was the leading city state, but her defiance of Nebuchadnezzar II for thirteen years shattered her commerce, and Sidon took her place. Tyre stood another great siege with the coming of Alexander the Great, but was at last forced to surrender to his army of investiture (333 B.C.).

The career of the Phœnicians as sea traders was ended. Indeed, their commercial supremacy in the Ægean Sea had been wrenched from them by the Greeks several centuries before. In 64 B.C., the Phœnicians came under the rule of the Romans.

The Phœnicians were distributors and middlemen. They added little to civilization, but performed a useful service by passing it on. To the realm of the spirit they contributed nothing. Their god was Moloch, to whom the Carthaginians once offered 200 sons of noble families as burnt sacrifice when the city was besieged by the Romans.

MINING TIN WITH A HOSE

A Chinese labourer operating a monitor on a tin-bearing cliff in Malaya. The stream of water tears the gravel down with ease, and the resulting mixture flows into a sluice where the tin ore is concentrated. The deep lode mines in this neighbourhood are the hottest known.

ARCHITECTURE THAT FROWNED

The portal built by Ptolemy III (247-222 B.C.) at Karnak. It is massive and overbearing, unlike the graceful Greek portal shown on page 114. The reliefs represent the king worshipping Theban deities. Karnak, the northern part of Thebes, was a centre of the worship of Amen.

GREEKS PLAYING A GAME OF BALL

The Greeks indulged in athletic pursuits, including running, leaping, wrestling, hurling the javelin, boxing, chariot racing and a game suggestive of hockey. They called leisure "schole." The word "school" is derived from it. There is food for thought in this significant fact.

CHAPTER 9

TRIUMPHS AND TRAGEDIES OF GREECE

Greece and its origins. Early Greek colonies. Trade and travel. The Greek view of life. Sparta, the totalitarian city. How Athens grew to greatness. Olympic games. Persia's attack and defeat. Marathon and Thermopylæ. Pericles and his city. Greek beliefs and superstitions. Peloponnesian War. Fall of Athens. Philip of Macedon.

TO THE early Greeks, a mixed race who called their country Hellas and themselves Hellenes, the Mediterranean was the embodiment of splendid isolation. They referred to it as "Our Sea," just as they termed everybody who was not a Greek a barbarian, though the word had a meaning less harsh than its modern definition. They knew no other maritime waterway, and it was a long time before they ventured beyond the Pillars of Hercules at the western end, and nosed their ships into the Atlantic.

Largely on account of the crumpled-up and bitten-in nature of the peninsula, and the complicated mountain ranges and deep inlets that more or less isolated them, the Greeks failed to realize that there is strength in unity. They therefore never formed a composite nation, and independently founded agricultural and trading colonies, though they made commercial agreements. The comings and goings of their merchantmen during what is generally known as the colonial period, which lasted from about 800 to 600 B.C., converted the Mediterranean into "a Greek lake." Miletus, in Asia Minor, with over eighty city colonies, grew into a busy emporium, to be rivalled only by Corinth and Athens. The first settlement may have been made by Cretans following the fall of Knossos. Beginning with agriculture, it developed into a sheep-raising area, and from the fleece of the animals, cloth was woven. As "hands" were short, slaves were brought from the neighbourhood of the Balkans. Sicily and the coast of the Black Sea became centres of Greek influence and for the distribution of goods. The south of Italy was known as Greater Greece.

Phasis, Trapezus (Trebizond), Tanais and Olbia commanded the leading trade routes. Cyrene was founded on the African coast and Naucratis in Egypt. The Milesians brought Odessa and Sevastopol into being;

GATHERING THE OLIVE HARVEST

Gathering olives in Greece, as pictured on a vase of the sixth century B.C. *A youth is sitting at the top of the tree, and he and two fellow workers are knocking down the fruit with sticks. Another helper is gathering the fallen olives and collecting them in a basket.*

the Megarians found a home away from home at Chalcedon and later at Byzantium.

The Phocæans, sailing in the opposite direction, founded Massilia (Marseilles), where they introduced into France the cultivation of the vine and the olive. They also started a colony in Spain near Malaga, and made Tarshish (Tartessos), at the north of the Guadalquivir, a centre for the distribution of metals.

In Greece itself cloth-weaving, metal-work, pottery, the sowing and reaping of wheat and barley, and the making of olive oil and wine provided plenty of work. Not that the Greeks regarded physical labour as a virtue. They had a word for it which may be translated as burdensome toil. On the other hand the craftsman never put out any part of his job to what we term sub-contractors. He would have spurned the idea of mass production or of being no more than an assembler of parts.

Cattle and metal as media of exchange gradually gave place to bars of copper and iron, and later to a coinage made of an alloy of gold and silver known as electrum.

The sole of a man's foot became a standard of measurement; his arms stretched sideways denoted a fathom (six feet).

At first the Greek trading ship was propelled by oars, but by the end of the sixth century B.C. the war galley was the only vessel of any size that employed them, although it had sails also. The British Museum treasures a vase on which is pictured such a vessel with twenty-three rows of oars in two tiers, together with a merchantman. Whereas the former has a ram carved to resemble a boar's head, the latter has a high bow and is obviously broad-beamed and capable of carrying lumber, grain and flax from the remote Black Sea. A pair of oars served as a rudder.

Tradition says that Naupactus, "the place of shipbuilding," received its name because it was there that the Dorians, who invaded the Peloponnese, built their vessels. It commanded the entrance to the Corinthian Gulf, and was the end of the road from the north which carried much traffic.

The patriotism of the Greeks, who were intense individualists, was narrow and local. They held themselves aloof. Each community in its own estimation was self-sufficient and superior to all others. Even when the peninsula came to be dominated by two city-states, and the influence of Sparta was paramount in the Peloponnese and that of Athens in the north, they remained rivals.

Their outlook on life was entirely different. Sparta, remote and hemmed in by mountains, was conservative. It believed in hardness and despised luxury. Physical culture was a passion. Weaklings were taken from their mothers as soon as they were born and left to die. Pity was a crime. Boys deemed fit to live left their homes at the age of seven and were placed in barracks, where they underwent a relentless drilling in the twin virtues of courage and self-control until they reached twenty. Then they became soldiers, having endured almost every form of fatigue and punish-ment. The demand for a healthy body, but not necessarily a healthy mind, extended to the women and girls, though less severely.

The Spartans must have been suspicious people, otherwise they would not have had two kings and five ephors or magistrates to watch their doings. King Pausanias was stoned to death because he was not sufficiently austere. The monarchs and a council of twenty-eight nobles constituted the ruling body. When it came to a question of peace or war, the assembly of citizens over thirty years of age voted yes or no. If the vote was affirmative, one of the kings was chosen commander and given absolute power. Helots, or serfs, who were one degree removed from slaves because they could not be bought or sold, did the menial work of the State and were given the privilege of marching with the army when hostilities broke out.

It may be that the Spartans made a

WEDDING PREPARATIONS OF A GREEK BRIDE

The rigid discipline in Sparta is commemorated whenever we use the word "Spartan" to denote endurance, the lack of comforts and an ascetic way of life. The demand for a healthy body, but not necessarily a healthy mind, extended to women and girls, though less severely. The reward of women's virtue, said Pericles, was to incur neither blame nor praise

virtue of necessity, if subjugation to the State is to be regarded as a virtue, and the State as absolute. It would seem that about the middle of the sixth century B.C. something happened that made them adopt this cold-blooded austerity. A rising without or a revolt within the valley, or perhaps whisperings of an encirclement policy on the part of neighbours, may have urged them to organize a military machine and to cast behind them all that they had hitherto deemed beautiful and of good report. Whatever the nature of the threat, the former policy was relegated to limbo, and Sparta did nothing further for culture.

Athens, the First Democracy

Attica, which was no larger than Yorkshire, was progressive. Athens, its main centre of activity, enjoyed an open site. The sea was almost within an hour of it, and there were two excellent harbours. Beginning as a monarchy, it became in turn an aristocracy, an autocracy and a democracy. The aristocrats displaced the monarchy and used their position to bolster up their own vested interests. Hesiod described them as "bribe-swallowing lords."

There was a public Assembly to be sure, but it had little or no influence in the direction of public affairs. Draco codified the unwritten laws. They were so drastic that the word "draconian" found its way into English as meaning very severe or cruel.

The appointment of Solon as archon, or chief magistrate, eased conditions considerably. His motto was: "Nothing in excess." Those who had been enslaved for debt were released, mortgages were cancelled and a man was not allowed to buy more than a certain amount of land. Instead of one law for the rich and another for the poor, the bold statesman demanded that the scales of justice should not be weighted against those without affluence or influence, and that all free citizens should sit in the Assembly of the City.,

Solon's Social Revolution

In this way democracy made a beginning, though the term had not the comprehensive meaning that it has since gained. The proletariat, which forms so large a proportion of all populations both ancient and modern, was not represented in any way. Its members were slaves, and as such deemed voiceless. It was an important step in the organization of mankind, for hitherto despotism had held sway. Slavery remained

and, long after the glory of Greece had departed, continued to remain as a part of the social system.

These reforms were not carried out at once. Desired adjustments seldom come on swift wings. They were aided and abetted by tyrants, popular leaders who overthrew the nobles. Their tyranny must not be regarded as cruelty, or even as exercised in the brusque fashion of a Napoleon or a Hitler. Peisistratus, for instance, had the cause of the common people as much at heart as any twentieth century humanitarian, yet he did not overlook the necessity for a navy and the importance of fostering commerce. He neglected the interests neither of the country nor of the town. While arranging for loans to enable peasants to redeem mortgages on their farms, he encouraged the building of a more substantial Athens, hitherto mainly a collection of hovels.

Instead of beginning with some high-flown ideal that would take a long time to bring to earth, Peisistratus started by improving the water supply. Conduits connected the city with the upper course of the River Ilissus, and aqueducts with streams from neighbouring mountains. Some of the channels were subterranean and furnished at various points with shafts for ventilation, and at their journey's end discharged into reservoirs cut in the living rock.

Fount of Nine Mouths

A spring in the city was named the Fount of Nine Mouths because of the number of its jets, and a colonnade was erected over the basin. Any person found polluting the supply was subject to severe punishments, for while the cause of epidemics was no more than guessed at, the connexion between certain diseases and impure water was strongly suspected.

All these things did not exhaust the energies of the tyrant. He interested himself in the people's amusements. Thus early did the question of the right use of leisure vex the mind of a statesman, though not necessarily from an entirely altruistic point of view, for idle hours may breed revolutionary tendencies.

He instituted what perhaps may be termed an enlarged and improved edition of a festival in honour of Dionysus, god of the vine, later to be known by the Romans as Bacchus. It was a general holiday, the forerunner of the Bank Holidays that are so much appreciated in Great Britain. Imagine all London flocking to Hampstead Heath

OLYMPIC GAMES REVIVED AFTER 1,500 YEARS

Every fourth year the Olympic Games were celebrated in honour of Zeus, the greatest of the Grecian gods. The first of which any record is preserved were held in 776 B.C.   In 1896 the Games, abolished by the Roman Emperor Theodosius, were revived in the restored stadium at Athens, and have since then been held every four years in various parts of the world.

on successive days to listen to plays, and you will have an idea of what the Great Dionysia meant to Athens, though it must be borne in mind that the population of Athens probably never exceeded that of a fair-sized provincial town in England.

On the southern slopes of the Acropolis, the rock on which stood the citadel guarding the city, in a vast open-air theatre, plays were performed in competition. The stage was of wood; below it was the chorus, which danced and chanted. The audience sat in tiers in a great semi-circle listening spellbound for hours if the drama presented was good, or dozing if it failed to satisfy.

To give them added height the performers put on a special boot, called the cothurnus, with thick wooden soles. Costumes differed little, except in colouring, from everyday garments. Masks were worn that represented the characters portrayed.

If it were necessary for a god to appear, a high platform was pushed on to the stage, or he descended from his remote regions on a kind of crane. When the Great Dionysia was inaugurated no charge was made for admission to the theatre, but later, tickets were sold for a few pence or presented to those who could not afford so modest a sum. The performances were religious observances. The stage was actively associated in its early days with worship.

In July of every fourth year the Olympic Games were celebrated in honour of Zeus, the greatest of the Grecian gods. The first of which any record is preserved were held in 776 B.C., in the valley of Olympia at Elis, in southern Greece, and the last in A.D. 394. The games became so popular that eventually all Greece was represented. If any quarrelling happened to be going on at the time an armistice was arranged so that the events might not be interfered with.

For a reason that is not evident, no married women were admitted, although maidens were not barred. The penalty for breaking this rule was death. Contests for members of the fair sex were included in a festival of their own.

The events included running, leaping,

MOCK-TRAGEDY ON THE GREEK STAGE

Notice the masks and padded costumes of the burlesque figures taking part in the farce. Plays of this kind were called mock-tragedies. They dealt with all manner of subjects, including the everyday affairs of life. The woman represents Hera (Juno), wife of Zeus.

PERSIA GAVE THE WORLD ITS FIRST DOME

The Tomb Tower at Damghan, Persia. Herodotus states that before their conquest of Lydia the Persians had no art, though it has been suggested that the word in this connexion means the refinements of civilization rather than what is usually understood by the term. Certainly art afterwards blossomed with the profusion of the rose in Persia, which gave architecture the dome. Onion-shaped domes, like those of the Taj Mahal, were also Persian in origin.

wrestling, hurling the javelin, throwing the discus (a kind of quoit), boxing, chariot racing, and weight lifting and throwing. A block of stone that turns the scale at 36 pounds has been found inscribed with the words: "Bybon threw me over his head with his left hand." The awards presented on the field were simple enough. They were no more than wreaths fashioned from leaves of the sacred olive tree which flourished in a grove near the temple of Zeus, and a branch of palm, but other favours also went with them. Statues of the victors were erected in the sanctuary, poems were written about them, and it was not unusual for a pension to be given by the cities they represented, or some other privilege, such as exemption from taxation, granted.

The Olympic Games, abolished by the Roman Emperor Theodosius, were revived in 1896, over 1,500 years later. The stadium in Athens, with accommodation for 200,000 spectators, was restored in marble. The Games, which are held at different centres, are open to the whole world, but it is regrettable and ironic that on more than one occasion war has prevented the meeting, more especially as the Games were conceived with the idea of promoting international brotherhood.

For fear it be thought that the ancient Greeks played only on special occasions, let it be added that those who could indulged in a game suggestive of hockey, swam, sun-bathed, ran and leapt for hours on end, and every day. "Those who could" were but a small part of the nation. Their leisure was paid for in great part by slaves, who toiled while others enjoyed themselves. The Greeks called leisure *schole*. The word "school" is derived from it. There is food for much thought in this significant fact.

ENTRANCE TO THE PARTHENON

Ictinus, the architect of the Parthenon, or Temple of Athena in Athens, gave symmetry to the building by having the columns lean inwards, slightly thickening them in the middle and making them taper at the top.

One of the greatest assets of the Greeks was their keen interest in life. The aphorism "Those whom the gods love die young" refers to age of mind and not of body. It means that those who retain their sense of wonder and a healthy outlook on affairs never fail to remain youthful though they live to be centenarians.

The tyrants came and went, to give place to Cleisthenes, who, among other reforms, inaugurated a Council of Five Hundred charged with attending to public business. The Assembly retained its decision in matters of peace and war, the making of laws, and the hearing of law suits.

" The democracy," says Professor F. M. Cornford, "consisted of the citizens (including the peasants) who owned the slaves. They were the 'people'—the *demos*. Democracy meant that the whole *demos* governed itself, and was not ruled by a minority. All common affairs and interests came up for discussion in an assembly composed of all the adult male citizens. They were self-governing in a very full sense, electing and holding responsible all their officials, and competent to decide all public questions by a free vote of the Assembly itself. Every citizen had the duty which now falls on Members of Parliament—the duty of expressing by his vote a considered opinion on all great public issues."

Cyrus, King of Persia

On the shores of the great inland sea the city states of Greece and their independent colonies waxed mightily. In the East another Power was also extending its influence. Cyrus, King of Anshan, in the mountains of Elam, a vassal of the Median emperor Astyages, had not only rebelled but possessed himself of his lord's territory. In 550 B.C. he was King of Persia. He became one of the outstanding figures in history.

His peasant subjects were moulded into a formidable army. Taught "to ride, to shoot and to tell the truth," they conquered Lydia, which was ruled by the king whose reputation for wealth is embodied in the phrase "as rich as Crœsus," and the Greek colonies of Asia Minor. Marching on Babylon, Cyrus defeated Belshazzar and ended the Chaldean Empire. The Hebrews were released, and went back to Jerusalem. Three years after the death of Cyrus his son Cambyses added Egypt to the Persian Empire, which by 525 B.C. reached from the Indus to the Ægean.

The conquerors were not merely commanders of great armies; they were keen business men as well. East met West along the roads maintained at great cost as lines of military and commercial communication. Postmen appeared, working in relays from point to point. Highway robbery became a less profitable profession. The old caravan route from Sardis to the Euphrates was extended to Susa, the new capital. Throughout its 1,500 miles it was provided with resting-places and watch towers.

Darius I, who followed Cambyses, has been termed the first benevolent monarch.

He ruled the biggest empire that the world had known, and was not disposed to hide his light under a bushel. Yet, while he did not belittle his own achievements, he remembered that he was a disciple of Zoroaster, or Zarathustra as the name is sometimes written. The king paid tribute to the deity whom he worshipped in much the same way as the foundation stones of Christian churches are laid "To the glory of God."

Zoroaster, as Dr. Percy Dearmer reminds us, was "the earliest and one of the greatest of the prophets that humanity has produced, and though his lofty principles and great discoveries were corrupted and overlaid long even before the time of Cyrus, Mazdaism continued to be the inspiration of Persian idealism."

The prophet, who may have lived about 1000 B.C., conceived that life was a great fight between light and darkness, and that man must ally himself to one side or the other. Fire was regarded as a symbol of God, and in modern Iran (Persia) a few priests continue to feed the sacred flame day

SUGGESTING GRACE AND DIGNITY

The Olympieion at Athens, of which only fifteen of the original 104 Corinthian columns remain. Begun about 530 B.C., it was added to at intervals, especially about 170 B.C., and not completed until about A.D. 120. It was of marble, and over 353 feet in length.

and night in their temples. Mithraism, to which reference has been made elsewhere, was a branch of this religion, and Manicheism, traces of which lingered in the mountainous regions of south-east Europe until the middle of the eighteenth century, was influenced by it.

Darius sent an expedition to explore the courses of the Kabul River and the Indus and then to proceed westward to the Isthmus of Suez. He restored to service the long-disused canal connecting the Nile with the Red Sea, coined gold and silver after the manner of the Greeks, whose architects he probably employed at Susa, and appointment of red, and blue, and white, and black marble." The drinking vessels were of gold.

After ruthlessly crushing a revolt of the Greek colonies in Asia Minor subject to Persia, Darius focused his unwelcome attentions on Athens. Lest his purpose should weaken it is said that a servant had to repeat, "Master, remember the Athenians," three times a day. Platæa alone gave practical help to the harassed defenders. It sent 1,000 men. Sparta, urged "not to allow a city most anciently established among the Hellenes to fall into slavery by the means of Barbarians," contributed 2,000 men. Although they arrived too late

THE GLORIOUS FRIEZE KNOWN AS THE ELGIN MARBLES THAT

Portions of the frieze that surrounded the Parthenon at Athens, one of the finest examples of low relief extant, and probably coloured when it was placed in position, may be seen in the British Museum. They were bought by the Government from Lord Elgin in 1816 for £35,000.

pointed satraps or governors to organize the twenty provinces which he created. As to their sources of supply of the precious metal the Persians were as secretive as the deep.

Of the great palace at Susa it is recorded that it had "white, green and blue hangings, fastened with cords of fine linen and purple to silver rings and pillars of marble: the beds were of gold and silver, upon a pave-it was a significant gesture. The threat of conquest by a foreign enemy achieved what nothing else had accomplished, though the realization of Greek unity failed to last. On the Plain of Marathon, some twenty-five miles from Athens, the invaders were defeated by Miltiades with no more than the semblance of an army. The Spartans were allowed a glimpse of the dead. They commended the work and marched home.

Staggered by their amazing victory and flushed with success, the Athenians failed to foresee that so implacable an enemy as Persia was scarcely likely to be thwarted in its ambition by a preliminary set-back. Themistocles, soldier and statesman, was convinced that the enemy would return when he pleased. A second onslaught was inevitable.

He begged and prayed his fellow citizens to prepare, and eventually undermined the fierce opposition that met his bold proposals. So a powerful navy was put on the stocks and the harbour at Piræus was fortified. "Whoso can hold the sea," said

combatants has been suggested as a more probable figure. A powerful fleet of perhaps 1,000 vessels, mainly Phœnician and Egyptian, was also at his command.

Some of the city states, including Sparta, rallied round Athens. A few hundred Spartans held the Pass of Thermopylæ, the key that unlocked the door to central Greece, and by sacrificing themselves, won undying renown. Athens, abandoned on the advice of Themistocles, was set on fire by the ruthless Xerxes, but at Platæa and Mycale on land and at the battle of Salamis at sea, the Persians were beaten.

Successful in uniting the Greek colonies

DECORATED THE GREATEST ARCHITECTURAL MASTERPIECE

It seems almost incredible that previous to the purchase of these magnificent works of art some of the figures had been used as targets, tourists had broken off pieces as souvenirs, and others had been ground to powder by Turkish builders for the purpose of making cement.

Themistocles, "has command of the situation."

The sequel came ten years later when Xerxes, the weak son of a strong father, crossed the Hellespont—now called the Dardanelles—on a bridge of boats, marched through Thrace, and entered Greece. He had a huge army, though the statement of Herodotus that it numbered 1,700,000 men is doubtless grossly exaggerated; 150,000

of Asia Minor and the islands of the Ægean into a confederacy for defence, Athens became mistress of the Ægean. As the treasury was kept for a time on the island of Delos, the confederacy was called the Delian League.

Thus were the foundations of the Athenian Empire laid, but neither well nor truly. The conflict with Persia dragged on until 449 B.C., when peace was restored and the colonial settlements ' regained their liberty.

The dominating personality in Athens at the time was Pericles, one of the ten *strategi* or generals who were elected annually to manage both home and foreign affairs. For thirty years he enjoyed the confidence of the citizens, but he would have failed to maintain this position had he not shown enduring qualities as a statesman, using the term in its widest sense. Pericles not only developed commerce, he also fostered art and the drama, and delighted in the company of poets, historians, architects and sculptors.

Pericles and the Parthenon

He encouraged the building of the marble Parthenon, which crowns the rocky and then fortified Acropolis. Deemed one of the most beautiful buildings in the world, it was begun about 447 B.C., and took nine years to finish. A great ivory and gold statue of Athena by Phidias, 38 feet high, stood in the temple, which was surrounded by a superb frieze. The enclosed outside porch was the treasury of the State and home of the maiden priestesses of the goddess Athena, the Minerva of the Romans.

Portions of the frieze, one of the finest examples of low relief extant, and probably coloured when it was placed in position, may be seen in the British Museum. It seems almost incredible that previous to the purchase some of the figures had been used as targets, tourists had broken off pieces of statuary as souvenirs, and others had been ground to powder for the purpose of making cement.

Temple, Church and Mosque

With superb ingenuity Ictinus, the architect, gave symmetry to the Parthenon by having the columns lean inwards, slightly thickening them in the middle and making them taper at the top. For including a portrait of himself and of Pericles on Athena's shield Phidias was arrested and died in prison. He had profaned the goddess.

The building, converted into a Christian church about the fifth or sixth century A.D., dedicated first to Santa Sophia (the Holy Wisdom) and afterwards to the Virgin Mary, was eventually transformed into a Turkish mosque. A considerable amount of restoration has been done in recent years.

The building projects of Pericles kept many skilful hands busily employed. "The different materials," says Plutarch, "such as stone, brass, ivory, gold, ebony and cypress, furnished employment to carpenters, masons, braziers, goldsmiths, painters, turners and other artificers. The conveyance of them by sea employed merchants and sailors; and by land wheelwrights, wagoners, carriers, rope makers, leather cutters, paviours and ironfounders: and every art had a number of lower people ranged in subordination to execute it, like soldiers under the command of a general. Thus by the exercise of these different trades, plenty was diffused among persons of every rank and condition."

On the south-western side of the Acropolis is a ridge known as the Pnyx. There, with no more exalted pulpit than a block of stone, orators thundered and guided or misguided the multitudes, as their successors do in many a London park today.

Greek Architectural Orders

The architects of Babylonia and Egypt thought in masses of material that symbolized power; those of Greece preferred grace and dignity, balance and proportion.

The three orders of their architecture were the Doric, Ionic and Corinthian, proceeding from the simple to the more elaborate and the ornate. Of none of these styles can it be said that what was aimed at was overdone or fell short of the mark, nor was stability sacrificed to secure the desired effect. The difference between the almost barbaric proportions and ornamentation of the Hall of Columns at Karnak in Egypt and the finesse of the Parthenon and the Olympieion at Athens is very noticeable, though it must not be overlooked that the one was completed several hundred years before the other.

The source of the Doric shaft, the abacus and the architrave has been traced to the Egyptian rock tombs of Beni Hassan. Even the fluting of the columns was not original, for one of wood dating from 2684 B.C. was found at Kahun. The arch, which in Ur goes back to the fourth millennium B.C., was made known to Greece by the returning armies of Alexander the Great. What the Greeks did not originate they refined, and in the long run culture is no more than a series of refinements.

On the whole the Greek gods were rather a jolly and colourful company, for while they were superhuman and immortal, they were neither omnipotent nor omniscient. Their attitude towards mankind was benevolent. They had their headquarters on the snow-capped summit of Mount Olympus. Zeus, whose name is derived from a word meaning sky, was the chief deity. Not all the gods had permanent residence on Olympus, though from time to time they were all summoned there for a general discussion on affairs.

The Greeks learned of these beings from the *Iliad* and the *Odyssey* of Homer. They were doubtless based on a judicious choice of local myths, some of which were probably very old when they were collated. Who Homer was we do not know. The name may be that of an actual individual or an alias for a number of collaborators who flourished about 1,000 years before our era. In any case the epics were regarded in much the same way as Christians esteem the Bible, although there was no suggestion of an inspired revelation.

The stories are exciting and human. Indeed, Lawrence of Arabia avowed that the *Odyssey* "by its ease and interest remains the oldest book worth reading for its story and the first novel of Europe." It tells much about the customs and beliefs of a primitive age, whereas the *Iliad* is largely a record of fighting. Again, as in ancient Egypt,

Babylonia and elsewhere, the sun is the object of man's awe and fascination. In the myths of Greece it is a golden chariot in which Apollo drives in the azure sky during the day; in the evening he vacates his fiery vehicle for the pleasure of playing the lyre.

There is a story of a great flood sent to destroy the wicked and a Noah and his wife in the persons of Deucalion and Pyrrha. In answer to their prayers the gods created men from stones, hence the tribes of the Æolians and the Dorians, the Ionians and the Achæans. These and a multitude of tales, including many that centred round local heroes and heroines, gripped the imagination and fired enthusiasm as they were told and retold by wandering bards.

While the terrifying gods who held mankind in fetters elsewhere had no place in the Grecian catalogue of deities, there was no system of morality such as is evident in the Old Testament, which was gradually being put together at about the same time as the Homeric poems. Yet this liberation of the mind was valuable, for it led to open discussion and tolerance. It broke with a hidebound tradition and paved the way for the higher morality as revealed in the

APOLLO'S TEMPLE AT CORINTH

The three orders of Greek architecture were the Doric, Ionic and Corinthian, proceeding from the simple to the more elaborate and the ornate. These columns are of the Doric order.

philosophies of such thinkers as Socrates, Plato and Epictetus.

The most sacred and secret of the religious rites were the Eleusinian Mysteries, celebrated at Eleusis, a few miles from Athens, where divine secrets were alleged to be revealed. The wild forces of Nature, such as the winds and water, were regarded with deep reverence. The eight-sided Tower of the Winds at Athens still stands, although the weathercock which adorned it is no more. It was the predecessor of the device which once formed an almost essential part of a church steeple.

Divination, by which knowledge of future happenings or guidance on a proposed course of action is sought, was widely practised. The most famous oracle was that of Apollo at Delphi. Here a priestess, aided by volcanic fumes that issued from a fissure in the temple, was "inspired," and her babbling interpreted by priests. There is evidence that considerable skill was shown by the diviners, who were addicted to giving answers that were non-committal and might suggest either of two opposite meanings.

Meanwhile quarrels between Athens and Sparta led to hostilities. Pericles suggested arbitration, but Thebes attacked Platæa and the issue was joined. No formal declaration of war was sent by Sparta, thus setting a precedent followed in our own time.

Athens and Sparta at War

Begun in 431 B.C., the conflict flamed, flickered, smouldered and almost died down, flared up again and ended in 404 B.C. The commercial rivalry of Athens with Ægina and Corinth was at least partly responsible for this lamentable state of affairs. During the protracted course of the Peloponnesian War, carried out with diabolical savagery on both sides, the inspiring Pericles and a third of the population of overcrowded Athens succumbed to plague, an expedition sent against Syracuse met with disaster, and the blockade of the port of Piræus threatened the once proud city with starvation. Besieged by land, her fleet captured, the sowing of corn and its importation rendered impossible, wasted by disease and a further tussle with Persia, the Athenian Empire came to an end in 404 B.C.

The triumph of Sparta was short-lived. Thebes, under Epaminondas, threw off the heavy yoke, but when that gifted leader was killed at the battle of Mantinea he left a feeble country ready to fall into the hands of the first skilful commander who should happen to come along. Such a one arrived in the person of Philip II of Macedon, a country north of Greece.

Demosthenes sought to bring the divided Greeks to unite against Philip, as they had fought together against Persia. He begged them to do something to save their liberty. Condemned on a false charge he fled into exile, to return later to repeat the same passionate plea and to end by suicide.

Philip succeeded in consolidating the Macedonians, created a powerful army, built a navy, gradually extended his territory, annexed seaboard cities, and, save Sparta, made a federal State of Greece with the object of liberating the Asiatic Greeks from Persia and conquering the Orient.

Had an assassin's hand failed in its purpose his son Alexander might have exclaimed with some truth that he had been left without further worlds to conquer, for already Philip's hosts were gathering to his standard for the invasion of Asia.

DEDICATED TO THE WINDS

The Tower of the Winds at Athens, built by Andronicus of Cyrrhus, an astronomer. The wild forces of Nature were regarded with deep awe and reverence by the early Greeks.

CHAPTER 10

TAKING THE WEST TO THE EAST

The first world conqueror. Battle of the Granicus. Tyre besieged. Alexander conquers Egypt. Darius murdered. Founding of new cities. Invasion of India. Nearchus' voyage of exploration. Expedition against Arabia. Death of Alexander. Arts and crafts of ancient India. Alexandria and its wonders. Break-up of the Macedonian Empire. Parchment originates at Antioch. Rhodes repels Antigonus. The Colossus.

P HILIP'S son and successor did far more than win military renown. Alexander created a vast empire, penetrated a considerable distance into northern India, opened up wide territories to trade, released money that had been locked in State coffers, created many new centres for the exchange of goods, and made the West more widely acquainted with the opulence and possibilities of the East. His undertaking was at once a scientific expedition, an exploration and a campaign. It lasted over eight years, during which the army covered more than 11,000 miles.

Greece Conquers Asia

When Alexander started on his conquest of Asia Minor his treasury was sadly depleted, and both his army and his navy were outnumbered, for Cyprus and Phœnicia, with their extensive fleets, were allies of Persia. Near the River Granicus, which the commander crossed in face of the enemy, the Macedonians taught their foes a severe lesson, though it was the hardest battle of the campaign. The Greek mercenaries who had fought for the enemy and were taken prisoners were sent back to Macedonia till the soil. Halicarnassus (Budrum) was a hard nut to crack, but it eventually yielded. It was set on fire by its defenders, an example followed shortly afterwards by the citizens of Marmaria.

At Issus the Persian King Darius III suffered defeat, and Alexander began the conquest of Phœnicia. Byblus was occupied, Sidon welcomed the invader, but Tyre was in no mood for humble submission. She would probably have proved a very serious stumbling-block to the Macedonians had not the fleets of other Phœnician cities and of Cyprus thrown in their lot with the invaders. After a siege lasting for seven months the Tyrian fleet was captured, thousands of citizens were butchered, and thousands more sold into slavery.

Alexander now began his march to Egypt, then under the yoke of the Persians. To the people of the Land of the Pharaohs Alexander appeared in the guise of a deliverer. Welcomed by Pelusium and Memphis, the capital, the liberator looked about for a site suitable for a Greek colony that would form a centre for the great influx of trade that was bound to come as a result of his conquests, and also be a half-way house between the old and new territories of his rapidly growing dominions He decided on a spot near the mouth of the Nile, and here he built Alexandria.

While he was reorganizing the government Alexander visited the oracle of Amon at Siwa, in the Sahara, where it is said he was hailed as a god, though the matter is disputed by some modern historians. This is supposed to have made a deep impression on him, for the Pharaohs had been regarded as divine. "Thus," to quote Breasted, "were introduced into Europe absolute monarchy, and the divine right of kings."

Fall of Babylon

The armies of Alexander and Darius came face to face at Gaugamela, on the Bumodus (Ghazir). Although they had vastly superior numbers, the Persians were overwhelmed, and Alexander entered Babylon and Susa, the latter city affording him treasure to the amount of 50,000 talents of silver (about £12,000,000). With poetic justice Alexander entered Persepolis, through the gates of which Persian hordes once poured for the invasion of Greece. No opposition was offered. It is said that wealth reaching some £25,000,000 fell into the hands of the victorious Macedonian Darius, however, was still at large, and his eastern satrapies—provinces under a

DARIUS FLEEING FROM THE FIELD OF BATTLE

The Persian King Darius III retreating from the battle of Issus (333 B.C.), which marked the end of Persian world domination. After this battle, Alexander began the conquest of Phœnicia. Part of a mosaic of the third century B.C. found at Pompeii.

viceroy—remained loyal. Hearing that he was at Ecbatana (Hamadan), in Media, Alexander pushed on, but his wily enemy again eluded him. Alexander made his way into Parthia, covering 256 miles in six days and leaving all but a few hundred men behind him in the race, to find that Darius had been murdered by Bessus, a satrap of Bactria (Bokhara). The traitor had been proclaimed general of the Persian army by the troops and had crowned himself as Artaxerxes.

Hyrcania, on the south shore of the Caspian Sea, submitted to the Greek king, and marching through Gedrosia (Baluchistan) he founded a second Alexandria, possibly the city now known as Kandahar. A third city, also of the same name, was ordered to be built at the foot of the Paropanisus (Hindu-Kush), over the pass by which generations of traders had gone from India to Bokhara and Ispahan.

Crossing the snow-clad mountains, Alex-

ander advanced into Bactria, toiled through the scorching desert, navigated the Oxus (Amu Daria), and entered Sogdiana (Turkestan), the furthest limit of the Persian Empire. Bessus was captured and afterwards put to death. On reaching the Jaxartes (Syr Daria), the victor founded the fourth city of Alexandria (Khojend), which he called Alexandria the Farthest, on the road that led over the Tien-Shan mountains to China.

Two reasons induced Alexander to continue his campaign. Persia had once ruled the wealthy territories of the Punjab, Afghanistan, and Kashmir, and his sense of the fitness of things did not allow him to be satisfied with anything less. This we may regard as his personal point of view. But it was also part of a wider policy. Trade would help to weld his great empire together.

In 326 B.C. he crossed the Indus, believing it to be a continuation of the Nile, so vague was geographical knowledge at that time. Then he made the passage of the Hydaspes

(Jhelum), inflicted a heavy defeat on an Indian prince who afterwards became his willing ally, and founded the cities of Nicæa (Mong) and Bucephala (Jhelum).

After crossing the Hyphasis (Beas), his army stubbornly refused to proceed further. The men were worn out and homesick, exhausted with the heat and turmoil of the long and trying campaign. For days the commander sulked in his tent, expecting the soldiers to relent. They did nothing of the kind. So Alexander turned back, not at the sword-point of his enemies, but at the behest of his friends.

The king was in less haste than his warriors. He took his time. He had been disillusioned about the Nile, and was told that the Hydaspes and Acesines (Chenab) joined the Indus, which flowed into an ocean by which the Euphrates and Tigris could be reached. A great fleet was built and the ships started off. The soldiers for whom accommodation could not be provided marched along the banks.

At the junction of the Acesines and the Indus he established the fifth city of Alexandria, and a sixth lower down. After reducing Sind he pushed on to Patala, where he gave orders for the building of yet another city, and then proceeded down the Buggaur until at last he reached the mouth of the King River of Vedic poetry.

Alexander now determined upon sending Nearchus, the commander of the fleet, on a voyage of exploration on what he called the Great Sea. His objective was the Persian Gulf, but he was also to "explore the coast to see what harbours and islands were there, and if any gulf ran into the land to sail round it; to find out what cities were on the sea coast, and see if any of the country was fertile, and if any was deserted."

One wing of Alexander's army marched by way of Afghanistan, and the other under his immediate command via Baluchistan. Another city of Alexandria was founded, and stores were left and wells dug for the use of the fleet, but he lost heavily in men owing to lack of food and water as they traversed the seemingly unending waste. After almost incredible agonies those who survived caught a glimpse of Pura, where

PANELLED GRANDEUR OF A PERSIAN PALACE

A section of the beautiful panelling at Persepolis, once the capital of Persia. If placed together the reliefs would form a panel almost 1,000 feet in length. After overwhelming Darius' army and conquering Babylon and Susa, Alexander with poetic justice entered the city through the gates of which Persian hordes once poured for the invasion of Greece

they rested to recover their strength before proceeding to Susa.

Nearchus and his crew had also suffered many privations, including the loss of three ships, while several others had been severely damaged. Their first encounter with whales was the sight of "the water of the sea being blown upwards as if being borne violently aloft from the action of bellows."

Nearchus' Amazing Voyage

The navigator landed on the Kirman coast, and after proceeding along the Persian Gulf, sailed up the Tigris to Susa. He had discovered the sea route from India to Babylonia, as his master had opened up vast territory on land. Probably no recipient was more worthy of the golden chaplet.

Preparing for the conquest of Arabia, Alexander proceeded to Babylon, where Nearchus had already arrived. The city became a hive of activity. Sailors were sent to develop the resources of the Persian Gulf. An army of men began the construction of a harbour planned on a scale sufficiently large to cope with any possible development for years to come. Ships were built.

Alexander's ambition to make the old city a vast emporium was not realized, for Seleucia, on the Tigris, became the leading centre for trade. Expeditions were sent to attempt to reach Egypt by circumnavigating Arabia, but none succeeded.

Full of plans for the development of his empire, the man who had sighed for other worlds to conquer and found them was stricken with fever. He listened with eager interest to the glowing story that Nearchus had to tell of his exploits. Then, a day or two later, on June 13, 323 B.C., only thirty-three years of age, Alexander the Great died.

Collapse of a World-Empire

The attempt to weld politically West and East had failed. Though Greek culture was widely diffused and reciprocal trade relations were established, though the conqueror wedded Asiatic women, introduced subject races into the Macedonian army, and sought in many other ways to establish a commonwealth of nations, his empire crumbled. Yet had it not been for him, as Professor Rudolph von Scala remarks, "No Roman world empire, no world-embracing Christianity, no Byzantine empire, with Asia Minor, Syria, Egypt as provinces, would have been possible."

Of the arts of ancient India we learn much from the *Rig-Veda*, the great Hindu religious poem composed perhaps about 1500 B.C. Chariots, carts, ships, battle-axes, swords, mailed armour, helmets, breast-plates, crowns, necklaces, bracelets and anklets of gold, and towers of iron and of stone are catalogued. Wig makers carried on their trade in India twelve centuries before the birth of Christ, as did dyers, tanners, engravers and painters.

Megasthenes, the Greek ambassador who reached the Court of Patna six years after the death of Alexander, was dazzled by figured garments of finest muslin, robes ornamented with precious stones and worked in gold, and jewelled vessels and ornaments. He notes that "underground" were "numerous veins of all sorts of metals" containing "much gold and silver, and copper and iron in no small quantity, and even tin and other metals, which are employed in making articles of use and ornaments, as well as implements of war."

Wonders of Ancient India

Officials supervised the manufactures of the energetic Hindus, and although there was not a Workmen's Compensation Act, heavy punishments were exacted for causing personal injury. "Of the artisans," Megasthenes reports, "some are armourers, while others make the implements which husbandmen and others find useful in their different callings. This class is not only exempted from paying taxes, but even receives maintenance from the royal exchequer."

What Alexander was unable to do at Babylon was achieved at Alexandria, which became a hive of industry as well as the centre of the world's commerce. Here glassblowers and carpet weavers, incense and papyrus makers, cameo cutters and craftsmen in metal went about their various tasks, while merchants were busy buying the products of Africa, Arabia, and India, and dockers unloaded the Nile Valley harvests.

In course of time the city had its stadium and other public buildings, a superb library of 400,000 works that attracted scholars from near and far, and a mighty lighthouse that proclaimed the importance of its shipping and trading interests and was regarded as one of the seven wonders of the world. The lay-out of the city was a worthy effort in town planning.

Some of the Greek States, jealous of Macedonian supremacy, had endeavoured to break away during Alexander's lifetime; all Greece revolted at his death. His generals, enamoured of power, warred among themselves and divided the Empire. From administrators they became kings: Antigonus in Macedonia, Seleucus in Syria, and Ptolemy in Egypt.

Though the countries were split and divided, the influence of Hellenic culture was not lost. Greek kings and Greek courts, Greek soldiers, philosophers, artisans, merchants and colonists were the human channels by which the stream of Western thought was conveyed to Eastern lands. Greek art influenced Buddhist artists, as has been proved by the excavation of shrines and monasteries at Swat, on the North-West Frontier.

Antioch, the capital of Syria, developed into an important trading entrepôt, and remained so until a series of earthquakes razed it to the ground. Pergamum, in Asia Minor, which a Greek army officer seized on the assassination of Seleucus, was not only great commercially but became an important centre of ancient civilization.

Its library was rivalled only by that of Alexandria. Its scribes, unable to obtain papyrus, used *pergamentum* (parchment), made from the skins of animals and consequently far more endurable than the vegetable fibre. The kingdom was eventually bequeathed to the Roman Republic, and renamed the province of Asia.

The island city of Rhodes also flourished amazingly after its deliverance by Alexander the Great. For a time its ships and mariners became the principal carriers of the Mediterranean. Its soldiers fought on the side of Ptolemy against Antigonus, and when the latter sent a fleet and an army against Rhodes the former did not forget his old allies but came to their rescue, with the result that the Macedonians were compelled to withdraw. To commemorate the event, and in honour of the sun god, the islanders erected the Colossus, that wonder of the ancient world, which crashed to the ground during an earthquake in 224 B.C.

THE PASSING OF ALEXANDER THE GREAT

Full of plans for the development of his empire, the man who had sighed for other worlds to conquer was fatally stricken with fever. Alexander the Great died on June 13, 323 B.C.

CHAPTER 11

THINKERS PLOUGH LONELY FURROWS

Socrates, teacher of Greece. "Know thyself." Trial and death of a world hero. Plato's ideal republic. Aristotle, explorer of Nature. Greek science and medicine. Archimedes the engineer. Origins of Chinese civilization. Confucius. Lao-tze the mystic. Gautama and his religion. What Buddhism teaches. Asoka, pacifist emperor. Who was the Pharaoh of the Bible? Code of Hammurabi. From Moses to Jesus.

DEEDS are more important than words, though often the latter lead to the former. That is why the man of action looms larger in the public eye than the philosopher.

Today the individual who accomplishes the spectacular gets a better Press, he is front page news; in ancient times he was the subject of livelier gossip at the street corners and in the market place. Yet it is evident that thinking must precede doing, even though the process be performed at lightning speed, as when a motorist by a dexterous turn of his steering-wheel saves a jaywalker from sudden death. Sustained thinking is not without complications. What is called inspiration is usually the result of continued concentration, and in no way deserves a name that implies incredible swiftness of enlightenment.

Greece Begins to Think

Pondering quietly in the midst of the busy, talkative life of some of the Greek city states, though by no means shut off from it unless by compulsion—which occasionally happened—a number of men puzzled over things in a way that most of their contemporaries regarded as sheer waste of time. They asked themselves questions about such matters as man and morals, Nature and the universe, and sought an answer. Many of these problems seemed to be no more than remotely practical. They had no apparent bearing on everyday life, and that was the only phase of existence that mattered to the rank and file. Mooning about brought neither bread nor olives.

About the year 469 B.C. a midwife living in Athens presented her husband, who was a stonemason and sculptor, with a son. They gave him the name of Socrates. The father's lot in life was to conjure beauty from rough material. It must therefore have struck him with a deep sense of irony that the older his boy became the uglier he grew. He had an almost flat nose, thick lips, bulgy eyes and a stocky frame. This grotesqueness was accentuated by a total disregard for the niceties of dress. Even when called up for military service, during which he served in three campaigns, Socrates failed to develop a military bearing. Weather did not seem to affect him. He wore clothes of the same thickness summer and winter.

The reason for this unusual attitude towards material things was that Socrates lived in a world of his own, the world of thought. He also, all unsuspected, was fashioning beauty from rough material. It seems strange that such a man should have married, but it would have been stranger still had his matrimonial venture proved successful. His wife Xantippe was a scold and seldom gave her spouse a minute's peace. Not that she saw a great deal of him. He was usually talking somewhere in Athens at a distance sufficiently far removed from wifely restraint and admonition.

Socrates, Wisest of Men

Both husband and wife have come down in history. The oracle of Apollo at Delphi avowed that: "There is no man wiser than Socrates"; Xantippe is regarded as the embodiment of shrewishness. Doubtless there were faults on both sides. The man would accept no fees from his pupils, did not even take up a collection to defray expenses, and the woman had to earn the living of both.

The philosopher's method was to gather a little congregation in a quiet spot and catechize them. They must have been a motley throng, with idle listeners in the majority, hangers-on anxious to kill time,

126

and a few ardent spirits anxious to learn. When the speaker became a "character" his fame grew and with it the crowd.

Socrates asked questions, listened to answers when they were forthcoming, and then put forward his own point of view, which was usually illuminating if contradictory. So far as we know he never "laid down the law"—it was Xantippe who did that after he had exhausted the patience of his hearers and returned home.

He never posed as the final authority. He suggested rather than stated. His daily text was: "Know thyself." In our day Socrates would be numbered in the ranks of the rationalists. Although no dogmatist, the philosopher was an ardent and fearless critic of shams and poses. He would have men put aside conventional morality and be honest with themselves: "Man's invisible conscience is, or ought to be, the ultimate measure of all things. It is not the gods but we ourselves who shape our destiny."

Socrates queried everything, was indeed a kind of personal interrogation mark always seeking an answer to Why? What?

When? How? Of course he was laughed at as well as applauded. Aristophanes, who wrote some forty plays, of which only eleven are extant, the sole survivors of all the Greek comedies, ridiculed him in *Clouds*.

Terming himself a citizen of the world, Socrates believed that if one knew the path of virtue one would necessarily follow it, that self-knowledge led to morality. He failed to realize that while conscience may prompt, the mentor may be disregarded. The "still small voice" is by no means automatic in operation. Knowledge and morality do not necessarily go hand in hand. If they did, man's record would be very different, and Lord Acton would not have been compelled to admit that for the most part history has been made by bad men.

When he was seventy years of age Socrates was accused of impiety and corrupting the minds of youth. At the trial he met the charges fearlessly. "If you propose to acquit me," he told the jury, "on condition that I abandon my search for truth, I will say: I thank you, O Athenians, but I will obey God, who, as I believe, set me this

PRISON OF A GREAT GREEK PHILOSOPHER

The cave at Athens in which Socrates was imprisoned on being condemned for impiety and corrupting the minds of youth. He told the jury that so long as he lived he would never cease from his occupation of philosophy. They found him guilty by a majority of 110 votes.

task, rather than you, and so long as I have breath and strength I will never cease from my occupation with philosophy. I will continue the practice of accosting whomsoever I meet and saying to him: 'Are you not ashamed of setting your heart on wealth and honours, while you have no care for wisdom and truth and making your soul better?' I know not what death is—it may be a good thing, and I am not afraid of it. But I do know that it is a bad thing to desert one's post, and I prefer what may be good to what I know to be bad."

Nothing Evil to the Good

He believed that death was gain, whether it were a dreamless sleep or a migration to another land where one would associate with a glorious companionship. He cited the names of various Greek heroes, and again his inquisitiveness came to the fore. "It would be an unspeakable happiness to examine these," he asserted, "or ten thousand others—for there, I fancy, they do not put to death those who thus question them. Be hopeful then, gentlemen of the jury, as to death; and this one thing hold fast, that to a good man, whether alive or dead, no evil can happen, nor are the gods indifferent to his well-being."

Unfortunately there is no record of the speeches of the philosopher's accusers. He was condemned to death by a majority of 110 votes. Allowed to receive friends, he chatted with them as though he had many years to live instead of no more than thirty days. He could easily, with their help, have escaped had he been so minded.

Socrates' Last Moments

The passing of Socrates was in keeping with his life. Greek criminals were not hanged or executed but given poison. When the cup of hemlock was offered to him, he received it with a steady hand. "What do you say about pouring out a part of this potion as a libation to some god? Is that allowed?" he questioned. He was told that only sufficient for the immediate purpose was made. "I understand," replied the brave old man, "but just to pray to the gods is allowed and is right, that the change of home from here to there may be happy; and this I do pray, and so may it be."

His last words were: "Crito, we owe a cock to Æsculapius; pay it and don't forget." Whether this was a final fling against conventional ideas, or was said in a humorous way because it was usual to

sacrifice to the god of healing after recovering from illness is uncertain. Socrates lapsed into unconsciousness. He had solved the last and greatest of his riddles.

So far as we know the philosopher committed nothing to writing. What he said was recorded for posterity by Plato, a wealthy young aristocrat, a grandson of Solon, and an oil merchant. His real name was Aristocles; that by which he is called is an abbreviated form of Platon, meaning broad-shouldered, a title bestowed on him by his sports master. As the disciple not only carried on but developed his master's teaching, it is difficult to disentangle their philosophies from each other.

In a grove called Academus, near Athens, Plato set up a school where he continued to teach until he was an old man. The name of the place is recalled in our word "academy," the garden or villa receiving its title from Academus, an Attic hero to whom the place is said to have originally belonged. He taught at the academy for forty years and, according to Cicero, died "pen in hand."

Plato's writings are principally in the form of dialogues between Socrates and his followers, but the most widely read and important of his books is his *Republic*, the forerunner of many literary Utopias.

Plato's Ideal State

The great thinker's ideal form of government has a benevolent tyrant at the head of affairs and a philosopher as guide and counsellor. Although he took no dismal view of man's future, and believed that man by a process of moral evolution went from good to better, Plato's republic is suggestive of the modern totalitarian state. It is certainly not a democracy. There were specific tasks for everybody. Each and all had to regard the rules and regulations laid down for them, be they freemen or slaves, warriors or weavers, under pain of penalty. The country is everything, the individual nothing.

Plato would have men study arithmetic, geometry and astronomy. He regarded the world as endowed with knowledge, and believed in a former existence and the immortality of the soul. There are contradictions in his teaching, as there are contradictions in all human philosophies. He did not believe, for instance, in returning good for evil, yet his own personal petition represented so high an ethical ideal that it is almost word for word that of the greatest

CONDEMNED TO COMMIT SUICIDE

The passing of Socrates was in keeping with his life. Greek criminals were not hanged or executed but given poison. When the cup of hemlock was offered to him, he received it with a steady hand and lapsed into unconsciousness. The philosopher had solved his riddles.

moral teacher of all time. "And may I," he prayed, "being of sound mind, do to others as I would that they should do to me." The parallel, known familiarly as the Golden Rule, is: "And as ye would that men should do to you, do ye also to them likewise."

Plato's most famous pupil was Aristotle, whose interests were so wide that they embraced physics, metaphysics, psychology, rhetoric, politics, ethics, poetics, natural history and logic, of which last he was the founder. His teaching made so indelible an impression on the thought of the Western World that for centuries it was supreme. His findings were regarded as virtually inviolable; he was a veritable pope of knowledge.

The bright light shed by the Renaissance disclosed cobwebs in the dusty corners of some of Aristotle's conclusions. His dictum that heavy bodies fall more swiftly than light ones, and that the rate of speed is in proportion to the weight of the object was steadfastly believed in until Galileo, between the years 1589 and 1591, proved by a simple experiment that objects of different weights falling from the same height reached the ground at the same time.

MAN—E

For nearly 2,000 years the authority of Aristotle had held. Although it is unthinkable that nobody had tested the assertion, certainly nobody in authority had been so rash as to contradict it in the light of what he must have found to be the truth.

This is not to minimize Aristotle's achievements, which, without exaggeration, may be termed prodigious. Darwin himself saluted his Greek predecessor. "From quotations I had a high notion of Aristotle's merits," he wrote, "but I had not the most remote notion what a wonderful man he was. Linnæus and Cuvier have been my two gods, though in very different ways; but they were mere schoolboys to old Aristotle."

When Alexander was thirteen years of age King Philip of Macedon made Aristotle his son's tutor. His maxims, then and afterwards, were in the main entirely unsuited to the special requirements of a pupil whose ambitions were almost boundless. What might be considered as applicable to a Greek city-state did not serve the best interests of an empire that was to embrace vast areas of East and West.

No believer in equality, Aristotle held that Asiatics were by nature slaves, incapable of virtue, and should be treated as such. The foreigner was ever the "barbarian," useful for providing human chattels, whom he termed "living instruments." It was beyond the power of Alexander or of any mortal to remove geographical divisions, but he did seek to remove the barriers of race and prejudice, a hope which remains unaccomplished to this day.

"To my father I owe my life," said Alexander, "to Aristotle the knowledge how to live worthily." Hundreds of natural history specimens were collected during his campaigns and dispatched to Aristotle, who had returned to Athens to establish the Lyceum, a school so called from its nearness to the temple of Apollo Lyceus. Here, wandering up and down the *peripatos*, or pavement, he discoursed to pupils who boasted no kingly rank.

Aristotle's Universal Mind

Aristotle had an encyclopædic mind. He attempted too much, but he achieved a very great deal. He tried to work out a complete scheme of the universe, searching for facts, prying for details, observing, collating and copying. He invented technical terms that became the language of the scientist and the despair of the layman.

His investigations varied from the four-chambered stomach of cows to the constitutions of 158 city-states. Whereas Plato avowed that "Trees and fields tell me nothing; men are my teachers," Aristotle learned from everything. Plato lived in the clouds, Aristotle on earth.

He believed that history moved in eternal cycles, "the age of man, government, and the earth itself with its blossoming and withering away," a theory also held by Plato, Empedocles and Zeno, and other Greek philosophers. "Man," he asserted in a sentence much quoted, "is a political animal, born in association with other men; he cannot attain either virtue or happiness as an isolated individual."

Thales Discovers Electricity

Accused of impiety, as Socrates had been, Aristotle fled to Chalcis, in the island of Eubœa, where he died in 322 B.C., having spent the greater part of his sixty-three years of life in learning and revealing what he had learned.

Speculation rather than experiment was the keynote of Greek science. Thales of Miletus, who combined research with the selling of salt, made discoveries in geo-metry, suggested that water was the origin of all things, wrote a book on medicine and predicted an eclipse of the sun. To the astonishment of all who heard the prophecy it was fulfilled. Nor were these the only matters in which he took an interest. He discovered electricity by noticing that when amber was rubbed it attracted any light bodies, and that the lodestone attracted iron in a similar way. Amber was then called electron, and from it the word "electricity" is derived.

Anaximander, a contemporary and fellow-citizen, is said to have made a sundial, and to have stated that the light of the moon was the reflection of the sun. Socrates may have been a pupil of Anaxagoras, who argued that natural causes were responsible for much that was attributed to the gods. He paved the way for the atomic theory suggested by Democritus, who avowed that the Milky Way was made up of myriads of stars, a discovery that may have been brought about by the invention of some rudimentary form of telescope. It was he who laid down the principle that "only that society is worth while which offers to the largest number of people the greatest amount of happiness obtainable with the smallest amount of pain."

Father of Medicine

His most famous pupil was Hippocrates, who flatly declined to certify his old master insane. Known as the Father of Medicine, Hippocrates was the first practitioner to systematize the treatment of disease, which he termed acute, chronic, endemic or epidemic according to its nature. Health was dependent on the correct proportions of what he termed "humours," namely blood, phlegm, yellow bile and black bile. The next time you refer to a man as phlegmatic or as holding a jaundiced view of things, try to remember the patient investigator of the fifth century B.C., who strove to rid medicine of magic formulas and incantations and helped to lay the foundations of sane practice by eliminating fancy from fact.

Hippocrates would have gone much further had he been allowed to dissect human bodies, but this was forbidden. The prohibition was removed later, and at Alexandria medical men could do what they willed with the corpses of criminals. Hippocrates was not too proud to admit failure or to confess that he was ignorant. "I have written this down deliberately," he notes,

PLATO AND HIS DISCIPLE ARISTOTLE

Plato's writings are principally in the form of dialogues between Socrates and his followers, but the most widely read of his books is his "Republic," the forerunner of many literary Utopias. His most famous pupil was Aristotle. His teaching made such an impression on the thought of the Western World that for centuries it was supreme. His findings were regarded as virtually inviolable. Aristotle is shown holding his "Ethics," and Plato his "Timæus."

CHINESE BURIAL FIGURE

A Chinese burial figure 1,300 years old. Legend has it that previous to about 2800 B.C. the people of the country were barbarians of the most primitive type.

"for it is valuable to learn of unsuccessful experiments, and to know the causes of their non-success."

Archimedes turned from pure science to invention almost under compulsion, applying his reasoning, as Plutarch phrases it, "to the uses of common life." Although it is said that he was the first to appreciate the power of a lever, stating that if he had a place to stand and to rest his lever on he could move the world, this is open to question. It is only reasonable to assume that the builders of the Egyptian Pyramids and others who had to deal with great masses of stone must have had knowledge of such an appliance.

What probably is meant is that the famous citizen of Syracuse developed the application of the tool. With a system of levers and pulleys he overcame the almost insuperable

difficulty of launching a heavy ship. He invented the Archimedean screw, by means of which water was raised by a screw or helix which turned in a tube from a lower to a higher level, and he discovered the law of specific gravity.

When Syracuse was besieged Archimedes invented powerful engines for its defence and suggested destroying the Roman fleet by means of burning glasses that would direct the sun's rays upon the vessels. Although his contrivances did not prevent defeat, they enabled the defenders to offer a spirited resistance.

When the victors entered the city Archimedes was stabbed owing to the mistaken zeal of a soldier who apparently was unaware that orders had been given that the life of the famous physicist was to be spared. He was found studying geometrical problems which he had roughly marked out in sand on a board. "Don't disturb my circles!" he begged.

In their different ways the thinkers of Greece illuminated a path that was to lead to the day of greater things in which we live. They were not unique in this. Far away, in what were then the remote countries of India and China, philosophers were also endeavouring to find out the meaning and purpose of life and to make it livable.

The brief survey already given of the history of Egypt and the countries of the fertile crescent of Asia Minor shows the great importance of rivers, the fingers that point to the sea. Two fertile streams were factors in the making of Chinese civilization. These are the Yangtze and the Hoangho, familiarly known as the Yellow River.

Between them, in the centre of the country, the first rude inhabitants probably settled. Legend has it that previous to the time of Fu-hsi, about 2800 B.C., the people were barbarians of the most primitive type, but that under his careful tutelage they were taught to farm and fish, to write, and more or less generally behave themselves.

China's Earliest Rulers

His successor, Shen-nung, known as the Divine Husbandman, continued to deserve well of his people and earned their eternal gratitude by inventing the plough while, during the rule of Huang-ti, his immediate follower, the development of arts and crafts went on apace. Boats plied their oars, and carts trundled along highways that could have been little better than parallel ruts

It is said that his consort obtained threads of gossamer from silkworms, the secret of which was closely guarded from any new-comer and led to the development of a big industry.

Between 1800 and 1700 B.C., a certain amount of trade was done in the importing of carpets, and some years previous to the introduction of ring money in 1110 B.C., jade was imported from Turkestan. Money as such was not in circulation in China until about 600 B.C., long after the country had started mining gold, silver, copper and tin. A century later iron was in general use. Traders were regarded as occupying a place at the bottom of the social scale.

Master K'ung

It remained for Confucius, most famous of Chinese seers, to show that business was something more than a necessary evil, and the social position of those engaged in it thereupon improved so much that traders were regarded as only one step below scholars; the last had almost become first.

The real name of the teacher was K'ung, to which his followers added Fu-tze, which means the Master. When Christian mission-aries journeyed into the Yellow Kingdom they turned K'ung Fu-tze into Confucius. Although he was born five and a half centuries before the coming of Christ, his ideal of life and conduct influences hun-dreds of millions of people today.

Confucius never ceased to teach his dis-ciples to study. "The love of humanity," he said, "not tempered with the love of study, is blind as to its foolishness." His whole teaching was based on his own intimate knowledge of the past. He delved deep into books that told, or pretended to tell, of the life of the nation for thousands of years before he was born, and thus began that love of yesterday that was to influence his whole outlook on life.

Having married early, he obtained a post as keeper of the grain stores for the ruler of the district in which he lived, and later became superintendent of en-closures and herds. Eventually Con-fucius made up his mind to devote him-self entirely to teaching, and asked to be relieved of his official position. He did not start a school, but became a tutor of young men of good family who could afford to travel. With them he toured the country.

We have a glimpse of the sad condi-tions of the people in three sentences written by Mencius, one of the great fol-lowers of the master. "The world had fallen into decay, and right principles had dis-appeared. Perverse speech and oppressive deeds were waxen rife. Ministers murdered their rulers, and sons their fathers. Con-fucius," he adds, "was frightened by what he saw, and undertook the work of reformation."

To "pacify all under heaven" was this ancient philosopher's way of referring to the more modern brotherhood of men Again, "Let young people show filial piety at home and respectfulness toward their elders when away from home," he advised. "Let them be cautious and truthful, their love going out freely toward all, cultivating goodwill to men. And if in such a walk there be time and energy left for other things, let them employ it in wise reading and acquiring accomplishments in art and in music."

There is much more to similar effect. Reverence for ancestors is the leading tenet of the Confucian philosophy; the worship of Heaven was for the Emperor only. "A noble-minded man," Confucius asserted, "has four rules to regulate his conduct; to serve his sovereign in such a manner as is required of a subject; to serve his father in the manner required of a son; to serve his elder brother in such a manner as is required of a younger brother; to set the example of dealing with his friends in such a manner as is required of friends."

SPIDER SEALED IN AMBER
Speculation was the keynote of Greek science. Thales of Miletus discovered electricity by noticing that when amber was rubbed it attracted any light bodies in its neighbourhood

It was not until the twentieth century, when thousands of women in the fighting line or conducting guerilla warfare challenged the Japanese invaders, that women were regarded as of much consequence in China. This may be traced, in part at least, to the doctrine of Confucius. "Man," says the sage, "is the representative of Heaven, and is supreme over all things. Woman yields obedience to the instructions of man, and helps to carry out his principles. . . . Woman's business is simply the preparation and supplying of wine and food. Beyond the threshold of her apartments she should not be known, for evil or for good."

The philosopher uses the term Heaven in preference to the name of God. The reason is that long before his birth the Supreme Ruler of the universe had always been known as Tien (Heaven) and that the creed Confucius taught related to moral conduct in this world.

When he was asked whether there was any one word that would serve as a rule of conduct, the teacher answered "reciprocity," which means equal rights. "What you do not want done to yourself," he added,

IN HONOUR OF CONFUCIUS
An ancient monument to Confucius, the most famous of Chinese seers. It is in Shantung, the province in which he was born.

"do not do to others." Lao-tze, a contemporary mystic, taught that one should repay evil with good, but Confucius retorted: "Then what will you return for good? Repay evil with justice, and good with good."

Confucius thought to bring about the moral and national reformation of China by good conduct. The subjects of the Emperor had definite responsibilities to the monarch, but those in authority also had obligations. "Let your desires," he writes, "be for what is good, and the people will be good. The relation between superiors and inferiors is like that between the wind and the grass. The grass must bend when the wind blows across it."

An opportunity to test their theories has not always come to the world's great thinkers; it was given to Confucius. The reigning Duke of Lu, impressed by the marked progress of the philosopher's teaching, appointed him chief magistrate of the city of Chung-tu. Eminently successful in this, he was given a post of almost unlimited authority.

Although one can scarcely believe the literal truth of the statement that during his administration "a thing dropped on the road was not picked up, and no two prices were charged in the markets," there is no doubt that the reforms he introduced were beneficial to the people of the country.

Wanderings of Confucius

Confucius believed that the example set at Chung-tu would compel the remainder of China to follow suit. With it would come the pacification of "all under heaven." His triumph was his undoing. Jealous of the marked progress of Chung-tu, the ruler of a neighbouring state set about undermining the authority of Confucius, and he succeeded in this only too well.

Reluctantly the sage bade farewell to the court and pursued his way. Doubtless he would secure a similar position elsewhere. For a time his hope sufficed, but as he went from state to state he found he was not wanted. His wanderings lasted thirteen years, and he knew what it was to go hungry and homeless.

While the Master was thinking out his scheme of life Lao-tze was perfecting his own plan. Both were searching for the road that leads to perfection, though approaching it by different routes.

The founder of what is now called Taoism once referred to the way as "very level and easy, but people love the by-ways." No positive definition of what is meant by "the way" is extant. Professor Max Müller came to the conclusion that in Nature "the way" meant the law and order evident in the universe, "sometimes also something very like Providence, only not like a personal God," and that "if the individual acts as he acts because he cannot help it, he acts in conformity with his Tao (the way)."

Three Precious Things

"There are three precious things," the philosopher remarks, "which I prize and hold. The first is gentle kindness, the second is economy, the third is humility."

During the passage of the centuries the teaching of Lao-tze has undergone many changes. It has borrowed much from Buddhism, which was introduced from India probably before the first century A.D. In a Taoist temple will be found images of the three Holy Ones, namely the Almighty, Lao-tze and the God of the physical world, just as there are often representations of the three Precious Ones in a Chinese Buddhist temple.

As a general rule the Chinese are not strict adherents of any one religion. They are apt to pick out what they consider to be useful to them from the creeds of which they have heard. Mohammedanism, introduced during the seventh century A.D., is estimated as having from 15 to 20 million adherents in China. Christianity was taken to that country by a Nestorian priest in 635.

While Confucius was working to better human conditions in China, a Hindu prince was striving towards the same end in another way. The lot of Siddhartha Gautama, the son of a petty ruler, was cast in pleasant places, but when he began to compare his easy existence with the care-worn lives of many of his father's subjects, the contrast filled him with despair. Why should he be in a position to demand and get, while others asked and seldom received? Why this distinction? Had life a meaning, or was it no more than a something that had to be endured? Was it possible that if he abandoned luxury and went into the highways and ditches he would find what he sought?

Gautama went through an agonizing mental struggle before he decided to abandon the pomp and circumstance of his social position. Then he went to his wife's room, where she was sleeping peacefully

AFGHANISTAN'S GIANT BUDDHA
This statue of Buddha, 172 feet in height, dominates the Bamian Valley. At one time the stone robe was covered with gold leaf.

with her recently born and only child in her arm, took a silent farewell and left.

He sought out learned ascetics and practised what they taught for several years. Happiness eluded him. Plain living and high thinking had availed him nothing. "Not nakedness," he asserted, "not plaited hair, not dirt, not fasting, not lying on the earth, not rubbing with dust, not sitting motionless, can purify a mortal who has not overcome desires."

One day, as he sat under a fig tree—afterwards to be known as the Bo-tree, the tree of knowledge—enlightenment came. Man was the slave of his cravings. The Greek Cynics taught much the same thing.

Get rid of craving, said Buddha, and peace will take its place. This was to be accomplished by following the eightfold path to holiness, which included not only right thought and right aspiration, but right speech, right behaviour, right occupation, right effort, right attention and right concentration. When selfishness has been completely overcome the state of Nirvana is reached. Nirvana is not annihilation, as Europeans once believed. It is serenity.

FOUR GREAT MOMENTS
A stele from Sarnath, India, representing Buddha's birth and enlightenment, his first sermon and his attainment of Nirvana.

Christianity teaches that when a man dies his soul leaves his body; the Buddhist holds that what departs is *karma*, that is, to quote Professor P. V. N. Myers: "something which is the net product of all the good and evil acts of the person in all his various existences—a sort of seed or germ from which will spring up here, on earth or in some heaven or hell, another being. There is no conscious identity, however, between the two beings. They stand related to each other as father to son." This belief was not new but was adapted from Brahminism, which taught the transmigration of souls. Hence the duty to regard all animal life as sacred.

Buddhism is a creed of great tolerance, given to proselytizing but not to persecution. Its adherents number some 150 millions, in China, Japan, Ceylon, and southeast and central Asia. It offers its followers, at least in its earliest forms, no idealized homeland, but a state of serenity which may be attained even in the present life. It teaches the brotherhood of man, and is entirely pacifist. Much has been added to its original tenets by various sects. It seems to have kept closest to its original form in Ceylon, and departed most from it in Tibet. The title of the Buddha, which means the Enlightened, was adopted by Gautama himself; of his followers, only a few can have fully appreciated the mystical nature of much that he taught.

India's First Emperor

It is unlikely that Buddhism would have made such immense strides had it not been for the influence of the Emperor Asoka, a tolerant and enlightened ruler who reigned from about 264 to 227 B.C. and sincerely believed in the wisdom of the gentle teacher. His grandfather Chandragupta had brought about the unification of almost the whole of India, absorbing the Greek colonies which Alexander had founded there. Asoka was seeking to extend its borders when the misery caused by war struck him so profoundly that he determined to sheath his sword for the rest of his reign.

He sent missionaries far and wide, and, not content with propaganda by word of mouth, had pillars and rocks inscribed with messages of peace and goodwill. He bade his officials to "direct the people in the good way, so as to strengthen fickle spirits. Likewise let the wardens of the marches behave. For the rule is this—government by religion, law by religion, progress by religion, safety by religion."

Asoka sought to convert by persuasion, called councils to determine the doctrines of the faith, and is said to have supported over 60,000 monks. As further proof of his sincerity the Beloved of the Gods, as he was called, founded hospitals for animals as well as for mankind, planted medicinal herbs and shady trees, and provided water by the digging of wells. He made his

LIGHT OF ASIA

This sandstone carving of the Sarnath school of about the sixth century A.D., *shows Gautama Buddha, India's prince-philosopher, calling the earth to witness his Buddhahood. His teachings are still followed today by hundreds of millions in the countries of the Far East.*

MAN—E*

LION PILLAR AT LAURIYA

Asoka, monarch of almost all India, erected pillars, such as this one at Lauriya, throughout his dominions, on which were carved precepts extracted from the Buddhist law.

religion a very practical affair. That he was broad-minded is proved by his aphorism that "Whosoever honours his own sect and condemns the sects of others wholly from devotion to his own sect, in acting thus, injures more gravely his own sect."

In Egypt there are remains of brick buildings in the excavated store city of Pithom believed to have been erected by the Hebrews before Moses led them out of the land of their oppression. The date may have been some time about the fourteenth century B.C., though this is in dispute, as is the identity of the Pharaoh of the oppression, whom some authorities hold to be Rameses II, who reigned about 1250 B.C.

Moses and Jesus

Apart from the Biblical record in Exodus, Leviticus, Numbers and Deuteronomy, we know very little about Moses, the great founder of Hebrew law and religion. The suggestion has been put forward that after he had been discovered as a baby in the ark of bulrushes, Queen Hatshepsut was his protector. The code of Hammurabi almost certainly exercised an influence on the rules and regulations laid down by Moses. This is no cause for wonder, considering that the Jews had passed many years in Babylonia.

The story of Jesus Christ needs no retelling here. Details of his life are so scanty that they fill no more than a few pages of the Bible. The precious literary fragments are not contemporary documents but compilations by followers who probably collected evidence from those intimately connected with the Master. Thus there is reason to believe that St. Mark's record is based on the reminiscences of St. Peter. It was probably the first to be written, and in its present form is held to date from A.D. 65 or 70. That Christ was an historical person is not disputed by serious scholars, and even those who do not believe that he was the Son of God, as he claimed, have testified to the matchless beauty and moral worth of what he taught.

We are told that "the common people heard him gladly." It was to the homeless, the hopeless, and the helpless that his message of goodwill and reconciliation with God particularly appealed, as it continues to do. The date of Christ's birth was probably 5 or 4 B.C., four years earlier than that which was chosen to mark the beginning of the Christian era.

MOST MODERN OF THE ANCIENTS

The columbarium at Naples known as Vergil's tomb. Vergil held that the purpose of Rome was to bring unity to all peoples, thus presaging the hopes of internationalism and the League of Nations. The authenticity of the tomb is questioned by most modern antiquarians.

CHAPTER 12

MAKERS AND BREAKERS OF ROME

Italy's early inhabitants. The Etruscans and their civilization. Coming of the Gauls. Romulus and Remus. Rome's kings overthrown. Patricians and plebeians. Cattle as standard of value. Rome versus Carthage. The Republic's foreign conquests. Land reform. Slavery and the slave revolt. Baths, roads and newspapers. Julius and Augustus Cæsar. Wealth of the Eternal City. Decline sets in. Christianity versus the State. Constantine, the first Christian emperor. Founding of Constantinople.

SICILY and the south of Italy had long been centres of Greek culture and commerce, but much had happened and was happening in the top and the knee of the great geographical boot that thrusts itself so conspicuously into the Mediterranean.

In the north, at some remote period, a primitive people had taken up residence in the marshy valley of the Po, the Lombardy and Venetia of today. They built rough-and-ready houses on piles similar to those of the lake-dwellers of Switzerland, surrounding each little village with a moat and a great wall of earth thrown up during the excavations and forming a double defence.

There would seem to have been two main groups, the Itali, who were the earlier, and the Etruscans. Each of these peoples was of unknown origin, as were also the Iberians from Spain, who likewise put in an appearance. Then there were the Ligurians, who filtered down from a vast territory that extended beyond the Rhine. The mountainous territory which they inhabited in Northern Italy was scarcely more than a wilderness of sticks and stones, of splintered rock and dense forests that enabled the immigrants to snatch but a meagre harvest. Some built rough huts of branches or reeds, while others contented themselves with the cold comfort afforded by caves. Illyrian tribes, probably travelling for the most part by sea, came in three waves of migration.

139

though the Veneti, the last of them, arrived by land some time in the eighth century B.C.

About 1000 B.C. the gloomy-minded and semi-barbaric Etruscans, believed to be the descendants of sea rovers and to have come from the coast of Asia Minor, made a home on the west coast, north of the Tiber, whence they spread to the islands of Corsica and Sardinia, at no great distance from their front door. That they were brought into touch with the civilizations of Egypt, Babylonia and Mycenæ is proved by objects

Carthage, and showed great activity in mining copper, working in bronze, iron and gold, trading and seafaring. Tradition has it that their kings ruled over Rome.

It was not until the fourth century B.C. that they were conquered and their territory absorbed. Their sea power came to an end when a fleet sent by the tyrant of Syracuse won a decisive victory off Cumæ, near Naples, the oldest of the Greek colonies in the west. The legacy they left to the Romans included the toga, the gladiatorial games,

SITE OF THE FORUM OF AUGUSTUS

Rome probably began as a group of settlements perched on its famous seven hills. As the population grew the villages joined together and became a town, and the town became a city. An open market fitted with wooden booths was provided on the site of the future forum.

found in their graves which clearly betray the influence of these countries. Probably the Phœnicians introduced iron to them.

One has only to compare the primitive art of the Etruscans with their later work to appreciate what they learned from the Greeks. Indeed, they became such skilful workers in bronze that the Greeks themselves were proud to possess the products of the Tyrrhenians, as they called them.

The latter eventually conquered or dominated a considerable part of Italy, founded a number of cities, became so powerful that they were admitted as allies by mighty

and the arch, a fine specimen of which is still to be seen at Volterra.

An interesting link between the Etruscans of yesterday and the Italians of today is the axe in a bundle of rods called fasces. The axe was for execution and the rods for scourging. Symbols of law and order, they were also the means of carrying them into effect. The word Fascism is derived from these instruments.

Gauls settled in the north, between the Alps and the Apennines. Perhaps, as Livy says, this branch of the Celts had been driven by hunger from the country now

THROUGH THE ARCH OF SEPTIMIUS SEVERUS

The remains of the Roman Forum seen through the arch of Septimius Severus, erected
A.D. 203. Beyond is the Temple of Faustina and the triumphal arch of Titus. Republican
institutions became ever more vague and shadowy, and under Septimius Severus (146-211)
faded away. He was proclaimed emperor by his legions, and his defeat of the Parthians is
pictured on the arch. He was in Britain for three years before his death at York, and his
name is connected with Hadrian's wall. Previous to his short reign from 79 to 81 Titus
had captured Jerusalem in the year 70, and served as military tribune in Britain and Germany.

MOST BEAUTIFUL OF ROME'S MANY FOUNTAINS
Fontana di Trevi, erected by Pope Clement XII in 1735, continues to operate by means of a channel of the Aqua Virgo, which filled the baths of Agrippa. In a recent year, when the Eternal City was menaced by a drought, the underground courses saved the situation.

known as France. Although they were excellent agriculturists, their habits were too predatory and warlike to be pleasant. When not in conflict with their neighbours they quarrelled among themselves.

It must not be inferred that these various and varied immigrations took place with the regularity of an invading army, or that the pedigrees of the newcomers were so pure and unalloyed as such simple names as Itali, Etruscans, Ligurians and so on would suggest. There was much intermingling. As Professor G. W. Botsford has pointed out, "the 'pure race' remains an unproved theory."

The story of the founding of Rome by Romulus and Remus, outcast children who were suckled by a wolf, is delightful but entirely legendary. Rome probably began as a little group of settlements perched on its famous seven hills. They were inhabited by a pastoral people known as the Latins, an offshoot of the already-mentioned Itali.

As the population grew, the villages naturally expanded, until at last they joined and became a town, and the town a city-state ruled by a king. An open market fitted up with wooden booths was provided on the site of the future Forum, and soon became an exchange for goods and gossip. Romans met Samnites and Greeks from the south, and Etruscans from the north.

The kings, legend tells us, ruled from 753 to 510 B.C., when the Roman patricians, or aristocrats as we should call them, revolted and proclaimed a republic. Two consuls and a senate of elders were charged with the welfare of the State.

The patricians had acted in no altruistic way nor with the general good of the public in mind. They had stepped in to safeguard their own vested interests. The plebeians, the ordinary folk of the city, were left to fend for themselves. When they deemed the time propitious, they asserted what they claimed to be their rights in no uncertain fashion. There was a general strike. If Rome would not give them justice they would found another Rome for themselves and organize their own way of running it. The threat was a serious one, and the Senate took the warning to heart. They made concessions, and were to make many more. In course of time plebeians found a place in the august body of the Senate, and it was enacted that one of the consuls should be of the people. Concession followed concession in a long struggle which extended over centuries and ended in the defeat of both contestants. Despotism won.

In the early days, before the introduction of coined money, the standard of value was cattle or sheep. Then came bronze, weighed in scales, which sufficed until the introduction of copper weights. Coins were probably used in the middle of the fourth century B.C. With cash came the inevitable money-lenders and brokers. Rome's first silver coins, struck about 268 B.C., bore on the reverse Castor and Pollux, the patron deities of trade and commerce.

The word "pecuniary," exclusively associated in our minds with money and money matters, is derived from *pecus*, meaning cattle, *pecunia*, signifying property in cattle and afterwards money, *pecuniarius*, relating to or consisting of money.

The Threadneedle Street of ancient Rome was the Janus Medius, in which stood the Basilica Æmilia, where the bankers had their offices. Visitors to the city may still ascend the marble pavement that once clattered with the hurrying tread of clients.

At first the bankers were merely money-changers. As industry and commerce expanded, they relegated their former duties to others and devoted their energy to the business of current and deposit accounts, and transactions in connexion with letters of credit and bills of exchange. The books of the bankers were always open to official inspection by the prefect of the city.

PUBLIC BATHS LINED WITH MARBLE

The baths of Caracalla in Rome were built in 212 and contained 1,600 baths. No fewer than 170 public institutions of this kind were erected in various cities in the time of Augustus. Some were lined with marble and floored with mosaic patterns, many of them of great beauty.

The plebeian craftsmen formed themselves into guilds. These institutions multiplied to such an extent that eventually there were eighty in the city of Rome alone. They do not appear to have come into being as organizations for securing an economic wage or otherwise protecting their members, but rather as benevolent societies whose main objects were the provision of an occasional feast or necessary funeral.

Rome's Contest with Carthage

The expansion of Rome overseas began during her long and bitter contest with aristocratic Carthage, her greatest commercial rival. In 241 B.C., as a result of the first Punic or Carthaginian War—Punic comes from the Latin word *Punicus* meaning Phœnician—Rome conquered all Sicily, a valuable asset which produced olive oil, wine and corn, and followed up the advantage she had gained by taking Corsica and Sardinia after hostilities had ceased. During the following two decades Carthage, already planted in Spain, compensated herself by a further advance and the seizure of valuable silver mines. The Cartagena of today commemorates the old Nova Carthago (New Carthage).

Despite early success in the second Punic War, which began in 219 B.C., the Carthaginian leader, Hannibal, who had sworn eternal enmity to Rome, failed to break the power of his opponents. Scipio Africanus conquered Spain for Rome, was victorious against the troops defending Carthage, and finally defeated the great general.

In 202 B.C. the once powerful Semitic trading power was forced to accept a humiliating peace. As the majority of her citizens were actively engaged in business, Carthage fought with hired soldiers. On the other hand Rome had a citizen army in which all males between the ages of seventeen and forty-six were liable to serve—men with a definite stake of some kind, however humble it might be, in the country.

Greece Becomes Roman

Beginning the war without a fleet, the Romans speedily built warships, taking as a model, so it is said, an enemy vessel that had run aground. Nothing if not practical, the landsmen sailors evolved the *corvus*, a kind of drawbridge which they used for boarding, often with great effect.

It was now the turn of Macedonia to be punished for her friendship with Carthage, and in 148 B.C. the country became a Roman province. Greece, nominally free, passed under Rome's control. Corinth, save for her art treasures, was destroyed in 146 B.C., as was Carthage, whose women cut off their long hair and handed it to the soldiers for bowstrings. Thus ended the third and last Punic War. "Captive Greece," writes Horace, the noble Roman poet, "took captive her rude conqueror, and introduced her arts to rustic Latium."

Syria, ally of Greece, was taught a severe lesson, and part of her territory was given to Pergamum, in Asia Minor, as a reward for the latter's friendship with Rome. This kingdom was left to the Roman people by Attalus III, and most of it incorporated in the Roman province of Asia.

Whatever may have been his lot previous to the formation of the Roman Republic, the agriculturist certainly did not have an easy time afterwards. Wars and rumours of wars frequently interrupted his peaceful pursuits, and it was required of him to don the sword and abandon the plough. If he returned it was to find his land weed-ridden.

Economic Disaster

When Carthage was vanquished and the power of Rome was in the ascendant throughout the lands of the Mediterranean, the outlook became even more gloomy. Foreign corn and cheap labour in the form of slaves from conquered countries played havoc with the farmers, who either drifted to the towns or cultivated the vine and the olive if the soil were suitable.

The brothers Gracchus, Tiberius and Gaius, nephews of Scipio Africanus, tried various agrarian panaceas, with little or no practical effect. Eventually, according to Professor Rodolfo Lanciani, 1,518 million gallons of wheat had to be imported every year from Egypt, and double that amount from Sicily, Numidia, Sardinia, Cyrenaica, and the lower valley of the Danube.

Rot had set in and was never eradicated. If wealth increased and commerce expanded, there was marked decline in religion and morals. To the ordinary man the gift of free or cheap corn, introduced at the end of the second century B.C., or of a daily dole of bread that came later, was poor compensation compared to the booty brought home by military commanders and the swollen riches of capitalists and profiteers, who lent money at extortionate rates of interest.

Beautiful villas and lovely gardens owned by others offered no consolation, but only added to his bitterness. The poor lived in buildings that resembled the slum tenements of Victorian days.

Slaves were not employed merely for domestic service and in the fields; their brawn and brains were utilized also in industry and in the construction of public works. When Rome was at the height of its glory the slaves of the Empire numbered many millions.

When the province of Asia was created, that in Christ was neither bond nor free, a runaway slave caught in the act was branded. A lash with metal beads was used when punishment for other offences was deemed necessary, or the neck and wrists of the helpless victim were fixed in a board reminiscent of the Chinese cangue.

To the wretched captives of foreign wars were added those who could not pay their way. Small wonder that under Spartacus

LOOTED FROM THE TEMPLE AT JERUSALEM

Jerusalem was captured by the Romans in the year 70. A sculptured frieze inside the Arch of Titus at Rome depicts victorious soldiers carrying away the table of shew-bread, silver candlesticks and the branched candlestick of gold from the devastated Temple of Herod.

Delos, frequented by the merchants of many lands, became a rendezvous for Roman traders. It is said that in a single day 10,000 slaves changed hands in this Ægean port alone.

The ghastly cruelties associated with the slave trade of darkest Africa at its darkest were no worse than the inhuman practices of ancient Rome towards its unfortunate human chattels. Before Christianity taught

70,000 slaves and others with more or less genuine grievances revolted and held their former masters at bay for two years. There was "a grandeur that was Rome," but there was also a shame.

"In exact proportion to the sum of money a man keeps in his chest," writes Juvenal, with bitter sarcasm, "is the credit given to his oath. And the first question ever asked of a man is in reference to his

RUINED HALL OF AUDIENCE AT CTESIPHON

*When a new and energetic Persian dynasty with its capital at Ctesiphon, on the Tigris,
threatened the Roman Empire on the east, Diocletian (284-305) thought it well to establish
himself in Asia Minor with a joint emperor at Milan. Rome's importance waned in comparison.*

income rather than his character. How
many slaves does he keep; how many acres
does he own; with what dishes is his table
spread? These are the universal inquiries.
Poverty, bitter though it be, has no sharper
sting than this, that it makes men ridicu-
lous. Who was ever allowed in Rome to
become a son-in-law if his estate was
inferior? What poor man's name appears
in any will?"

Communications are the arteries of
commerce. Ostia was developed into an
important seaport by the removal of the
sand-bar that was like a bit in the Tiber's
mouth. The Via Appia, the first of the
famous military roads, and the Aqua
Appia, the first aqueduct, were due to the
censor, Appius Claudius Cæsus, who
started building them in 312 B.C. The most
beautiful of Rome's many fountains, the
Fontana di Trevi, continues to operate by
means of a channel of the Aqua Virgo,
which filled the baths of Agrippa, the
general of Augustus. A few years ago,
when the Eternal City was menaced by a
water famine, the underground courses
of the old Romans saved the situation.

In the first century of our era, the
Emperor Claudius constructed a waterway, both subterranean and overhead, that
brought water to his palace from a distance
of over forty miles.

It is not only in comparatively recent
years that the cleanliness which is supposed
to be next to godliness has been encouraged
by the opening of public baths. No fewer
than 170 were built in various cities in the
time of Augustus. Some baths in ancient
Rome were lined with marble and floored
with mosaic. That of Diocletian accommodated over 3,000 people and took over five
years to erect. "We are dissatisfied," said
Seneca, "if we do not tread on gems in our
baths."

Roman roads are still the admiration of
civil engineers. The foundation was of fine
earth beaten in. Then came a layer of large
stones mixed with mortar. Small stones,
also mixed with mortar, formed the third
stratum. Powdered brick, chalk and lime
constituted the *nucleus*, on which was the
surface or *summum dorsum*. The highways
varied in width from eleven to fifteen feet,
and at various distances travellers on foot

were provided with seats on the footpath and riders with stones by which to mount.

Traffic laws are not modern. In the time of Julius Cæsar no wheeled traffic was allowed to enter the Market Place during the ten hours after sunrise.

Rome had its newspapers. They were engraved tablets. The journalism was of the "tabloid" variety, brief and to the point, and related such events as a law exempting poor citizens from tax payments, the death of Julius Cæsar (without details), and a disastrous fire in the Aventine. The great orator Cicero posted outside his villa at Tusculum a record of notable occurrences, including births, marriages and deaths, and used an abbreviated system of writing. State officials recorded current happenings and employed copyists.

The Roman Republic lasted five centuries. Factions and grave unrest rendered it as unstable as it was unwieldy. It was difficult, if not impossible, to get quick decisions. The actions of the consuls were not always unanimous. There was no effective financial control. The administration of overseas provinces was lax and open to gross abuse. Pillage and profiteering were common. The armies and their generals got out of hand. Strife within and without the country threatened to overload and break down the cumbrous, creaking machine. The marvel is that it functioned at all after the wear and tear, the patching and mending of 500 years.

Julius Cæsar, who had been subduing the Gauls and had carried the eagles to the Rhine, crossed the Rubicon, the limit of his authority, and after fighting a civil war marched on Rome. He thereby created a precedent in 45 B.C. for an Italian socialist named Benito Mussolini in 1922. Cæsar tore up the constitution and started to reorganize the government, believing that the old methods were no longer adequate to control an ever-expanding empire.

It may be that he trampled on traditions with too heavy a foot. In a matter of months he was dead, stabbed by conspirators who

TRIUMPHAL ARCH OF THE EMPEROR CONSTANTINE

Constantine (306-337) established a new capital on the site of the old Greek colony of Byzantium. He called it Constantinople, now known as Istanbul. Its position was excellent from a strategic point of view, but the move from Rome meant a break with a long tradition.

thought that they were saving their country, as many another assassin has believed throughout history. On the day of the funeral the public set fire to the Senate House where he had been murdered. The confederates had but postponed the issue.

Vergil and His Age

The work begun by Cæsar—dictator, imperator (the ancient form of emperor) and regarded after his cremation as a god— was carried on by his heir and successor Augustus. Following his victory at Actium over Antony, a member of the triumvirate who was plotting and dallying with Cleopatra in Egypt, Augustus ruled in peace for over forty years, proceeding quietly but steadily on the path of reform.

He encouraged learning, more particularly the culture introduced from Greece, and the intellectual life of his time was heightened by the literary productions of Vergil, Horace, Livy and Ovid. For this reason the period is often referred to as the Golden Age of Latin literature.

The political preference of Vergil, perhaps the most modern of the ancients, was for a despotic government; his ideal of happiness for ordinary folk was the tilling of the fields. He would have it that the purpose of Rome was to bring unity to all peoples, thus presaging the hopes of internationalism and the League of Nations. In Naples a structure of rough stone is pointed out to the tourist as the tomb of the author of the *Æneid*, though its authenticity is seriously questioned.

Of Rome it was said that Augustus "found the city built of brick and left it built of marble." He did much for the consolidation of the provinces, for he repaired and widened the Alpine passes over Mont Genèvre, Mont Cenis, St. Bernard and the Brenner, and founded Turin, Aosta, Ivrea, Trento and Verona on their southern frontier to guard them.

Rome's Golden Age

As Rome grew in wealth and importance more and more money was spent on luxuries. Buildings were bigger, their fitments more elaborate. The quarries of the world contributed their choicest marble for the adornment of the walls, which were often further decorated by fresco paintings. Simple or elaborate designs pieced in stone cubes called *tesseræ* covered the floors.

In domestic and civic architecture Greece alone remained unrivalled. Rome could not transport buildings from Hellas bodily, but many fine statues were transplanted.

Rome continued to extend her territory. At the time of Augustus about 1,875,000 square miles were under her dominion. Province was added to province. The boundaries of the Empire reached their greatest extent under the Emperor Trajan, who died in 117 A.D. and whose times were adjudged by Gibbon to have been the happiest attained by mankind.

The whole of the countries bordering the Mediterranean and the islands in it were Rome's. The sea was a Roman lake, as Mussolini sought to make it again. In the east her frontiers included Palestine, Syria, Mesopotamia and Armenia; in the north parts of what are now Rumania, Hungary and Germany; in the west Spain, Gaul and Britain; in the south the north coast of Africa, Egypt and a strip of Arabia. The legions of Imperial Rome were known from the coast of the Caspian to the Irish Sea and the borders of the Atlantic Ocean.

Beginning of the End

The first 200 years of the Christian era brought peace and prosperity to the Roman Empire. It was a lull before a gathering storm whose rumbles may have been heard but were disregarded.

The respite saw the blossoming of many centres of active life in lands remote from the centre of affairs, more especially in Gaul and southern Spain. But Rome, by the very nature of things, was a power based on militarism, and the army, now largely recruited from aliens, got the upper hand. It began to make and unmake emperors. Despite divine right, it was the exception rather than the rule for wearers of the purple to die on their couches, so many of them met with violent deaths. At one period four different emperors were chosen by various sections of the army.

Republican institutions became ever more vague and shadowy, and under Septimius Severus faded away. The long frontiers of the vast imperial estate became sources of weakness rather than of strength. They were not easy to defend. There were many gaps between the lines of forts that extended from the Danube to the Rhine. Moreover there were not always sufficient troops to garrison them at full strength.

A new and energetic Persian dynasty with its capital at Ctesiphon, on the Tigris, threatened on the east. The Emperor Diocletian therefore thought it well to establish

HEATHEN TEMPLE THAT HELPED TO ADORN A CATHEDRAL

The main portal and interior of the Temple of Dionysus at Baalbek, one of the most beautiful of ancient buildings in Syria. It was built about 200 by the Emperor Caracalla. The sculptures are extraordinarily rich, although terribly mutilated. Material from Baalbek was taken by Justinian (527-565 to adorn the cathedral of Sancta Sophia or Divine Wisdom at Constantinople, but the Turks were responsible for much of the disfigurement.

himself in Asia Minor, with a joint emperor at Milan. Both were peasants, the one from Dalmatia and the other from Thrace. Each had an assistant, who was regarded as an heir, stationed at points of vantage to deal with the barbarian peoples in the neighbourhood of the Rhine and the Danube. Rome became scarcely more important than a provincial city.

New World Capital

Finally, the Emperor Constantine, an illegitimate who murdered his wife and child, made himself sole ruler and established a new capital on the site of the old Greek colony of Byzantium. He called it Constantinople; today it goes under the name of Istanbul. Seated as it was, like Rome, on seven hills, its position was excellent from a strategic point of view, but the move meant a break with tradition.

The religion of Jesus of Nazareth, like bread cast on the waters and found after many days, reached Rome. It was regarded in the same light as the hundred-and-one different religions that had their devotees in palaces and hovels. But the new would not blend with the old. Provided incense was offered to the emperor, who had adopted the Eastern idea of the divinity of kings, no questions were asked. An Aurelian could sanctify the sun, a Marcus Aurelius bow to Mithras, a patrician pray to the family gods or take part in the ritual of the most exotic cult. The Christians acknowledged one God, who sat on no earthly throne, and refused to worship or offer incense to Cæsar.

"The Christians to the Lions"

A modicum of incense, no larger than a pinch of snuff, placed on the altar fire would have saved them. They refused, and as a consequence were regarded as revolutionaries bent on overturning the State. The policy of tolerance did not extend to them. They followed their own path; it sometimes led to the Colosseum and the lions; some were smeared with pitch and became human torches, others were crucified. Still they prayed in their underground passages.

Constantine the reformer, who had not hesitated to build a new Rome, gave Christianity its golden opportunity. The "pestilent superstition," as the Roman historian Tacitus termed it, emerged from the catacombs. The emperor allowed all men to follow whatever religion they preferred, and he himself became a Christian.

The blood of the martyrs had proved to be the seed of the Church, but with the fruit there appeared the tares also. When the flames of persecution flickered and went out the followers of the Prince of Peace began to quarrel among themselves. Doctrinal differences arose. It was forgotten that the letter killeth, but the spirit giveth life. In agreeing to disagree they became embittered. So instead of one organization under a single head the Church was eventually split in twain, and the Roman Catholic, or Western, Church, and the Greek Orthodox, or Eastern, Church went their separate ways.

Constantine spent a great deal of other people's money on beautifying the new capital, which was dedicated in 330, two years after the foundation of the first cathedral of Sancta Sophia or Divine Wisdom. It was burnt down, rebuilt and destroyed again. The present superb building, the pride of Byzantine architecture and now a museum, was built by Justinian, whose name is also associated with a famous digest of the laws of the empire.

Church, Mosque, Museum

He ransacked the Roman world for the adornment of the sanctuary. Material from Heliopolis and Baalbek, Athens and Delos was transplanted. Parts of the heathen temples of Diana and Jupiter found honoured places in the Christian temple. For nearly six years thousands of bricklayers laboured at the walls, while other craftsmen lined them with costly marbles or coloured mosaics. Gold and precious stones adorned the altar. Silver was used like mortar—40,000 pounds of it. The dome was of pumice stone reinforced by the lightest bricks that could be obtained; its centre stood 180 feet from the ground.

Nothing was too good or too costly for the place, which became known as the Jewel of Christendom. The great building was erected to the glory of God; a colossal equestrian statue of the emperor was erected in its forecourt to the glory of Constantine. The Turks spared the one but not the other when they took Constantinople in 1453. They broke up the statue and melted it into cannon. The church was converted into a mosque. Plaster and white-wash were daubed over the mosaics, which remained concealed for nearly 500 years until permission was granted by Kemal Ataturk, first President of the Republic of Turkey, for the covering to be removed.

HOLY CARPET PILGRIMAGE TO MECCA

The Holy Carpet is a series of coverings used in ceremonies that take place every year in the great mosque at Mecca. It makes an annual pilgrimage from Cairo, where it is kept at other times. Tradition says that the Mahmal, or litter, is that on which Mohammed prayed.

CHAPTER 13

HUMANITY ON THE MARCH

Migrations of peoples. Goths, Huns and Vandals. Rome's legacy to modern times. Social life in the late Empire. Reasons for Rome's decline. Buried cities of the East. Mohammed and Islam. Arab conquests and civilization. Cæsar's invasion. Romans in Britain. Gaul and Germany. Charlemagne restores the Empire. Viking invasions.

DURING the last few years multitudes of hapless people have migrated from one part of the world to another, not because they wanted to do so, but through dire necessity.

Hordes of refugees, victims of the hatred, malice and uncharitableness of political oppression, unwanted in the lands they once called home, have wandered over Europe. In 1940 Great Britain sheltered over 74,000 refugees from Germany, Czechoslovakia and Poland.

These mass movements may have far-reaching consequences. Wholesale migrations, usually less peaceable in intention, took place in the early centuries of the present era. European and Asiatic denizens of plain and forest emerged from their fastnesses and spread confusion and conflict far and wide. We do not know the cause of these human floods, spates and trickles.

For whatever reason the Goths, who had probably made their first home in Sweden and Norway, crossed the Baltic and split up into two main sections, known as the Ostrogoths, or East Goths, and the Visigoths, or West Goths. The former settled for a time north of the Danube, beyond the Roman frontier. Then came pressure from the Huns, a wild people from the recesses of further Asia, who asked that they might be allowed to settle on Roman soil. Permission was granted on condition that they gave up their weapons.

The Visigoths also crossed the river, and under the able leadership of Alaric captured and plundered Rome in 410. Over fourteen centuries later, charred wood and cinders found during the excavation of old sites in Rome still preserved the acrid odour of burning. Marching into Gaul and Spain, the invaders settled there, making their capitals Toulouse and Toledo respectively. Forty-five years after Alaric's adventure

IN FULFILMENT OF A VOW
A votive altar in the Casa dello Scheletro, Herculaneum, one of the cities overwhelmed by the eruption of Mount Vesuvius in 79.

another Teutonic tribe thundered at the walls of Rome and sacked the city. They were the Vandals, who had debouched from the shores of the Baltic and had made themselves free of the Roman province of Africa after having been turned out of Spain by the Visigoths. The trident of the Mediterranean passed into their hands.

The Franks of the lower Rhine gradually expelled the Romans in Gaul and began laying the foundations of France. Slavs from what is now Soviet Russia marched into the lands that were later to be marked on the map of Europe as Poland, Czechoslovakia and Yugoslavia. The Ostrogoths made good their claim to north-eastern Italy, but were afterwards overthrown by the Emperor Justinian, who also dispossessed the Vandals in Africa. Under Attila, the Scourge of God, the Huns threatened Constantinople. They were kinsmen of the Tartars against whom the Great Wall of China was built hundreds of years before.

Passing into Gaul, the Huns were defeated near Châlons in 451 by the sustained efforts of Visigoths, Ostrogoths and Romans, who united in a common cause. It was one of the world's decisive battles, though Attila did further damage before he died, particularly, in the province of Venetia. Fleeing from his terror, refugees made their way to a group of dreary islands in the north Adriatic. On piles driven in the marsh a future generation was to create the architectural glories of Venice.

Such are the broad outlines of the Great Migrations. The whole known world was in movement and travail. The Northmen raided Britain; the Arabs were astir; the Far East was waking from its slumber.

Rome's Last Emperor

The name of the legendary founder of Rome was Romulus; it was also that of the last Emperor of the Western Roman Empire. He was a boy and reigned less than a year. In 476 Odoacer (Odovacar), King of the Goths, ruled over an independent kingdom in Italy, though the Emperor at Constantinople still made the empty claim that he ruled both East and West.

Rome was the channel by which the culture of Greece reached Western Europe. That was her enduring legacy to mankind, but she also added her own contributions to civilization. Abstract thought made little appeal to an essentially practical people.

Some of the bridges and aqueducts erected by Roman civil engineers remain. Their drainage system was the most perfect then extant. Some of the roads, untouched for centuries, were afterwards resurfaced and continue to bear the weight of heavy traffic. The itinerary of Antonine gives a list of over 370 roads with a length exceeding 52,900 miles. The gauge of the Roman chariot is the standard gauge of most of the world's railways.

Some rural areas in the present year of grace are less adequately provided with

DUG OUT OF A SOLIDIFIED RIVER OF MUD AND ASHES

The house with the mosaic atrium, or vestibule, at Herculaneum. The pavements were inlaid with multi-coloured mosaics and the walls decorated with frescoes and mosaics of glass. Herculaneum was probably about one-third the size of its bustling neighbour, Pompeii.

fire-fighting appliances than was ancient Rome. The brigades had double-acting force pumps, hand-grenade extinguishers, buckets, ladders, mattresses for smothering flames, and mats for catching people who had no other means of escape.

Medicine, being largely of an experimental nature, was not greatly favoured by the Romans. Julius Cæsar gave it a fillip by granting citizenship to practitioners of the healing arts, most of whom were Greeks or Asiatics. Hospitals for soldiers led to similar institutions for civilians. There were women doctors and barristers.

Schoolmasters did not rank high in the social scale; their profession was regarded as on a level with the menial pursuits of acrobats and fortune tellers. The highest esteem was reserved for the several branches of the legal profession, whose services to Roman law were to lay the foundations of the jurisprudence of the Western World.

In the Empire's closing days the citizen was of no account other than as a taxpayer or a soldier. Callousness, indeed, would appear to have become part and parcel of the mental make-up of the people as well as of the State, for the citizen himself had no regard for the sufferings of prisoners, slaves or gladiators. He lacked pity, the greatest of human qualities, or it may be that he suppressed it. In any case the result to the sufferers was the same.

World Unity Foreshadowed

Local customs, both secular and religious, were seldom or never interfered with provided they were not regarded as harmful to the welfare of the State. The Emperor Caracalla admitted to Roman citizenship all freemen throughout the Empire, and although this was no more than a means of raising more money by taxation, it led in the minds of some to the conception of the world as a unity, thereby suggesting the possibility of the brotherhood of man.

Marcus Aurelius Antoninus, the emperor turned philosopher, caught a glimpse of a far-off tomorrow when he avowed: "My city and country, so far as I am Antoninus, is Rome, but so far as I am a man, it is the world." Christianity upheld this ideal in its own special way, and in pursuance of it the Holy Roman Empire came into being at a later stage.

The failure of the central authority, the decay of the peasantry, the growing scarcity of precious metals, the sharp division of the peoples into the very rich and the very poor, the breakdown of discipline and of moral fibre, suicide and infanticide, the sapping of health by malaria brought by mosquitoes that bred in the marshes—these and the cankers already mentioned caused the Roman Empire to decay and fall like a rotten tree in the forest, yet leaving behind acorns from which grew mighty oaks.

Faded Cities of the East

Empires wax and wane, and finally disappear. Often enough the material creations on which mankind sets so much store perish or leave no more than a few sad and tarnished memorials, while the things of the mind, unseen but potent, survive. The earth is strewn with the battered relics of civilization in its many phases.

Mud houses occupy the court of the fortress temple of Palmyra, famed city of Zenobia. Petra, the "rose-red city half as old as time," with its rock-hewn temples

and tombs within the heart of the mountain, is deserted. Perched on a plateau 3,000 feet high, it was once a prosperous depot of the caravan trade with the Red Sea, Egypt, Damascus and Palmyra. Baalbek, which the Romans called Heliopolis, perhaps of Phœnician origin, was another important entrepôt. Lying in a quarry is the largest building stone in the world. Its weight is calculated at over 1,000 tons.

Of deeper human interest are Herculaneum and Pompeii. Both were overwhelmed by the eruption of Vesuvius in A.D. 79, but whereas the majority of the inhabitants of the town nearer the volcano made good their escape, many of the Pompeians were overwhelmed.

Buried beneath a heavy pall of lava and cinders for centuries, the streets, shops, houses and amenities of these pleasure resorts again bask in the sun beneath the burnished blue of the Neapolitan sky. The pitilessness of the tragedy was revealed when pick and spade got to work.

Horrors of Pompeii

Here were twelve men, women and children huddled in a heap, a mother clasping a baby, trapped in a narrow passage. Five youths, seeking to protect their heads from the fiery fury with roofing tiles, were found in a garden that but an hour before was aglow with flowers. A young female slave, with the belt around her waist that indicated her menial state, her hands shielding her face, gained her freedom in death.

The comedy of life, its needs and amenities were also evident. The oldest loaf of bread, a public laundry, a motto which reads "Be thou chaste and keep thine eyes from lewd glances at thy neighbour's wife," safety-pins, the precious stones and tools of a jeweller's shop, mosaic fountains, a wine bar with bronze and glass jars and mine host's till—these and other things bring the apparently remote life of 1,800 years ago very near. Perhaps it was not so markedly different from our own.

While Teutonic tribes were overrunning Europe, an Arab merchant named Mohammed was seeing visions and slowly convincing himself that he was called upon to deliver his people from idolatry. His theme was simple. "There is no God but Allah (God), and Mohammed is His Prophet." In Mecca, a city of idols and a centre of the caravan trade, he preached a monotheistic belief in one God, as Moses and Jesus had done. Moses led the Israelites to the Promised Land. Jesus avowed that His kingdom was not of this world. Mohammed blazed a trail that led to the creation of a powerful and extensive empire.

Islam is Arabic for submission. The word defines the sum and substance of Mohammed's teaching. There is an impression that it is a creed entirely propagated by swashbuckler methods. This is wrong. Islam offered unbelievers the choice be-

man with a mission is not usually a favourite. The dreamer of the desert became so unpopular that he was compelled to flee to Yathrib. That event, known as the Hegira, or flight, took place in 622—the year 1 of the Mohammedan calendar. Later Yathrib was renamed Medinat al-Nabi, the Prophet's City, or Medina.

Prayer, charity, justice, abstinence from wine, cleanliness and kindness to animals

EVACUATING THE DOOMED CITY OF POMPEII

Whereas the majority of the inhabitants of Herculaneum made good their escape, many of the Pompeians were overwhelmed by the mud and lava which tore down the slopes of Vesuvius and the burning cinders that rained on them from above. The city had scarcely recovered from the effects of an earthquake in 63 and rebuilding was still in progress when the blow fell.

tween conversion and war, a situation summed up in the phrase: "Koran, tribute or sword." Neither Christian nor Mohammedan can point the finger of scorn at the other. In the Crusades each fought like a fiend, and both in the name of God. Islam has many tenets in keeping with those of Judaism and Christianity.

The prophet did not find his task easy. A

were among the tenets of the faith he preached. His sermons made a great impression. He pictured a material heaven and hell. In the former all things dear to the Arab's heart were provided, and those who died for the cause went straight to it.

Civil war broke out between Mecca and Medina, and although at first Mohammed proved anything but a successful general, the tide turned in his favour when Medina withstood a siege of twenty days and the enemy marched home in despair.

In 630 Mohammed entered Mecca as a conqueror. Almost his first action was to destroy the idols in the great shrine known as the Kaaba, but he spared the Black Stone which, from time immemorial, had been an object of veneration. Two years later he was dead, leaving behind him many sayings and prophecies which were collected in the Koran, the Moslem Bible.

Empire of the Caliphs

Taking the title of Caliph, which means successor, Mohammed's father-in-law Abu Bakr and those who came after him overran the whole of Spain, part of France, North Africa, Egypt, Arabia, Syria, Mesopotamia, Armenia and Persia.

The capital of the Mohammedan Empire was at first Damascus and then Baghdad, now the chief city of Iraq. Caliphates were established at Cairo and Cordova, in Spain. Under Haroun-al-Raschid, Baghdad, situated on the Tigris at no great distance from Ctesiphon and the ruins of Babylon, developed into a place of outstanding importance that rivalled Constantinople. The time was that of the *Arabian Nights' Entertainments* and of Sindbad the Sailor, whose exploits are based on those of a much-travelled merchant named Sulaiman.

The Caliph of Baghdad lost his temporal though not his spiritual supremacy in 1058, when the eastern part of the Mohammedan Empire was conquered by the Seljuk Turks, whose chief adopted the title of Sultan.

Beauties of the Alhambra

On occasion the Mohammedan chiefs wielded their power with an iron hand that was not always enclosed in a velvet glove, but their rule is notable in many ways. Palaces, tombs and mosques as far apart as India and Spain testify to the fine qualities of their architecture. The tomb of Mohammed Adil Shah at Bijapur has the largest dome in the world.

The subtle beauties of the Alhambra in Spain, plain without and splendid within, perched on its towering hill with the snow-capped Sierras in the distance, have been described and painted almost times without number, and will continue to be. Slender columns and fretted arches, porcelain tiles of blue and green, purple and gold combine to make the Red Castle—for this its name means—an architectural delight.

The first observatory in Europe was erected by Arabs at Seville. Universities were founded at Cordova, Cairo and Baghdad. Learned Greek works were translated into Arabic; Aristotle was a special favourite. The Arabs excelled in mathematics, chemistry and pharmacy. Their contributions to medicine included the diagnosis of measles and smallpox. "Alchemy" is a word we have borrowed from Arabic. Paper from rags was first manufactured at Baghdad, and the cotton plant was introduced from Asia.

Haroun-al-Raschid ordered that every new mosque should have a school attached to it. Missionaries and merchants reached China, and traders founded colonies on the east coast of Africa. When the Polos arrived at Pekin in 1275 they found that some of Kublai Khan's highest officials were Mohammedans, and Magellan, the first circumnavigator of the globe, was amazed to learn that the King of Borneo was of the same faith.

Islam is the religion of one-fifth of the human race. To Mecca, sweltering in its parched valley at 133 deg. Fahrenheit in the shade, as many as 100,000 pilgrims flock to make the annual pilgrimage, which every Mohammedan is bound to do if he can afford it. Some travel by steamer and caravan—others arrive by motor-bus.

Cæsar in Britain

What of the lands shrouded in northern mists? Cæsar tells us in his *Commentaries*, which were written for propaganda purposes, that his reason for visiting Britain in 55 B.C. was "because he discovered that in almost all the wars with the Gauls help was furnished them from that country." It was really a reconnoitring expedition.

Cæsar's first stay in the island was for a few weeks only. He returned in the following year, and in less than three months had exacted the payment of a yearly tribute to Rome. There were "countless" people, he tells us, "exceedingly numerous" buildings, and the number of cattle was "great." Tin and iron were produced, and brass and iron rings of various weights used as money. "As in Gaul, there is timber of every description except beech and fir. Most of the inland inhabitants do not sow corn, but live on milk and flesh, and are clad with skins. All the British, indeed, dye themselves with woad, which occasions a bluish colour, and thereby have a more terrible appearance in fight."

The far-off island received no further military attention from Rome until A.D. 43, nearly a century after Cæsar's visits, when the possibilities of trade awakened the interest of the financiers and merchants of the Imperial City. Gradually the sphere of Roman influence was pushed to the Humber and the Dee. Finally the line of the Forth and Clyde became the most northern boundary, although for practical purposes it did not extend for any considerable period farther than a turf wall of over

Winchester. The only Roman *municipium* or fully corporate town was Verulamium (near St. Albans).

It is easy to exaggerate the importance of this phase of development of Britain's story. Extensive areas in the north and west scarcely felt the Roman influence. Yet no previous period had afforded so many advantages to the majority of the inhabitants. Agriculture and the mineral wealth of the country were developed; superb roads stimulated trade; flax, the cherry and the

"THERE IS NO GOD BUT ALLAH"

A Moslem at prayer at the tomb of a sheik on the edge of the Libyan desert. Islam is the religion of one-fifth of the human race. Every devout Mohammedan prays five times a day, his head bowed towards the sacred city of Mecca where the prophet spent his later years.

seventy miles between the Tyne and the Solway Firth, built by the Emperor Hadrian. The great rampart, rebuilt in stone, still remains on guard across the hills and moorland of Northumberland.

The Romans made no attempt to force their culture on the far-distant province. Each tribe was a self-governing community which conducted its own affairs from the convenient centre of a chief town such as Wroxeter. Silchester, Dorchester or

vine, the rose and the lily, the elm, chestnut and poplar were introduced, as well as various vegetables.

Corn had so many acres devoted to it that Britain became known as the Granary of the North. Marshes and fens were drained, forests cleared, dangerous wild animals exterminated, and the breeds of cattle improved.

By the fifth century A.D. Britain had nearly sixty important towns. There were

LASTING MEMORIAL TO THE ROMANS IN BRITAIN

The line of the Forth and Clyde became the most northern boundary of Roman Britain, although for practical purposes Roman rule did not extend for any considerable period farther north than a wall of over seventy miles between the Tyne and the Solway Firth. The great rampart of stone still remains on guard across the Northumberland hills and moorland.

fine public buildings, shops and warehouses, the large centres of population had drain-pipes of lead, and many of the more spacious houses had central heating. Hot air, supplied by hypocausts, was conducted under the floor and through the walls. If coal were used it apparently came from outcrops on the surface.

Probably the chief military, naval and commercial port was Richborough, then on an island, where ships could sail up the Stour to Canterbury. Burnt wheat, discovered while excavating buildings outside the fort, suggests that they were probably storehouses used for corn awaiting export to Gaul. There may have been a mint. The figure of Britannia on English money was copied from a Roman coin of Antoninus in the second century.

The chief industries of Roman Britain were agriculture and grazing. Time and time again British wheat proved a saving grace to Gaul when famine threatened or was an accomplished fact, thanks to the devastation of invading Alemans and Franks. The mines were worked, a fairly large trade was done in wool, potteries were started and there was much coming

and going across the Channel. London, which probably began as a neolithic settlement in the neighbourhood of Hammersmith, became an important place.

The Roman occupation came to an end about the middle of the fifth century of our era. The empire was in dissolution. Rome's soldiers were required nearer home. With the departure of the legions Britain had to look after herself.

Gaul, denuded like Britain of Roman troops, also had to fend for herself. Visigoths, Burgundians, Franks and many another tribe dubbed barbarian made themselves free of what is now the fair land of France. Then the seemingly inevitable struggle for supremacy took place.

For years Clovis, the vigorous King of the Franks, waged relentless war against the petty kings who stood in his path. As rough in manners as he was brave in battle, he appears to have bargained with God for victory. If he won he would turn Christian. The Alemans were defeated, and Clovis fulfilled his promise by compelling his followers to forsake their heathen deities. He and 3,000 of his stalwart warriors were baptized on Christmas Day, 496.

Whether he was sincere in his conversion or not, it was certainly an astute move. Clovis became the champion of the Roman Catholic Church. This secured him allies, and in a clash with the Visigoths at Poitiers the fierce warrior king put an end to the career of Alaric II with his own hand. Paris became a place of some importance as the capital of a kingdom. Roman and Germanic legal customs were codified and became known as the Salic Law.

When Clovis died in 511 he had founded the first permanent State in what had been Roman Gaul. It continued to expand, but under a succession of weak monarchs rule passed to the mayors of the palace. One of these mayors, Charles Martel, or "the Hammer," routed the Moslems at Tours in 732 and introduced an army reform that was to have far-reaching consequences.

Previously the warriors had been freemen who could be called upon to fight in time of war. They were all foot soldiers. He conceived the idea of creating a body of cavalry by giving land to his most powerful dependents on condition that they each maintained a properly equipped war horse, placed themselves at his disposal whenever required, and swore an oath of fidelity to him. So began the feudal system.

His son, Pippin the Short, with the consent of the Church, quietly ousted the nominal king by sending him to a monastery, and in return marched against the Lombards, who were threatening Rome. Defeating them, he presented the Pope with territory in central Italy afterwards known as the Papal States. The Pope thus became for the first time not only a spiritual ruler but a temporal sovereign.

ROMAN SOLDIERS IN ACTIVE SERVICE GARB AND CEREMONIAL ARMOUR

Roman helmets were usually made of iron, and the cuirass or breastplate was of leather plated with bronze. Greaves were thin plates of bronze formed to the shape of the legs, and during the Empire were worn only by centurions. Shields were of leather stretched on a curved framework of metal, and often bore an ornamental metal boss in the centre.

The turmoil and confusion of the so-called Dark Ages may be said to have come to an end during the enlightened reign of Charlemagne, which witnessed the beginning of the Middle Ages and the dawn of modern Europe. For over 350 years after his death, so it is said, he continued to sit crowned, sceptred and mantled, on his throne in the crypt of the cathedral at Aachen (Aix-la-Chapelle), the town which he had chosen for the capital of his empire.

Pippin and His Son

Pippin the Short was clever; his son's mentality was that of a genius. In fifty campaigns, extending over thirty years, Charlemagne fought to create and weld an empire that varied little in extent from that ruled by Napoleon at the height of his power a millennium later. He conquered raiding Saxons and rebellious Bavarians in Germany, insurgent Avars on the Danube; crossed swords with Moslems in Spain, rescued the Pope from threatening Lombards in Italy and became their king.

In 800 Charlemagne was crowned Emperor of the Romans in old St. Peter's at Rome by Pope Leo III. Thus the former Western Empire was in a sense restored. No ruler appreciated learning more than Charlemagne. The British-born scholar-monk Alcuin was persuaded to leave York, and spent the remainder of his life helping to found monastic and cathedral schools, assisting Charlemagne with his correspondence, and giving him the benefit of sane advice. The emperor and his court were pupils of the school attached to the palace.

How Charlemagne Ruled His Empire

Charlemagne was a conciliatory and constructive conqueror. The General Assembly, consisting of important laymen and ecclesiastics, met twice a year to discuss affairs but not to legislate: that was done by the monarch himself. His rules and regulations, called capitularies, number over 1,100. Counts were held responsible for the various districts into which the empire was divided; counts of the marches defended the frontiers.

When the energetic ruler was gathered to his fathers in 814 his grandsons divided the empire. By the Partition of Verdun (843) Charles took the western portion, which we know as France; Lothair, a long and narrow strip in the centre, reaching from the Netherlands to south of Rome and including lands that were to be the source of many complications; Louis, the territory east of the Rhine, which was to become the kingdom of Germany.

Under Otto the Great, a Saxon who drove back invading Magyars from Asia and who eventually settled in Hungary, the possessions of Lothair and Louis were loosely united in 962 and became the Holy Roman Empire. It was an affair of hundreds of disunited bits and pieces, ruled by dukes and prelates who nominally elected the emperor and whose spiritual and temporal ambitions often resulted in conflict and war.

Nevertheless this ramshackle organization —perhaps disorganization would be more correct—held together for over 800 years. It lasted until 1806, when it was quashed by Napoleon I, who referred to Charlemagne as "our august predecessor."

When the last Roman standard left Britain's shores, Picts from the north and Scots from Ireland invaded the land. Help was sought from the Jutes, who had probably already begun to settle in the south of Britain. They took with one hand what they gave with the other, and stolidly refused to budge from Kent when the danger was over. Saxons and Angles from north Germany plundered, raided and settled in England.

Coming of the Vikings

In 787 or thereabouts the Vikings put in an appearance, "like stinging hornets," says Simeon of Durham. Hitherto they had been almost unheard of outside their own countries of Norway, Sweden and Denmark; now many a land was to know and fear them. Finland and Lapland were already planted with their colonies. They settled in Ireland, the Isle of Man, the Faroes, Shetlands, Orkneys, Hebrides and various parts of England. For a time the whole of Scandinavia and the British Isles acknowledged Cnut (Canute) as their king. The rule of the Norsemen in Britain ended in 1042 with the death of Harthacnut. Cnut's son and second successor.

The Vikings made themselves at home in Normandy, pushed overland to Constantinople and thence penetrated to every part of the Byzantine Empire. In the ninth century the Swedes founded the Russian State at Novgorod, and Vikings made themselves known in Spain. The Norsemen discovered Iceland and Greenland. Sailing westward, they even came across North America about 1000 A.D., nearly half a millennium before Columbus's voyage.

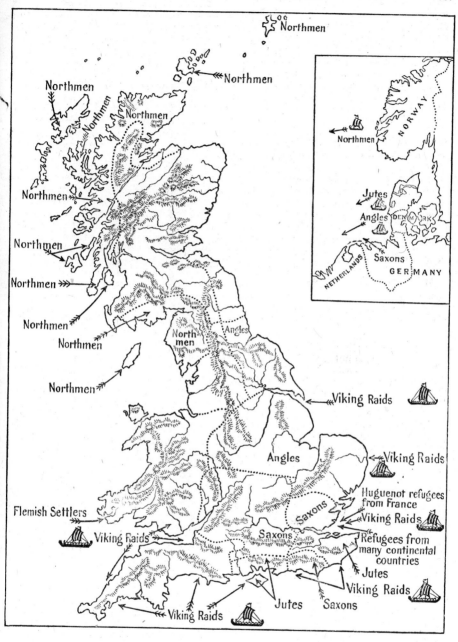

WARLIKE AND PEACEFUL INVASIONS OF BRITAIN

When the last Roman garrison left Britain's shores about 442, Jutes, Saxons, Angles and Northmen invaded the island. In later centuries refugees, often the victims of cruel oppression, made their entry by more peaceful means. This map shows the districts most affected by the arrival of newcomers, among them French Huguenot silk-workers and weavers from Flanders.

MAN—F

CHAPTER 14

LIFE IN THE MIDDLE AGES

Popes and missionaries. What the monks did. Castle and cottage. Peasant life. Rise of universities. Parliament takes shape. Trade and craft guilds. Manorial system. Britain's woollen trade. Early capitalists. Crusaders and adventurers. The Black Death. England's first popular rising. The Hansa towns. Mongol invaders. Genghis, Kublai and Tamerlane. Towers of skulls and corpses as monuments.

THERE are many delusions about the Middle Ages. Some people sigh for the "good old times" that this phase of the human story is supposed to represent. But Merrie England was not so merry. Other folks stigmatize anything that is not the last word in modernity as medieval and fusty. They are equally wrong.

The courtly sport of falconry, the clash of weapon against armour in tournaments, the melody of minstrels, and the pomp that attended the serving of a twelve-course dinner were not for the many. To them life was drab and humdrum; it was circumscribed in a way it is difficult for us to appreciate. This is not to undervalue what was achieved as a whole, which was considerable. The bridge of the Middle Ages links ancient times with modern.

Gregory, Pope and Statesman

The Roman Catholic Church was, in a sense, a spiritual Roman Empire, of which the Bishop of Rome—the Pope—was the emperor. Some of the pontiffs, such as Gregory the Great, were doughty champions of Christianity and of civilization. Gregory was both theologian and statesman, a substance in the government of Rome, whereas the eastern emperor was no more than a shadow. He wrote, founded monasteries, negotiated with the threatening Lombards, and sent missionaries to various lands, including Britain. Although Christianity had been introduced there long before, Gregory's chief representative, St. Augustine, became the first Archbishop of Canterbury.

Gregory, before he was raised to the highest office in the Church, had been, as a layman, first prefect of Rome, and then a monk and the founder of several monasteries, of one of which, at Rome, he eventually became abbot. These monasteries followed the rule of St. Benedict, a noble Roman who, distressed by the low state of the society in which he lived, fled from the Eternal City to a cave in a desert tract, where he followed for several years a life of prayer and penance. Disciples gathered round him; he drew up for them his famous "Rule" under which for many centuries nearly all the monastic houses of the Western World were to be governed. By the time of his death, about 543, several monasteries in various parts of Italy were already putting into practice his motto, "Work is prayer"; and by degrees they came to number hundreds, scattered over every part of Western Europe.

In the scriptorium, or writing-room, of the monasteries that were built in increasing numbers, monks chronicled events and patiently copied the works of Latin authors or the Holy Scriptures. Nuns did similar work in the nunneries. The Bibles, or portions of them, went to the churches or were bought by wealthy private individuals.

Pilgrim Holidays

Pilgrimages were undertaken as much in a spirit of holiday as of piety. Canterbury, Westminster, Glastonbury, Ely, Lichfield, Lincoln, Holywell, York, Durham, these and many other places in England and elsewhere had special virtues for the believer. Year after year, so it is said, 200,000 pilgrims thronged the road to worship at the shrine of Becket in Canterbury Cathedral.

Monks, priests, wandering friars, artists, sculptors, carvers and actors propagated Christianity in their several ways. Plays on Biblical themes were performed in the churches and later on movable platforms in the streets, so that the Bible stories became familiar to the illiterate majority.

Stained glass windows in churches gleamed with representations of Biblical characters: the Good Shepherd with a lamb in His arms; Moses with a flowing beard;

Elijah in his fiery chariot. On the walls pictures of the bliss of the saved and the pangs of the damned reinforced the message delivered from the pulpit. Beauty was sought with pen, brush and trowel.

Although England and Wales had a population of less than two million in the twelfth century, hundreds of large collegiate and monastic buildings were erected and many parish churches rebuilt. Some of the loveliest cathedrals were begun in the twelfth and thirteenth centuries.

Some masons, carpenters, glaziers, tilers and plumbers spent the whole of their working lives on one job, others wandered about from place to place, and on occasion were subject to forced labour by the Crown.

"Let all guests," ordered St. Benedict, founder of the Benedictine Order, "who come to the monastery be entertained like Christ Himself, because He will say: 'I was a stranger and ye took me in.'" The cost was heavy, for both rich and poor availed themselves of the hospitality proffered. The work of manifold organizations for the relief of distress, including flag days, bazaars, entertainments, leagues of pity and what not, which exist now was undertaken in medieval times by one institution —the Church. It preserved culture, a great deal of credulity, and charity, "and the greatest of these is charity."

The parish church was in a very real sense a communal building, the centre of many activities. Here courts were sometimes held, weapons were stored, the wills of the parishioners were kept, as well as a common coffin for carrying corpses to the grave, and fire-hooks for pulling burning thatch from blazing cottages.

A blot on the crowded pages of the Middle Ages was the Inquisition, carried out in an excess of ardour for uniformity of pattern to maintain what was held to be the purity of the Faith. The policy of the Church was: "Thou shalt think as I think."

It was the established authority on all intellectual matters. Heretics were roasted, not to make a Christian holiday as Christians had been flung to the lions to make a Roman holiday, but to save them from themselves.

The castle, introduced into Britain from Normandy at the time of Edward the Confessor, is as truly representative of the

ONE OF THE CRADLES OF THE BRITISH NAVY

One of the entrances to Sandwich, which, with Hastings, Dover, Romney and Hythe, were established as the Cinque Ports in 1078. Winchelsea and Rye were afterwards added. Some of them had already furnished men and ships to Alfred and Edward the Confessor. For fifteen days in any one year they were bound to supply free of cost 1,197 men and boys and fifty-seven ships. If they were retained for a longer period the expense was borne by the King.

THE MIDDLE AGES IN TWENTIETH-CENTURY ENGLAND

Oxen are still used in some parts of Britain for farm work, as they were in the Middle Ages. "Every day I must plough a full acre or more, after having yoked the oxen and fastened the share and coulter to the plough!" says the dialogue of an Anglo-Saxon writer.

Middle Ages as is the Church. The feudal system, whereby, in return for land granted for his use, the medieval aristocrat provided soldiers to fight for the king, led to the building of great houses capable of offering a spirited resistance in case of attack. This naturally brought about the evolution of engines of war such as the giant sling called the trebuchet. So castle walls were made higher and stronger, and different styles were tried. Square towers gave place to round towers, and so on.

The wits of besiegers had to conjure up still more powerful devices. When gunpowder and cannon arrived the days of the castle as a fort were numbered.

The comforts of life in the Middle Ages were few. The peasant lived in a wooden hut and sat on a form, which at night he converted into a bed by putting a straw pallet on it. His pillow was a log. Even in church he had to stand, though a low stone seat was reserved for the ill and aged, hence the saying: "The weak to the wall." If he were lucky a peasant had two meals daily, dinner at ten or eleven o'clock and supper in the afternoon about four. His fingers

took the place of a fork, which useful article was not invented until the time of James I. Piers Plowman lived on bread and cheese, vegetables, curds and cream, which he ate with a wooden spoon from a wooden bowl. Such modern importations as tea or coffee were unknown: ale was the usual beverage, and the monks of an abbey near Burton put an X on the barrel to indicate its quality—X, XX or XXX still indicates the strength of the liquor.

Football, "a bloody and murthering practise," "beastely fury" and "a develishe pastime" according to the few who disliked the game, was extremely popular, although it was frowned on by those in authority because it interfered with archery. Time and again edicts were issued to suppress it. Chess, brought to Europe by the crusaders, and backgammon were popular. Children enjoyed Punch and Judy shows, battledore and shuttlecock, skipping and top spinning.

The university was a medieval product. Just as the philosophers of ancient Greece started their academies by gathering a few interested pupils around them, so scholars in the Middle Ages congregated students and founded schools that were the beginnings of universities. When they had developed sufficiently to attract the attention of a pope or emperor they usually received a charter, although several seats of learning were recognized long before this distinction was conferred.

The first European university was that of Salerno, in Italy, which probably came into existence in the ninth century and was famous for medicine. At Bologna, notable for law, the university was run at first by the students. The university of Paris grew out of the schools attached to the cathedral of Notre Dame. Students flocked from all over Europe to listen to its lecturers.

Oxford University was in existence in 1200, but the precise date of its origin is unknown. Cambridge was brought into being by rebels from Oxford. Both borrowed much from Paris. Plain living and high thinking was the rule. Not until 1565 was the stone-floored dining-hall of Caius College, Cambridge, provided with a brazier of charcoal that helped to keep the apartment above freezing point from All Saints' Day to February 2.

Feudal society as a whole was built up in a kind of pyramid of ranks or classes, each class being dependent for its privileges and livelihood on that below. At the top of the pyramid we find the king. He depended for support upon his barons or tenants-in-chief who received their lands from the Crown. Below them were lesser nobility or country gentlemen who held land from the baron in return for military service. These in turn could rent out part of their land.

Tenants-in-chief who held land directly from the Crown, mesne tenants who held land under a superior tenant, thegns who received land in return for military service, villeins, bordars and cottars, who held less than fifteen acres and paid dues and owed service to their lords, and the *servi*, or slaves, all found a place in the scheme.

AT WORK IN A CHESHIRE SALT MINE

Man's possessions and activities were already various in the Middle Ages. Horses, cattle, ploughs, mills, quarries, vineyards, salt works, fisheries and iron mines are included in the records of eleventh-century wealth. The two most important salt-mining areas in Britain are Worcestershire and Cheshire; salt is also worked at Midlothian in Scotland.

Although at a later period personal service could be commuted for a monetary consideration, the military obligations of the feudal system were not legally abolished until the reign of Charles II.

The first parliament, as distinct from what had been no more than councils since the Norman conquest, was summoned by Simon de Montfort, Earl of Leicester, in 1265, but there was no popular election as we understand the term. The sheriffs, as officers of the king in each county, were commanded to return, in addition to bishops, abbots, earls and so on, two knights for each county and two burgesses for each city or borough.

England's First Parliament

"Simon," writes Bishop Mandell Creighton, "first recognized that the representation of all classes in the State was necessary to form a complete parliament. He called to it representatives of the towns as well as of the shires. When once this step had been taken, Parliament was fully formed. Many years had to pass, and many struggles had to be gone through, before Parliament gained for itself regular powers and definite times of meeting. But it was under Simon de Montfort's hands that it first reached its full growth. All praise is due to him that he had the insight to see its full meaning and importance."

This gathering took place fifty years after King John had attached his seal, showing himself on horseback in full armour, to Magna Carta. The Great Charter restricted —on parchment, for its provisions were often broken—the power of the sovereign and made him accountable for his actions. It did not create trial by jury, as has been asserted; it granted benefits mainly to the members of the privileged class who had drawn up the document, and it left the king's humbler subjects very much as they were. But it was a milestone on the highway of constitutional progress, because of the admission that the monarch was not an absolute ruler, and it also served as a guide post to future liberties.

It was not until 1302 that Philip IV of France summoned the towns to send burghers to take part in his council, and thus inaugurated the States-General. The Third Estate, or commons, had little practical influence until the breaking out of the French Revolution towards the end of the eighteenth century. The States-General indeed, ceased to meet from 1614 to 1789,

so despotic had the monarchy become. In Spain the commons were represented by lawyers in the Cortes of León in 1188, but no rules were fixed as to the constitution of the assembly. Iceland claims one of the earliest national assemblies. It held its first parliament in 930.

Man's possessions and activities were already various in the Middle Ages. Horses, cattle, ploughs, mills, quarries, vineyards, salt works, fisheries and iron mines are included in the records of eleventh-century wealth. Mention of goldworkers, bee-keepers, female minstrels, neat-herds (cattle keepers) and swineherds shows the varying nature of occupations.

Trading was carried on to a very large extent by means of markets and fairs. Over 2,800 grants for them were made by the Crown from the twelfth to the fifteenth century. The salt trade must have been very extensive. The mineral was required for the purpose of preserving meat for winter use, and for the most part had to be brought from the coast. Eventually huge pigeon-cotes were built in order that the birds might provide a much desired alternative dish. Their use was restricted to barons, lords of the manor and the clergy. Still later pepper was employed as a preservative. This spice had much to do with the formation of the East India Company in the reign of Elizabeth.

Medieval Craft Guilds

In the towns the merchants and the craftsmen or citizens had organized themselves in societies called guilds. Each guild looked after the interests of its members, and by King John's time they had become very powerful. In many places the merchant guild became the governing body of the city, its head official the mayor, and its office or guildhall the headquarters of the local administration. Unlike those of early Rome, these organizations regulated the various trades, and when granted a royal charter could enforce their rules and regulations on all and sundry in the borough. They restricted business to some extent because they could exclude competitors.

The craft-guilds, however, eventually succeeded in destroying the trade monopoly of the masters. Despite their faults, a keen sense of their responsibilities and pride of workmanship did much to prevent the taking of mean advantages at the expense of the public. Craftsmen kept to their own trades although a dispute concerning the

SOUTHAMPTON'S PROSPERITY WAS FOUNDED ON WOOL

Southampton docks as they are today. Throughout the Middle Ages England held the proud position now occupied by Australia in wool production. While a large quantity was shipped from the ports of Lynn and Boston, Southampton far outdistanced them in export traffic.

amount of new leather a cobbler might use for repairs without infringing the privileges of the cordwainers lasted over 200 years.

Agriculture is the master industry, however—man's prime necessity after air and water. In England the land was usually divided into areas known as manors, which consisted of three big fields divided by balks of turf into strips of about an acre, but the holdings of neither lord nor tenant were together. They were scattered about the three fields, one of which was always left fallow. A third of the land was therefore uncultivated. A rotation of crops was practised, so that the same kind of grain was never sown two years in succession.

Meadow, pasture and any waste land and wood were used by all, including the lord of the manor, whose domain generally consisted of one-third of the arable land while the remainder was used by his tenants, who also cultivated the lord's strips without pay. In ploughing, sowing and reaping the lord's interests came first. The tenant's wheat had to be ground at the lord's mill and his grapes crushed in the lord's winepress; both services had to be paid for. If repairs to roads or bridges were necessary the tenant lent a hand—without pay.

Most of the tenants were serfs. They were bound to the land, and if it changed hands were taken over by the new owner. On the death of a serf the lord could claim the dead man's best beast and the rector of the parish the second best, a state of affairs which might leave the bereaved family virtually penniless. If his direct heir had sufficient money to pay the necessary tax he could inherit the holding. A serf could secure his freedom in several ways, one of which was by becoming a member of a guild and residing in a town for a year and a day without being reclaimed. It does not sound very easy to accomplish.

The terrible scourge known as the Black Death was to affect appreciably the condition of the agricultural labourer. It reached Britain in 1348 via China, Constantinople and the Continent. Over a million people perished in England; many villages and

AT THE SPINNING WHEEL

The spindle and distaff for spinning are pictured on Egyptian monuments. The distaff came to be regarded as an emblem of womanhood, hence the female side of a family was called the distaff side, and an unmarried woman was called a spinster.

hamlets became as desolate as Tara's halls. East and west, the plague accounted for 62 million lives—four times as many as the world epidemic of influenza in 1918–20.

Already the villein of the manorial system, unable to leave his lord, had made an advance towards emancipation. He had burst some of his bonds. Farm hands who survived could demand almost any wage they chose to ask. This led to the passing of various Statutes of Labourers whereby it was enacted, among other clauses, that those who did not possess sufficient property on which to live were compelled to work for the wages in operation two years previous to the outbreak. Branding on the forehead was the penalty for refusal to do so.

This iniquity, to which unjust and heavy taxation was added, brought about the Peasants' Revolt. When that came to an end, land previously devoted to the growing of corn was in many places given over to the rearing of sheep, and sometimes common land was enclosed for the purpose. The sequel was a drifting to the towns.

In the production of wool throughout the Middle Ages England held the position now occupied by Australia, and heavy fines were imposed on both seller and buyer if it were sold below the standard price. The duties of the first customs officials were to collect tolls, see the wool weighed and sealed before it was placed on board ship, and prevent smuggling. While a considerable quantity of wool was shipped from the east coast ports of Lynn and Boston, Southampton far outdistanced them in the amount of traffic handled for export. In Bugle Street the fourteenth-century Wool House where the fleece was stored and weighed may still be seen. There a sisterhood of twelve women packed the "balons" of wool before export.

An additional fillip was given to the trade in 1353, when the staple, or centre at which all wool was bought and sold, was removed from Bruges to England. Ten towns, including Southampton, Newcastle-upon-Tyne and Exeter, became the only places where such business could be transacted, but the market for Northern Europe was shifted a few years later to Calais.

In primitive Britain weaving was performed without let or hindrance, but as it developed into an industry all manner of rules came into being, to be discarded and replaced by others as circumstances warranted. Often enough the regulations varied according to the district. In Bristol, weavers had to work in rooms facing the street as a precaution against fraud. There were fines for deficiencies in weight, size and colour. The cloth was of various qualities, and sometimes identified with the name of a place, such as Worsted, in Norfolk.

Weaving and Dyeing

The principal colouring matter was woad, prepared from the plant of that name. Indigo came later, to be superseded in its turn by synthetic dyes, although woad is still used for "setting" purposes. Dyeing was a distinct trade.

The fulling process was performed either by men who trampled upon the cloth in a trough, thus thickening it, or by a mill operated by water. It was afterwards cleansed by fuller's earth, mainly obtained from Surrey. The cloth was then stretched and the loose fibres removed with teazles.

Edward III has been termed the father of English commerce. The woolsack on which the Lord Chancellor sits in the House of Lords was instituted during Edward's reign as a reminder that the woollen industry was "the sovereign treasure of the kingdom." In a comparatively few years English cloth was a lively competitor with that spun on the looms of the Netherlanders at Ghent, Ypres and Bruges. Not the least important of the causes of the Hundred Years' War, which started in 1337, was the rivalry that existed between the English and French for the increasing wool trade in Europe.

In time the capitalist and the middleman made their appearance, often enough in one and the same person. The guild became more and more exclusive. The capitalist was the clothier, who bought wool, delivered it to the home workers, collected it in due course as cloth and then sold it. Hitherto for the most part the spinner and weaver had produced for definite customers, who would call for a friendly chat and see the goods in the making. There were intimate mutual interests. The "personal touch" gradually became a thing of the past. The producer span and wove for a somebody who was a nobody, so far as he was concerned. The clothier, provided the cloth was satisfactory, paid for it and departed, possibly without a word of appreciation. The operative was no longer independent.

As early as 1340 an attempt had been made to introduce what came to be known centuries later as the factory system. In that

NORWEGIAN HEADQUARTERS OF THE HANSEATIC LEAGUE

The old building of the Hanseatic League at Bergen. It is the second house on the left. The ramifications of the confederation were far-reaching, and the articles which it bought, sold or bartered were almost equal in number to the 130 trading stations which it maintained.

year Thomas Blanket and his brothers, taking advantage of a measure that enabled foreign clothworkers to settle in England, set up machines in their houses at Bristol and engaged operatives. Blanket's name is now a household word by reason of the article that continues to bear it.

Early Crusades

Outstanding among the historical happenings of the Middle Ages was the sequence of great crusades to rescue the Holy Places from the hands of the infidels. In early days Christians had been encouraged to visit Jerusalem. They were mostly harmless and carried good money in their scrips. But since power had passed to the Seljuk Turks, the pilgrims had been cruelly ill-treated. Islam had taken to the field and spread westward; now it was the turn of Christianity to gird on its armour and march eastward.

Jerusalem fell in 1099. Its capture opened the way to great commercial development. Palestine and the coast of Syria were no longer closed doors to trade. Sardinia and Sicily, previously captured by the Moslems, had been wrested from them. The soldiers were mainly recruited from France, while the enterprising and wily Genoese supplied them with munitions and provisions, which they landed at Antioch. A Latin monarchy was established at Jerusalem, largely with the aid of Italian traders, who thereby secured important commercial privileges.

The Franks governed neither wisely nor well, and in 1187 Jerusalem was captured by the Mohammedans under Saladin. Two clauses of the three years' truce that was agreed upon were important. The coast was to remain in the hands of the Christians, and Italian merchants were to be allowed to trade with the people of the interior.

Crusaders Seize Constantinople

Evidence of further greed on the part of the Italians is afforded by the fourth crusade, which seized Constantinople in 1204 at the instigation of the Venetians. The next two blows in the long series of Holy Wars were aimed at Egypt; both failed. Gradually the few remaining Christian cities in the east fell into the hands of the Moslems. Venice and Genoa, making the better of two possible worlds and bargains, secured commercial treaties with the conquerors. Alexandria became the clearing house of trade with the East, and

remained so until 1517, when it was captured by Selim the Terrible, the conqueror of Syria and Egypt. When Sir Hesketh Bell was Governor of Northern Nigeria, he saw horsemen wearing shirts of mail and helmets from the time of the crusades.

Two episodes in connexion with the six major attempts must be mentioned. They are amongst the most tragic in history. Led by a French shepherd boy named Stephen, 30,000 children embarked at Marseilles in seven vessels to conquer the Saracens. Their armaments were little wooden crosses, but the leader was convinced that innocence would conquer the machinations of wicked men. Two of the craft were wrecked and their passengers drowned. The other ships arrived at Alexandria, where the children were sold as slaves.

Another 20,000 boys and girls left Germany for the same purpose, but on foot. Those who did not perish as they made their stumbling way across the Alps staggered into Genoa. There they were persuaded to return. Some did so; many never saw their earthly homes again.

Forerunners of the Renaissance

If the political morality of those who reaped no small material advantage from the crusades cannot be regarded as high, even when judged by the standard of their own day, it must be remembered to their credit that it was to the merchant princes of the Italian littoral that Europe owed the beginnings of that wonderful new birth which we call the Renaissance. The suppression of the Barbary pirates by the Venetians enabled them to play so important a part in the crusades by securing maritime intercourse between West and East.

England was to benefit by the long succession of holy wars. In a manuscript written early in the fourteenth century we read: "The Pisans, Genoese and Venetians supply England with the eastern gems, as sapphires, emeralds and carbuncles; from Asia were brought the rich silks and purples; from Africa the cinnamon and balm; from Spain the kingdom was enriched with gold; with silver from Germany; from Flanders came the rich materials for the garments of the people; while plentiful streams of wine flowed from their own province of Gascoigny (Gascony); joined with everything that was rich and precious from every land, wide stretching from the Hyades to the Arcturian Star."

The right of the boroughs to assess their

own taxes in return for the payment of a stated sum led to the first popular rising against constituted authority. It took place in London in 1196, the poor alleging that they had to find not only their own levy but that of the wealthy also. Their leader, an old crusader, was hanged.

Most Englishmen of this period had no great love for foreigners. This was not due to racial or other prejudice, but to concessions which merchants from overseas had purchased from the Crown. The first German town trading association or Hansa to obtain such privileges was that of Visby, in Gothland. This was the Baltic centre of the commercial men of Cologne, Lübeck, Hamburg, Bremen, Wismar and other cities whose organization became the powerful Hanseatic League. It convoyed its vessels by armed ships, fought pirates to the water's edge, or turned pirate if circumstances warranted, and even declared war upon occasion.

Situated in a position that commanded the chief trading route between the Near East and Northern Europe, Visby was a place of opulence. "The Gothlanders weigh gold with twenty-pound weights," says an old ballad, "and play with the choicest gems; the pigs eat out of silver troughs and the women spin with golden distaffs." Two of our commonest commercial terms are associated with Gothland. "Sterling" is a corruption of "Osterling," or dweller by the Ostsjö, or Baltic, and "shilling" is the skilling of the Gothlanders.

German Traders in the North

The enterprising Germans secured a foothold in Sweden, and foreign trade during the development of the towns of eastern Scandinavia was mostly in their hands. Stockholm, founded in the twelfth century, took on a Germanic complexion which is still evident. The merchants of Lübeck bought up the iron smelted in the forests, and secured exemption from taxes and other privileges.

In pursuance of rights granted to them in 1229 the Hanseatics took up permanent residence at Novgorod, the scene of the greatest fair in Europe. They remained there until Ivan the Terrible, the first to assume the title of Tsar (Cæsar) of Russia, pitched them out neck and crop because they refused to fulfil his exacting requirements in the matter of taxation. Nearer their headquarters, representatives of the League fastened on Bruges, in Flanders.

ONCE BUSY BRUGES

Starting in the tenth century with cloth as its principal industry, Bruges became the most important centre in Northern Europe for the commercial products of the south.

Starting in the tenth century on its long commercial career with cloth as its staple industry, the city became the most important distributing centre in Northern Europe for the products of the south.

When the Order of the Golden Fleece was inaugurated at Bruges by Philip the Good, Duke of Burgundy, in 1429, the city had some 150,000 inhabitants, and it was said that 150 vessels entered the harbour in a single day. Sixty years later Maximilian, Regent of the Netherlands and later Holy Roman Emperor, wreaked his vengeance on the town because the burghers had not submitted kindly to his rule; had, indeed, imprisoned him. The sand silted up the mouth of the river. Financial and commercial supremacy departed. Bruges became Bruges the Dead, a place of picturesque peace. Its once proud position was taken by Antwerp, until the soldiers of Philip II of Spain, then ruler of the Netherlands, pillaged and burned it in 1576.

At first the representatives of the various German towns had separate quarters in London. Then they made their home in the Steelyard where stood the municipal scales on which all exports and imports were weighed. Situated on the left bank of the Thames and occupying the site of the present Cannon Street railway station, it was the finest position for their purpose in England. Secure behind high and stout walls, the factors lived, making money and homes, friends and enemies. Many a Londoner envied them their secure position and their half-dozen branch establishments at York, Hull, Great Yarmouth, Norwich, Ipswich and Bristol.

The League fought Denmark over a matter of herrings and won; it waged war with Henry IV of England over its privileges and was victorious. But troubles within the union, largely brought about by jealousy, the awakening of the nations to their opportunities, the discovery of new trade routes, and the Thirty Years' War sowed the seeds of decay, though the great federation took a lot of killing. The last three members of the League, Hamburg, Lübeck and Bremen, survivors from the break up in the seventeenth century, joined the German Customs Union in 1881.

For many a long day the Mongols, or Tatars, of the East exercised a kind of horrible fascination over the peoples of the

WALL THAT STRETCHES FIFTEEN HUNDRED MILES

Part of the Great Wall of China, planned to keep the Tatars at bay. It was begun in the third century B.C. *and finished in the sixteenth century* A.D. *Some of the mountains which it crosses in the course of its length of 1,500 miles rise to 4,000 feet above sea level.*

West, perhaps because these latter suffered much at the hands of the intruders. Towards the end of the twelfth century a hunted fugitive named Temujin spent thirty years mastering the refractory warrior hordes of the mountains and deserts of Mongolia, and having achieved his object proudly announced himself as Chingiz (or Genghis) Khan, which may be translated as Emperor of All Men. He conquered half the world and founded the greatest empire that had as yet been known.

With his nomadic but skilfully organized hosts, mounted on stocky ponies and armed with powerful bows that discharged arrows with heads of tempered steel, he raided China, caring nothing for such obstructions as the Great Wall and barricaded cities. Then he turned his thoughts and his cavalcade westward. With a quarter of a million men Chingiz covered 2,000 miles and swept down on Bokhara, Samarkand and other famed cities under the Islamic rule of Mohammed Shah.

An ageing man, with territories stretching across Asia and into Europe from the Yellow Sea to the Black Sea and south to the Indus river, the relentless Emperor of All Men started out on yet another campaign, during which he died in 1227. He had dethroned twenty-seven kings.

Like a devouring forest fire the Mongols under Batu Khan, leader of the Golden Horde, spread death and destruction in lands far removed from their native haunts. Georgia, Armenia, Bulgaria, Hungary, Poland, Russia knew the thunder of their pony cavalry and the terror of sword and torch. Flame followed massacre.

Kublai and Timur

Kublai Khan, another grandson of Chingiz, united all China. He moved the seat of government from Karakorum, which his grandfather had built in Mongolia, to Cambaluc (Peking or Peiping). An enlightened despot, Kublai asked the Pope to send him one hundred teachers. Two friars started out but failed to reach their destination, and what might have been the greatest Christian missionary effort of all time in the Far East was brought to nought.

The Mongols held sway in China until 1368, when a revolution brought in the Ming dynasty. Time and again they invaded the territory, yet the last ruling dynasty before the establishment of a republic in 1912 welcomed them as allies.

In Russia the Khan of the Golden Horde

STATUE AND TOMB
The famous Ming Tombs in China mark the resting places of the emperors of the dynasty of that name. They are situated on the Holy Road near Peiping (Peking).

was overlord until the fifteenth century, although the attacks of another Mongol chief named Timur, also known as Tamerlane, did much to undermine the power of the Mongols in that part of the world. He raided Persia, Mesopotamia, Asia Minor, Syria and India and caused unutterable misery. His favourite amusement seems to have been the raising of towers of skulls and corpses as monuments of his cruelty.

Of less, but more honourable, renown was his grandson Ulug Beg, who combined the quiet study of astronomy with the more active interests of an architect. One of his buildings, in a ruinous condition, is a faded glory of the former capital of Uzbekistan.

CHAPTER 15

ANARCHISTS OF THE MIND

Waldo, reformer of Christianity. Francis, saint and poet. Roger Bacon, forerunner of modern science. Dante and his epic. Wycliffe, herald of the Reformation. Huss, patriot and martyr. Beginnings of printing. Luther, Calvin and the Reformation. The New Learning in Italy. Leonardo da Vinci. New views of earth and stars. Galileo invents the telescope. The Popes and temporal power.

PROGRESS is mainly based on the upsetting, revision or enlargement of old ideas. As such it is a potential menace to the existing order of things. From early days bold spirits have endeavoured to burst the bonds which the generality of mankind have regarded as more or less natural heritages. It is easier to bow down to authority than to resist it. The world owes much to intellectual anarchists, though some bombs have killed the throwers.

Waldo and St. Francis

From the mists of the twelfth century there looms the shadowy figure of Peter Waldo, who sought to interpret the life of Christ in a very literal way. A wealthy merchant of Lyons, he first had the Gospels and various passages from the Early Fathers translated into his own language. Then he distributed his wealth to the poor, and with a number of followers of both sexes went on tramp.

Unorthodox in some of his opinions, Waldo was condemned by the Church, though few who heard him could doubt the sincerity of an evangelist who sought to copy the Master. Despite oppression and partial extermination, generations of Waldenses made their way from country to country shielding the flickering flame of their faith, which has been guarded in the remote Alpine valleys to this day.

After having led a gay life, been a soldier and a prisoner of war, Francis, son of Pietro Bernardone, a rich cloth merchant and moneylender of the Umbrian city of Assisi, came to hold opinions regarding wealth similar to those of Waldo, who had perished three years before the erstwhile King of the Revels was born. His experience in the hands of the enemy made him think rather more seriously on the lot of people less favoured than himself, an impression bitten in as by acid at the sight of a leper. He flung aside the garments of property and donned the rags of poverty.

Setting out as a wandering preacher, doing odd jobs for churches as a means of livelihood, Francis of Assisi savoured with humour the spiritual food which he gave to all and sundry. His sermons were full of the sheer joy of living; he even preached to birds and beasts. Gathering together a band of Poor Brothers, he sent them far and wide in pairs, taking the church to the quiet countryside and the cloister to the babbling market place. A loyal son of Rome, the founder of the Franciscan Order of friars was an impassioned social reformer in an age which believed with St. Hildegard that "God orders every man, so that the lower estate shall not raise itself above the higher, as once did Satan and the first man, who sought to rise above their estates." Sister Death—his own beautiful term—gathered St. Francis to her arms in 1226. He was canonized by the Pope two years later.

Prophet of Modern Invention

Among those who were educated at Oxford and Paris in the thirteenth century was Roger Bacon. He joined the Franciscan order, and sitting in his cell pleaded the cause of science and was promptly regarded as in league with the devil. "There shall be rowing without oars," he wrote, "and sailing without sails; carriages which shall roll along with unimagined speed, with no cattle to drag them; instruments to fly with, with which a man shall by a spring move artificial wings, beating the air like the wings of birds; a little mechanism, three fingers long, which shall raise or lower enormous weights; . . . and bridges over rivers, which shall rest neither on piles nor columns."

Bacon experimented with gunpowder and spectacles, was accused of black magic, and, with the alchemists, sought to discover the philosopher's stone that would convert all baser metals into gold, and the elixir of life that would cure all the ills of man. Condemned by the Church, forgiven, and again condemned, the learned but unorthodox friar asserted that as the earth was round it would be possible to sail westward from Europe to India. Incorporated in a later work, this statement was read by Christopher Columbus, who copied it in a letter which he sent to his patrons Ferdinand and Isabella of Spain. Bacon is therefore entitled to a share in the discovery of America.

Civilization is applied knowledge. The alchemists were the first experimental chemists, despite their mystical beliefs. They failed to find what they sought, but their efforts were not devoid of value. These dabblers in science made quite a number of important discoveries, including nitric, sulphuric and hydrochloric acids.

Dante's great poem the *Divine Comedy* is a masterly picture of medieval times portrayed by a genius, "the splendid tomb of a world passing away, the cradle of a dawning brighter world to come." The prophet of Italian nationalism hundreds of years

before it came about, he was as opposed to the accumulation of wealth as were Waldo and St. Francis, and he fought for the rights of the masses against the aristocrats. Exiled for his political sympathies, he dreamed of the future federation of mankind, for the world became his country "as the ocean is the country of the tribes of the deep." He died of fever at Ravenna in 1321.

The main object of the Council of Constance, which met in 1414 at the instigation of King Sigismund of Hungary and finished its deliberations four years later, was to consider the reform of the Church. Among its decisions was one that the bones of John Wycliffe should be disinterred from their resting place in Lutterworth, Leicestershire. "In obedience hereunto," writes quaint Thomas Fuller, they were burnt and cast "into Swift, a neighbouring brook running hard by. Thus this brook hath convey'd his ashes into Avon; Avon into Severn; Severn into the narrow seas; they into the main ocean. And thus the ashes of Wycliffe are the emblem of his doctrine, which now is dispersed all the world over."

The reformer whose remains had been so uceremoniously disposed of had criticized

ONE OF THE GIFTS OF THE RENAISSANCE

The printing press brought about one of the most sensational revolutions known. Britain was late in the field, for it was not until 1477 that William Caxton produced England's first printed book. This complex machinery, for producing books and periodicals by the gravure process, has gone a long way from the crude hand-presses of the 15th century.

the worldliness of the Church in no uncertain fashion. He challenged with the forthright energy of a Yorkshireman the temporal power of the Pope. "Monks, canons, friars have become a burden to the Church," he thundered. "They are ever absorbing more wealth and land." He translated the Bible into the common tongue, and while doing so came to the conclusion that the Scriptures were the final authority on spiritual matters.

Wycliffe and His Preachers

His itinerant preachers, clad in long russet gowns, taught wherever they could secure a hearing. Those who did not share the views of his followers called them Lollards, a contemptuous term meaning babblers, and borrowed, it may be, from a religious sect in Antwerp of which Walter Lollard was the leader. Wycliffe wished to right what he considered to be wrongs in the Church; he had no wish to break away from her.

Among those who were deeply influenced by the teachings and writings of the English reformer was John Huss, who was sentenced by the same Council of Constance to be burnt at the stake. Rector of the University of Prague, Huss was also minister of the neighbouring Bethlehem Chapel, where the Czech language was used instead of Latin. The preacher was a little too emphatic and liberal in his opinions.

Martyrdom of John Huss

Given a safe conduct that guaranteed his return to Bohemia, Huss was summoned to Constance. Flung into a cell near a stinking sewer, he was eventually cross-examined by the Council, found guilty of heresy, unfrocked and handed over to the secular arm. The Bohemians regarded the sentence as a challenge, and in 1419 a spark was applied to tinder that flamed for twelve years. The war was the first of a series of frenzied religious conflicts that spread over two centuries.

In July, 1915, on the fourth centenary of the death of Huss, a Slovak coachman's son named Thomas Masaryk again raised the standard of revolt in Bohemia, then part of the Austro–Hungarian Empire. He too could have written, as did Master John Huss, that when he was a hungry student he "made a spoon out of bread till I had eaten the peas, and then I ate the spoon also." The motto of the Czechoslovak Republic when it came into being in 1918 was that of the Hussites: "Truth Wins." Masaryk was the first president.

Twenty years later the Powers, great and small, watched while Germany made another contribution to culture by seizing over 11,000 square miles of Czech territory. Hungary helped herself to 4,567 square miles and Poland to 418 square miles.

While Huss was rocking Church and State, it so happened that a certain mechanical device was given to the world. It did more than advance the work of the reformers, for it brought about one of the most sensational revolutions known. The names of various individuals have been suggested as the inventor of movable types for printing, including John Gutenberg of Mainz, who, in 1438, was certainly at work on an idea that, while new to the West, was known in China in the eleventh century.

Early Printed Books

The industry spread rapidly. In 1467 Rome produced its first printed book, followed four years afterwards by Venice. Britain was late in the field in this, as in much else, for it was not until 1477 that William Caxton produced England's first printed book, *The Dictes or Sayengis of the Philosophres.* Apprenticed to a mercer, Caxton had risen to be acting governor of all English merchants in the Netherlands by virtue of a charter granted to the Guild of Merchant Adventurers. It was in the house of Colard Mansion, the owner of a press at Bruges, that he made the acquaintance of the craft that was to work such wonders for the liberation of thought.

Desiderius Erasmus of Rotterdam, born in 1466, would have "the peasant sing a ditty from the Scriptures when ploughing, the weaver at his loom hum something therefrom, and the traveller shorten his journey with their stories." Termed the first of Europeans because he made himself at home in each of the many countries he visited, Erasmus avowed that: "The world is coming to its senses as if awaking out of a deep sleep. Still there are some left who resist pertinaciously, clinging conclusively with hands and feet to their old ignorance. They fear that if *bonæ literæ* (good books) are reborn and the world grows wise, it will come to light that they know nothing."

The first scholar to print an edition of the New Testament in the original Greek, Erasmus also compiled for uneducated folk a paraphrase that was ordered to be put in every parish church in England, edited the

SPEEDING THE NEWS TO THE PUBLIC

The delivery or folder of a modern rotary printing press. From it issue complete news-papers or periodicals at the rate of many thousands an hour. The plates from which the impressions are made are curved and fixed on revolving cylinders, hence the term rotary.

works of some of the early Fathers, wrote incisive essays and penned an abnormal number of letters to the leading men of the time.

Erasmus stood for reform within the Church, but could not go so far as Martin Luther, with whom he had much contro-versy. Whereas Luther regarded reason as "the Devil's chief whore," Erasmus esteemed it as a leading virtue. He saw where Luther's berserker rage was driving him and had no mind to follow, preferring

the rapier to the bludgeon. Among the in-numerable activities of Erasmus was that of a pioneer of hygiene. With morals he associated manners and education.

A subtle and scholarly critic, the famous Dutchman conceived an international commonwealth, a United States of Europe. This idea was diametrically opposed to that of the contemporary Florentine statesman Niccolo Machiavelli, who regarded the nation as the unit of society, and whose low opinion of mankind is summed up in *The*

GIOTTO'S TOWER

The beautiful detached campanile of the thirteenth-century cathedral at Florence. It represents the finest work of Giotto di Bondone (d. 1337), painter and architect.

Prince as follows: "Our experience has been that those great princes who have done great things have held good faith of little account and have known how to circumvent the intellect of men by craft, and in the end have overcome those who relied on their word." It was on Machiavelli's teaching that both Adolf Hitler and Benito Mussolini based their political policies.

Luther, Monk and Reformer

Martin Luther was a titanic figure, big in build and personality and also in contrary qualities that made him intensely human. "Not for a thousand years," asserted this son of a Saxon miner, "has God bestowed such mighty gifts on any bishop as He has on me, a poor beggar and lowly monk." He bluntly asserted that the authority of the Bible was greater than that of the Pope and the Church, and he tried to spring-clean the ecclesiastical organization and sweep the minds of the faithful clear of the doctrinal cobwebs that a multitude of counsellors had spun round the teachings of Christ. Man is justified by faith; "believe and have confidence," he said.

Neurotic in temperament, a mystic who revelled in music and enjoyed a mighty swig of beer, Luther was a man of heroic courage who stoutly fought the sale of indulgences that purported to secure the remission of sin. On the last day of October, 1517, the Augustinian monk challenged the theologians to a public debate on the matter, and with hammer and nails fixed on the substantial door of the castle church at Wittenberg a list of the ninety-five theses, or propositions, which he intended to defend.

Revolt of the Peasants

The most paradoxical of men, who would almost persuade one to believe that consistency is the genius of mediocrity, Luther apparently failed to perceive that when he condemned the Roman Church wholesale he was exalting the Book on which, despite its divers ways of interpretation, the Church's teaching and his own was necessarily based. On the question of interpretation the Protestant sects were by no means at one, and they remain divided.

Pope Leo X issued a bull, or edict, excommunicating Luther, which the recipient promptly burned. He invited Charles V, Holy Roman Emperor, to head the opposition, and was summoned to the Diet (assembly) at Worms and outlawed. The peasants, incited by his fiery message,

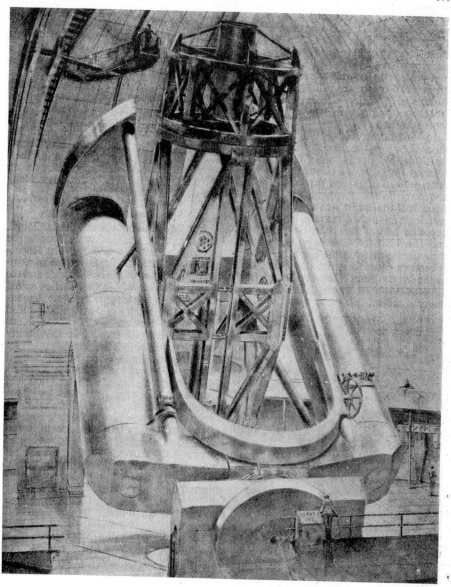

LARGEST TELESCOPE IN THE WORLD

The largest telescope is on Mount Palomar, California. After five years of intensive study it was found that the sky is darker there than anywhere else in the south-west of North America, and therefore afforded a better background for photographic work. The 200-in. mirror is the biggest glass disc ever cast, and necessitated the building of a furnace thirty feet in diameter. Into this forty tons of raw materials were placed and kept for three weeks at a temperature of 2,800 degrees Fahrenheit. After pouring the mixture into a specially prepared mould it was allowed to cool very gradually. Seven months later the mirror was taken from the annealing oven preparatory to grinding and polishing.

revolted and were crushed with ruthless severity, in which Luther was not their supporter but their opponent. Frederick III, called the Wise, Elector of Saxony, and a number of other princes gave him support and protested against an attempt to quash an imperial decree made in the absence of Charles, that territorial rulers should control the religion of their subjects; hence the term Protestant.

In 1530 Luther's friend Philip Melanchthon drew up the Augsburg Confession which defined the Lutheran belief; it was rejected by Charles. Twenty-five years later, when Luther was dead and the old and broken-hearted monarch who had ruled half the world was on the verge of entering a Spanish monastery, it was agreed at a diet held at Augsburg that the rulers and free cities of Germany should make their choice between the opposing creeds. It brought peace for a time but culminated in the Thirty Years' War that lasted from 1618 to 1648, in which Catholic France under Cardinal Richelieu fought on the side of the Protestants to secure territorial acquisitions from Spain.

In all sincerity John Calvin, an invalid Frenchman, sought to run Geneva as a "city of God." His Protestant principles were as intolerant as those of the creed the reformer despised. A wretched Spanish reformer, Michael Servetus, was burnt at his orders because he denied the doctrine of the Trinity. Calvin would have the Church rule man's every thought and deed. His doctrine of predestination, whereby some are foreordained to eternal life and others to eternal death, obviously rests on an exaggerated view of Christ's words: "Many are called, but few chosen."

Spread of Calvin's Teaching

For Calvin the world was primarily evil, but the strict code of morals which he propagated served a purpose. The Huguenots of France, the Presbyterians of Scotland, Dutchmen of the Netherlands and the future colonists of North America seized Calvin's teaching with avidity. As a counter-irritant the Society of Jesus was founded within the Roman Church by Ignatius Loyola, a Spanish soldier, in 1534, thirty years before Calvin's passing.

Giordano Bruno is perhaps the most elusive of the sixteenth century thinkers who sought to break with tradition and puzzle out things for themselves. Styled the knight-errant of modern philosophy, he donned the black and white habit of the Dominicans, was excommunicated, toyed with the Calvinistic faith, and wandered across half Europe breathing the most unorthodox opinions. He was born at Nola, within easy distance of Vesuvius, and his mental activity resembled the fires of the volcano, at one moment slumbering and at the next in full blast.

Bruno at Oxford

At Geneva he attacked a professor of philosophy in print, and was flung into prison for his pains; at Paris his discourses on physics, metaphysics, astronomy and much else attracted the attention of Henry III of France. Restless both physically and mentally, and greatly given to upsetting people, Bruno crossed to England, where he printed a brochure on the art of memory, dedicated to the vice-chancellor and fellows of Oxford University. In this he introduced himself as "a breaker of presumptuous and stubborn ignorance" who, while professing love to all men,

PALACE OF THE POPES

The citadel-like palace of the Popes at Avignon. The Papacy moved its seat of authority from Rome to Avignon in Southern France in 1309, remaining there till 1377.

"looks not to the anointed head nor to the consecrated brow...but thither where man's true countenance is to be found, towards his soul, and the perfection of his spirit." He lectured at the famous seat of learning, but the authorities failed to appreciate his paradoxes, while he on his part cordially disliked certain dons "smelling of Greek and beer, and owning to the manners of ploughmen."

Regarded in London as an atheist, Bruno returned to Paris, and did his best to upset the physical doctrines of Aristotle. Marburg, Wittenberg and Prague heard his invective. Bruno was excommunicated, but instead of keeping quiet, boldly crossed the Alps to Venice, where he bitterly offended a patrician named Giovanni Mocenigo, who denounced him before the Inquisition.

Bruno and Spinoza

Bruno was passed on to Rome, where seven years later he was condemned. "It may be you pronounce this sentence upon me with more fear than I receive it," he told his judges. Bruno, who was burned at the stake on February 17, 1600, had sought a spiritual unity in nature; God and the universe are one and the same thing.

Gentle Benedict Spinoza, of Amsterdam, the very antithesis of fiery Bruno, elaborated the theme, with the sequel that he was ejected from the Jewish community with maledictions and curses. Novalis, the German romantic poet and novelist, termed Spinoza "the God-intoxicated man."

Some of these pioneers played an important part in the remarkable outburst of activity in almost every phase of life that characterized the period known as the Renaissance, a French word meaning regeneration or new birth. Beginning in the fourteenth century it flowered in rich profusion in the fifteenth and sixteenth centuries. The term Renaissance was formerly applied to the revival of ancient culture, but now includes the general extension of knowledge that then took place.

Patrons of New Learning

In their flight to Western Europe refugee Byzantine scholars from Constantinople, which fell into the hands of the Ottoman Turks in 1453, brought with them classics that had been forgotten. They were read and translated with great enthusiasm. The "new learning"—much was old—was greatly stimulated by the patronage of Cosimo and Lorenzo dei Medici, rulers of Florence.

APOSTLE OF THE REFORMATION
Martin Luther, who bluntly asserted that the authority of the Bible was greater than that of either the Pope or the Church.

Among the literary men who helped in the great movement, in addition to those briefly mentioned above, were Francesco Petrarch and Giovanni Boccaccio, and a multitude of artists, sculptors and architects, including Giotto di Bondone, Lorenzo Ghiberti, Donatello, Fra Filippo Lippi, Sandro Botticelli and Donato Bramante. Shakespeare was a representative of the Renaissance at its full flowering.

Leonardo da Vinci, born in 1452 in the little Italian village which his name commemorates, was a wholesale genius with a prodigal partiality for attempting many things and completing relatively few. He tackled everything that interested him, from painting to engineering, from anatomy to bombs, and invented a steam gun and a spit for roasting meat before a fire. He studied the flight of birds, examined their anatomy, and worked out principles for the construction of aircraft. Leonardo filled books with notes on an infinite variety of subjects, and although his observations were not always correct, they betrayed an insatiable thirst for knowledge that makes one wonder whether he did anything but think and work.

Leonardo, Artist and Scientist

It is regrettable that in his fondness for experiment he used for his painting of "The Last Supper" a new oil process which nearly lost the work to posterity. With Michelangelo and Raphael he helped to beautify the Sistine Chapel at Rome, and was the first great artist to represent the human figure in the round. Leonardo remarked on the matter: "We have just discovered that the earth is not flat, neither must we any more paint men flat." It seems strange that a man with so sensitive a touch should have been able to break a horseshoe with his hands.

In the short space of twenty-five years that separated 1546 and 1571, a trinity of remarkable astronomers were born, namely Tycho Brahe, Galileo Galilei and Johann Kepler. Only three years before the earlier date Nicolaus Copernicus, the first modern observer to put forward the theory that the planets revolved round the sun, had passed away. Aristarchus, the Greek philosopher, had mooted the idea before the dawn of our era, but it had been scoffed at.

New Astronomical Theories

The statement of the Polish astronomer was staggering, for hitherto it had been believed that the earth was the centre of the solar system, as Ptolemy had taught. It upset man's idea of his importance. Tycho Brahe, a Dane, refused to believe that the earth goes round the sun, but he did valuable work by compiling a catalogue of the positions of over 1,000 fixed stars.

In many of his observations he was assisted by Johann Kepler of Wurttemberg, who supported the Copernican theory and showed after a prolonged study of Mars that the planets moved in ellipses and not in circles, as was believed. Referring to one of his discoveries, Kepler notes in his book on *Celestial Harmonies* that: "It may well wait a century for a reader, as God has waited six thousand years for an observer."

Galileo had the inestimable privilege of being the first astronomer to use a telescope, an appliance which is believed to have come about by accident. Jan Lippershey, a Dutch maker of spectacles, had an apprentice who casually placed a double concave lens and a double convex lens in such a position that he saw a weathercock on a church steeple magnified and upside down. This gave Lippershey an idea, and mounting the glasses in tubes he made the first telescope.

When news of the discovery reached Galileo in 1609, he immediately set about constructing an "optic tube," through which to his great delight he observed the mountains and valleys of the moon. It is still kept at Arcetri. The first observatory to be built in Europe was a wooden tower on the roof of the University of Leiden, Holland, erected in 1633.

Galileo came into conflict with the Roman Church because he held that the Copernican system was a truth and not a theory. He recanted, but moral resistance never breaks down without preserving a few mental reservations, and the investigator continued with his studies until blindness prevented further work.

Papacy Settles in France

The attempts made by the Papacy, at once greatly loved and greatly feared, to maintain its supremacy in temporal affairs had led to much bitterness. Its unbending attitude in doctrine had rent the Church in twain. The Church sought to control states, kings to control the Church. Emperors of the Holy Roman Empire, with the welfare of Italy in view, deposed popes or ensured their election. Under French influence the Papacy moved for a while its seat of authority from Rome, the hallowed city associated with St. Peter and its early struggles, to Avignon, a town without tradition just outside the French frontier. For a time there were rival popes.

In 1870, when the kingdom of Italy came into being and incorporated the Papal States, the Holy Father refused to recognize the monarchy and retired to the Vatican. He never came out of it. Thus a tradition of imprisonment grew up that was not officially broken until after the Lateran Treaty had been signed by Mussolini and Cardinal Gasparri in 1929, when Pius XI became Sovereign of the Vatican City State covering an area of a little over 108 acres and sheltering 518 subjects.

It is in the hearts of men rather than in the seat of authority that the Church lives.

RIDING ON THE BACKS OF FOUR ELEPHANTS

The Grand Khan who befriended Marco Polo travelling on the backs of four elephants. It will be noted that the artist had only an imperfect idea of the size of the animals, otherwise he would not have represented them as being only about the same height as a horse.

CHAPTER 16

UNVEILING THE UNKNOWN

Early British travellers. Missionaries and explorers. "Marco Millions." Henry the Navigator. Discovery of America. Cabot founds British Empire. First voyage round the world. Spanish gold. Merchant adventurers. Seeking the North-West Passage. Drake rounds Cape Horn. Traders and pirates. The Pilgrim Fathers. Canada and Australia. Commercial undertakings that fathered the British Empire.

So far as the British Isles are concerned the injunction of Christ to take His message to the uttermost parts of the earth led to some of the earliest journeys of exploration, though it was to save souls and not to gain knowledge that the religious set out. Like St. Paul, they were "in dangers oft" from footpads and pirates, wind and weather, and the following of primitive trackways.

The first known travel book to be penned in Britain was due to the vagaries of a gale towards the end of the seventh century. It blew Arculf, a prelate of Gaul, out of his homeward course from Palestine and compelled him to land at Iona, off the west coast of Scotland. Here the self-sacrificing zeal of the Irish St. Columba had founded a Christian community. Abbot Adamnan listened to the bishop's narrative with amazed interest, wrote it down, and presented the manuscript to Aldfrith of Northumbria, "the wisest of kings." The scholarly and industrious Bede made a precis of the work for his *Ecclesiastical History*, and also a separate version which was widely copied for the use of pilgrims. The flourishing trade of Alexandria and its flaming pharos, or lighthouse, of world-wide fame, particularly attracted Arculf.

Alfred the Great employed two dauntless Norse navigators, Othere and Wulfstan, as explorers, and according to William of Malmesbury sent Sigebert, Bishop of Sherborne, to India, whence he returned with many gems. Othere apparently reached Archangel via the White Sea and the Dvina River, while Wulfstan sailed up the Baltic, the Gulf of Riga and the Gulf of Bothnia.

Early English Voyagers

Athelhard, more commonly known as Adelard of Bath, a writer on philosophy who flourished in the twelfth century and to whom we owe a treatise on the astrolabe, an instrument for taking the altitude of heavenly bodies, appears to have wandered from France to Spain, Italy, the north of Africa, Greece, Arabia, Mesopotamia and Syria. His own account has disappeared, though that of Saeewulf, a Worcester trader and in all likelihood a contemporary, is treasured in the library of Corpus Christi College, Cambridge.

A far longer journey was undertaken by the Franciscan friar John de Piano Carpini. He was sent by Pope Innocent IV in the spring of 1245 to the court of the cultured Kublai Khan, near Karakorum, in Mongolia, and succeeded in reaching it in the summer of the following year. In 1253 another friar, William of Rubruck, was sent by Louis IX of France to the Mongol emperor. Both of these plucky travellers left accounts of their exploits. Part of the Caspian Sea had been explored a few years earlier, but Brother William added considerably to European knowledge of the country in the region of Astrakhan and Erzurum and of the Caucasus.

Travels of the Polos

Thus the way was open for the journeys in Asia undertaken by the Venetian traders Nicolo, Matteo and Marco Polo, respectively father, uncle and son, in the thirty-five years between 1260 and 1295. To a fellow prisoner in Genoa, Rusticiano of Pisa, we owe the narrative dictated by the youngest of the wanderers. It was the first book to deal in a thoroughly comprehensive way with the vast territories that stretch for thousands of miles and had aroused curiosity for centuries by reason of their apparently inexhaustible wealth.

The work inspired Christopher Columbus, whose printed copy, copiously annotated in the margins, is in the library that bears his name at Seville. The Polos brought news of Japan, and it was to reach that country and others that the former Genoese weaver sailed from the sunny shores of Spain in the midsummer of 1492.

The two brothers, after a business visit to the Crimea, proceeded to Sarai, Kazan and Bokhara, where they were asked by envoys of Kublai Khân to return with them to China. The great potentate received them kindly, and bade them go back with a request that the Pope would send learned men to instruct his people.

Marco Polo accompanied the travellers on their next extensive tour. They made their way to Old Hormuz, on the Persian Gulf, and proceeded via Kirman, Khorasan, Balkh, Badakhshan, the plateau of Pamir, Kashgar, Yarkand, Khotan and the terrible desert of Gobi. They reached Shangtu, where the gorgeous summer palace of the Khan was situated, a little over four years after they had set out from the coast of Syria.

Marco's Return Home

The appearance and intelligence of Marco attracted the favourable attention of the Mongol ruler, who sent him on various missions that enabled him to see great stretches of the country, and he was later promoted to the important post of Governor of Yangchow. A suggestion made by the Polos that the Khan should use catapults in warfare such as the Romans had employed was put into practice in the reduction of Siang-yang. When it surrendered the Venetians reaped no small reward in wealth and honours.

The Polos did not see Venice again until about 1295. When they arrived they invited their friends to a feast. As the dinner progressed the adventurers changed their gorgeous clothes several times, on each occasion cutting up the garments they had previously worn and distributing the material among the attendants.

"The proceedings," we are told, "caused much wonderment and amazement among the guests. But when the cloth had been drawn and all the servants had been ordered to retire from the dining-room, Messer Marco, as the youngest of the three, rose from the table and, going into another chamber, brought forth three shabby dresses of coarse stuff which they had worn when they first arrived. Straightway they took sharp knives and began to rip some of the seams and welts, and take out from them jewels of the greatest value in vast

DERIVED FROM THE NAME OF A GREEK TITAN

Greek mythology had it that the giant Atlas supported the pillars of the Universe, and in early books of maps it was the practice to have an engraving of Atlas holding up the globe. In this way the term Atlas originated for volumes of maps. The geographer Mercator, who lived in the sixteenth century, was the first writer to make use of the word in this sense.

quantities, such as rubies, sapphires, carbuncles, diamonds and emeralds, which had all been stitched up in those dresses in so artful a fashion that nobody could have suspected the fact."

When the rivalry of the great trading republics Venice and Genoa culminated in blows Marco Polo, now nicknamed Milioni, took a hand in the fighting and was made prisoner. His book was used in compiling several of the charts then in course of preparation, some of which, including the celebrated Hereford *Mappa Mundi* (about 1307), marked a considerable advance on any previous attempts.

Franciscans in China

The next merchant to reach China was probably Peter of Lucolongo, who penetrated to the Far East with Friar John de Monte Corvino. They spent some time in India, and from there sailed in a vessel "flimsy and uncouth, without nails or iron of any sort, sewn together with twine like clothes, without caulking, having but one mast, one sail of matting and some ropes of husk." Another Franciscan who reached China in the early days, travelling by way of Persia and India, and returning via Tibet, was Friar Odoric.

There is a story that in 1344 a certain Robert Machan eloped with Anne d'Arfet, and setting sail from Bristol landed on the then unknown island of Madeira. The voyage in 1360 of Friar Nicholas of Lynn, or Lymne, with the object of finding the North Pole is less improbable. The little island off the coast of north-west Africa was discovered or rediscovered, as the case may be, in 1420, by Gonçalvez Zarco. The instigator of the expedition was Prince Henry, surnamed the Navigator, a son of the King of Portugal. His observatory at Sagres, near Cape St. Vincent, was a school for potential navigators, whom he infected with his own passion for discovery.

Beginning of the Slave Trade

The Azores were explored, and ship after ship left in an effort to reach "farthest south." In 1441 one of Henry's captains put in at Cape Blanco (Rio de Oro), and a trafficking in natives was begun which was to have far-reaching consequences. It started an iniquitous trade—though one upheld by the morals of the age—that put a stop for many a long day to the internal development of Africa, and it led to the discovery of the sea route to India, for there

was to be no looking back in the desire to find what lay beyond. Cape Verde was doubled by Diniz Diaz in 1445, and in the following year Alvaro Fernandez proceeded some hundred miles farther. Alvise Cadamosto sailed up the Senegal river and discovered the Cape Verde Islands in 1456.

The inspiration of the Navigator continued long after his death. In 1484 the Congo was reached by Diego Cão, who claimed the territory for Portugal, and in 1485 he landed at Walvis Bay. Two years later Bartholomew Diaz, driven by a gale, rounded the Cape of Storms, afterwards renamed the Cape of Good Hope by John II of Portugal, and entered Algoa Bay. Defeated in his wish to proceed by the threats of a mutinous crew, he had to return or be flung overboard.

Among those who shared the triumphs and disappointments of this great adventure was a certain Bartholomew Columbus. On his return his brother Christopher poured out to him the burning desire of his heart to reach the Far East by sailing to the Far West. He had dogged the footsteps of kings and courtiers without success, yet the urge within him prompted further effort. Would Bartholomew cross to England and try to interest Henry VII in the project?

Columbus and His Brother

Nothing loth, Bartholomew set off, and was captured by pirates. Ill and penniless, he at last reached England, and managed to keep body and soul together by drawing maps and selling "sea-cards" for compasses, which had been introduced into Europe by the Arabs, probably from the Chinese. Finally he was granted an audience, and Henry's suggestion that the prime mover in the scheme should attend in person was "accepted with joyful countenance. But because God had reserved the sayd offer for Castile," his son relates, "Columbus was gone in the meane space."

With a company of jail-birds and ne'er-do-wells in three tiny ships he set sail on August 3, 1492, firmly believing that he would reach Japan and China. He found neither. On the twelfth of the following October he landed on one of the outposts of the New World, which he named San Salvador, now unromantically called Watling Island. Papal authority decided that all lands newly discovered or unknown to the west of a line drawn 300 miles west of the Azores should belong to Spain, and those on the eastern side to Portugal.

England, a little suspicious of all things new, a little lethargic in arousing herself to fresh endeavours, made no immediate move in this partitioning of the world. Again a sailor born in Genoa, though a naturalized Venetian, pointed out to Henry VII that his country's destiny was on the water. Mecca, a land-locked Arabian city on a caravan route, had inspired this trading mariner. To that great emporium of trade slow and cumbersome camels brought goods from regions afar. The Holy City of the Mohammedans and its crowded mart set John Cabot puzzling about the possibility of reaching farther Asia by way of

latter port in the *Matthew* on May 2, 1497. In the last week of June the little crew of eighteen discovered Newfoundland and claimed it for the island kingdom. For this service Cabot received £10 (about £125 of our money) and a yearly pension of £20.

In 1498 Cabot paid another visit to the "New Isle," reached Labrador and Baffin Land, and cruised along the coast of Nova Scotia and New England. Cipangu (Japan) eluded him, as it had done Columbus.

A little over two months after Cabot had set out on his first voyage to America a Portuguese fleet of four vessels left the Tagus intent on finding a sea route to India. Its

ZOOLOGICAL GARDEN OF A CHINESE EMPEROR
The menagerie of the Grand Khan visited by Marco Polo, as pictured in an old French volume. The appearance and intelligence of the Venetian traveller attracted the attention of the Khan, who sent him on missions that enabled him to see great stretches of the country.

the western sea, as Columbus had puzzled.

He received letters-patent from Henry that made him commander of an expedition "to seek out, discover and find whatsoever isles, countries, regions or provinces of the heathen and infidels, which before this time have been unknown to all Christians." The king bore part of the expense out of his privy purse, allocating one-fifth of the net profits to himself, and "dyuers merchauntes, as well of London as of Bristowe, adventured goodes and slight merchandises."

Cabot and his three sons sailed from the

commander, Vasco da Gama, had already proved a doughty fighter. Despite storms and militant discontent, he rounded the Cape of Good Hope and made Melinda, on the east coast of Africa, where good fortune in the guise of a pilot in the service of Indian merchants awaited him. Arrived at Calicut, the commander took possession of the land in the name of Manuel I. "Calico" takes its name from this seaport of southwest India.

Undeterred by da Gama's story that he had been compelled to fight his way out of the harbour, the King of Portugal ordered thirteen ships to be made ready to sail for India. At all costs factories, otherwise trading posts, were to be established. Pedro Alvarez Cabral, under whose command they were placed, set his course too far westward, and in 1500 reached Brazil, which had already been discovered a few months before by Vincente Yañez Pinzon, a Spaniard who had sailed with Columbus on his first voyage. Unaware of this, Cabral took possession of the territory, which he called Terra de Vera Cruz. After losing several vessels he reached Calicut, founded a factory, and left forty of his people in charge. All were afterwards murdered.

Vasco da Gama at Goa

When news of the tragedy reached Portugal, da Gama was sent off to avenge the insult. He acted with savage brutality, bombarding the town, massacring the inhabitants, and capturing many native vessels. He was made Viceroy of India in 1524, but his term of office was short, for he died at Cochin in the same year.

Brazil, a less attractive country because its natural resources other than its timber were unknown, was not forgotten in an age when national claims were being staked in so many new directions. A Portuguese colony was planted there in 1503. Rumours of the existence of such a country had long been prevalent in England; indeed, enterprising Bristol merchants had fitted out expedition after expedition in the unavailing hope of finding "the island of Brazil."

During the two opening decades of the sixteenth century Spanish navigators went from strength to strength. In 1512 or thereabouts Juan Ponce de Leon made the first exploration of the coast of Florida; in 1513 Vasco de Balboa, anxious to escape his creditors and urged on by native stories of fabulous wealth, crossed the Isthmus of Panama and discovered the Pacific; in 1516 Juan Diaz de Solis found the mouth of the Rio de la Plata.

Sailing Round the World

It was reserved for a Portuguese to carry out the first circumnavigation of the globe. It is true that Ferdinand Magellan had renounced his nationality for that of Spain over some real or fancied grievance connected with services rendered by him in the East Indies and Morocco, but the land of his birth honours him as one of the most distinguished of her many adventurous sons.

It is quite likely that he had taken part in the assault on Malacca, in the Malay Peninsula, the capture of which had opened the way to the renowned Moluccas, or Spice Islands. The possibilities of the rich territory attracted him, and he and his friend, Ruy Faleiro, approached Charles V with a scheme for reaching it by sailing westward. The notion appealed to the emperor, who furnished Magellan with five ships, the largest of which was of 120 tons. With an eye to business, a varied cargo of miscellaneous goods was stowed away for bartering with the natives.

They sailed in September, 1519, not very happily. Faleiro quarrelled and detached himself. The channel which Magellan believed would lead him to the Pacific failed to materialize. Compelled to seek shelter in a bay off Patagonia, the discontent of the crews flamed into mutiny. Magellan fought the rebels and won.

First Rounding of Cape Horn

Eventually the intrepid commander came across the mouth of the strait which now bears his name. One ship had been lost; another funked the passage and turned back. The three remaining vessels proceeded carefully, threading their way for as many miles as there are days in a year, and on November 28, 1520, the men who had begged the commander to give up the project rejoiced greatly. The Pacific, bathed in golden sunlight, with scarcely a ripple on its surface, lay in front of them.

Scurvy-ridden, the band of scarecrows sailed the sea of their desire for three months before they came across the Ladrones—probably Guam, later to become a naval station of great strategic importance. The King of Cebu, one of the Philippines, received Magellan kindly, and in return the navigator undertook an expedition against the island of Mactan. There he met his death, fighting.

Juan Serrão and Barbosa, Magellan's brother-in-law, assumed joint command, and were murdered by the king or by mutineers: the evidence is inconclusive. Setting fire to one of the remaining ships, the survivors under Juan Sebastian del Cano set sail and reached the Spice Islands, but not before they had been compelled to abandon their consort, whose leaky condition rendered her unsafe for further service. The *Vittoria*, of eighty-five tons, was a little more seaworthy, but not much. Finally, after having crossed the Indian Ocean and

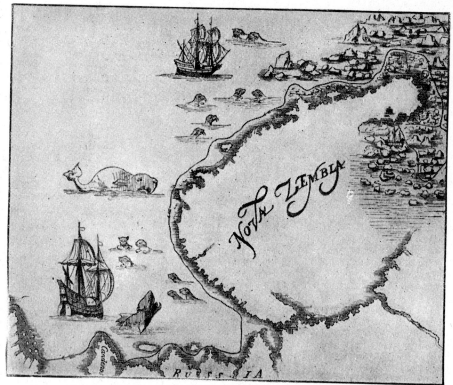

AN EARLY ATTEMPT TO MAP A NEW DISCOVERY
An early map of part of the coast of Novaya Zemlya, or New Land. It may have been sighted by Richard Chancellor before he anchored near the site of the present-day city of Archangel and made a sledge journey of nearly 1,500 miles to meet Ivan the Terrible.

rounded the Cape of Good Hope, the pioneer circumnavigators reached Seville in September, 1522, little more than bags of aching bones and jangled nerves.

Whence did America, discovered by the Vikings, and after a lapse of nearly five centuries rediscovered by Columbus and Cabot, take its name? It was derived from Amerigo Vespucci, who claimed to have sailed with Pinzon in 1497 in an expedition that reached the mainland several days before Cabot. After a further voyage he transferred his affection to Portugal, and in 1502 apparently reached "farthest south."

"On the first day of April," he tells us, "I discovered a Terra Australis, which we coasted for twenty leagues. We found it all a bold shore, without seeing any port or inhabitants."

Writing to Lorenzo dei Medici, Vespucci referred to his discovery as "a new world," and the letter was published. A copy fell into the hands of Martin Waldseemuller, a German scholar, who duly announced in his *Cosmographiæ Introductio* that a fourth continental division had been discovered; "wherefore I do not see what is rightly to hinder us from calling it Amerge or America, namely the land of Americus, after its discoverer Americus." The suggestion was acted upon. Vespucci died as Chief Pilot of Spain, but it is extremely doubtful whether the honour conferred upon him in the matter of the name was deserved.

The only region which appeared to offer the wealth which Spain sought in the New World was Mexico, and thither Hernando Cortes was sent in 1518. He founded Vera Cruz, conquered the country, and won a wealthy Spanish dominion. Seeking for the "South Sea," he discovered the peninsula of Lower California in 1536. When Charles V had no further use for the great adventurer he so far dismissed him from his thoughts as to fail to recognize him. According to the story, his reply to the emperor's peremptory: "Who are you?" was nothing more than this: "I am a man who has gained you more provinces than your father left you towns"—which was discourteous but deserved.

Pizarro and the Incas

Another vast storehouse of natural wealth was discovered and unlocked by a needy adventurer, Francisco Pizarro. He had accompanied Balboa to the Pacific, tried his hand at stock raising, served as a soldier, and made two unsuccessful attempts to conquer Peru before he set out on his final and victorious effort in 1531. His acceptance of treasure to the estimated value of over £3,000,000 as a ransom for Atahualpa, the Inca emperor, proved the resources of the country; his non-fulfilment of the obligation proved his own unscrupulous methods. He was murdered in 1541, the year in which his fellow-countryman Francisco de Orellana concluded the navigation of the mighty Amazon in a makeshift brigantine built of bits and pieces.

Meanwhile expedition after expedition had set out in quest of the unknown. Between 1526 and 1530 old John Cabot's son, Sebastian, explored the rivers La Plata, Parana and Paraguay. The Marshall Islands, in the North Pacific Ocean, were sighted in 1535. In the same year Jacques Cartier, one of the most illustrious of French explorers, discovered the island of Anticosti, in the Gulf of St. Lawrence, and reached Hochelaga, now a suburb of Montreal, the largest city in the Dominion of Canada.

Europe Discovers Japan

Marco Polo brought the earliest knowledge of Japan to Europe. The country was first visited by Europeans about 1542 by sheer necessity. Three Portuguese sailors in a junk, blown out of their course from the coast of China, were compelled to make a forced landing. Seven years later, preceded by Mendez Pinto, a Portuguese merchant, Francis Xavier, the great Jesuit missionary, began his work there, and was followed by Spanish and Dutch traders, who found the native merchants already carrying on business with China, India and the Philippines.

European influence did not last for long, though it developed Nagasaki into a thriving port. In 1612 orders were given that Christianity was to be stamped out, and

that natives were not to leave the kingdom or have communication with white men other than the Dutch, who were allowed to remain on a tiny island after the last Portuguese and Spaniard had shaken the dust of Japan off their feet in 1639.

The country maintained this policy of isolation from the Western World until the middle of the nineteenth century. One notable exception was made. Near Yokosuka may be seen two stone lanterns that mark the last resting place of an Elizabethan seaman. "The Pilot's Grave," as it is called, contains whatever may remain of the dust of William Adams, the first Englishman to settle in what was then the land of cherry blossom and the Samurai.

Misfortune rather than desire led him there. Adams set out as pilot major of a Dutch fleet loaded mainly with woollen cloth for Spanish America. The ships were scattered by a storm, and at the suggestion of a sailor who had previously been to Japan, Adams decided to make an attempt to reach the country. The *Charity* made the coast of Japan in April, 1600.

First Anglo-Japanese Treaty

Adams was summoned to appear before the shogun, or hereditary commander-in-chief. His manly presence and the straightforward answers he gave to questions made a favourable impression on Iyeyasu. In 1613 the *Clove*, an East Indiaman, arrived at Hirado. With the help of Adams a charter was secured which gave permission "to the subjects of Great Britain for ever, to come into any of the ports of our empire with their ships and merchandise, without let or hindrance to them or their goods, and to abide, buy, sell and barter, according to their own manner, with all nations; to tarry here as long as they think good, and to depart at their pleasure."

A factory was established, but it lost heavily and was closed. Adams married a Japanese woman, became a master shipbuilder, taught astronomy and mathematics, and made voyages to the Liukiu Islands and Siam before his death in 1620.

In 1551 Sebastian Cabot was appointed Governor of the Mysterie and Companie of the Marchants Adventurers for the Discoverie of Regions, Dominions, Islands and Places Unknowen, which had just been founded. He suggested that the company should first turn its attention to "the northern part of the world by sea to open a way and passage to Cathay by the north-

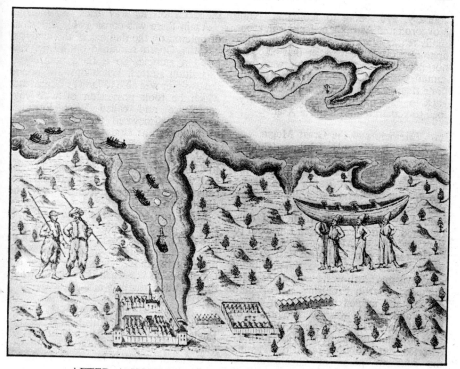

AFTER A VOYAGE OF 1,400 MILES IN OPEN BOATS

William Barentz, a Dutchman, sought to reach China by the North-East Passage. He died in the attempt after wintering in Novaya Zemlya, but the survivors made a voyage of over 1,100 miles in open boats and reached a Lapp settlement on the peninsula of Kola.

east," and the idea was approved. Three small vessels, the largest a cockleshell of 160 tons, were fitted out and victualled for eighteen months. The command was given to Sir Hugh Willoughby, with Richard Chancellor as pilot general.

The beginning of the voyage was not auspicious. A gale struck the ships near the Lofoten Islands and they parted company. The possibility of separation had been foreseen, and it was arranged that all should make for the Norwegian port of Vardo. Chancellor arrived and waited in vain, and then headed for the White Sea, eventually landing near the site of Archangel. At the invitation of Ivan the Terrible the explorer sledged nearly 1,500 miles, and was told by the emperor that he would welcome the introduction of English goods. He returned home, and the facilities he obtained led to the formation of the Muscovy Company.

Willoughby was far less fortunate. He sailed up and down the coast of Lapland and at length entered a haven "wherein were very many seal fishes, and other great fishes; and upon the main we saw bears great deer, foxes, with divers strange beasts, which were to us unknown, and also wonderful." Evil weather set in. Three parties "returned without finding people, or any similitude of habitation." Thus closes the journal of Sir Hugh Willoughby. Russian fishermen found it, together with the frozen bodies of him and his crew.

In charge of another of the Muscovy Company's ventures was Anthony Jenkinson, a seasoned merchant and mariner who had obtained trading privileges in Turkey. His purpose was to penetrate into Central Asia. From Kholmogori, where the company had its trading post, he proceeded in a small boat up the Dvina river for over a thousand miles.

The next stage of his long and lonely journey was made by sledge to Moscow, where the Tsar received him with marked courtesy. Proceeding to Kolomna, Nijni Novgorod and Astrakhan, Jenkinson eventually reached Bokhara. It was a bitter disappointment to the traveller that he could not penetrate into Persia, but wars and rumours of wars compelled him to postpone the idea. He therefore made his way back to England, the first of his countrymen to penetrate into Central Asia.

Elizabeth and the Great Mogul

Within Jenkinson's lifetime Thomas Stevens had been the pioneer English traveller to reach India by rounding the Cape of Good Hope. Ralph Fitch, James Story, John Newberry and William Leedes, merchants of the Levant Company, succeeded by the overland route and duly delivered a letter from Queen Elizabeth to the Great Mogul, Akbar.

The real or fancied North-East Passage having failed to materialize, the possibility of a navigable north-west channel was again discussed. Martin Frobisher, a Yorkshire sea captain, argued the point for fifteen years, and in 1576 was given command of three ships, the largest of about twenty-five tons burden. One was wrecked and another deserted, but Frobisher sailed on. Passing the southern point of Greenland, he reached the bleak coast of "a new land of marvellous great heith," which was taken to be Labrador. Sailing northwards until the weather made further progress impossible, he turned into the bay which now commemorates his name, hoping that it would lead "into some open sea on the backe syde."

Gold—or Rubbish?

Coming across an island, some of the crew landed to explore. Five men were seized and carried off. Taking as hostage an Eskimo who was paddling about in his canoe, the commander reluctantly hoisted sail, carrying with him a quantity of "mynerall" that he thought might be of commercial value.

The "mynerall" was examined. "Gold!" said some. "Trash!" said others. Certain London merchants decided to risk money on a further expedition, particularly as it was noised abroad that Queen Elizabeth was willing to lend a ship of the Royal Navy for the purpose. Frobisher Bay was reached and Meta Incognita, the Unknown Land, taken possession of in the name of Her Majesty. Some 200 tons of alleged ore were brought on board, and the squadron

sailed off on its way back to England.

Again there was considerable difference of opinion on the findings of the analysts, but the Queen remained optimistic. She loved a gamble. So a third and bigger expedition started. When outward bound the explorer was able to land at Greenland, which he took possession of with easy conscience and called West England. Frobisher discovered the channel afterwards known as Hudson's Strait, and felt certain that his efforts were to be rewarded by his finding the great North-West Passage to China. He proceeded for some 300 miles and was then compelled to put back because his crew refused to remain loyal if he did not return.

More iron pyrites—the "mynerall" was nothing more valuable—was loaded, and Frobisher left the bleak and inhospitable shores for ever. The cheers that greeted him on his arrival in England gave place to contemptuous silence when it was proved that the ore was virtually worthless.

Drake in the Pacific

He had not rendered his final services to England. The Elizabethan adventurer seldom rested until his body was mouldering in the earth or rotting in the sea. Frobisher was vice-admiral to Sir Francis Drake in his expedition to the West Indies and fought against the Spanish Armada. He was wounded at the siege of Brest, and after lingering a few days died at Plymouth.

With a green silk scarf on which were embroidered the words "The Almighty be your guide and your protector to the ende" as a talisman, Francis Drake weighed anchor from Plymouth Sound in December, 1577, on a mission to find new territory for his queen on the Pacific coast of America, and incidentally to settle one or two old scores with the Spaniards. There was no grievance against the territorial acquisitions of Spain and Portugal, but Englishmen held that if they wished to do so they had a perfect right to trade anywhere on God's earth without let or hindrance.

That no compatriot had attempted to navigate the ill-favoured Straits of Magellan appealed to the fiery Devonian. Drake accomplished the tortuous passage in sixteen days. The Pacific belied its name. The ships were blown out of their course and sent scurrying far to the south-east of Cape Horn.

Until then it had been believed that Terra del Fuego was the northern part of

From an Original Painting   J. Taylor sculp.

FIRST ENGLISHMEN TO REACH INDIA
The first Englishman to reach India was Thomas Stevens, who did so in 1579 by rounding the Cape of Good Hope. Four years later Ralph Fitch, James Story, John Newberry and William Leedes succeeded by the overland route and delivered a letter from Queen Elizabeth to the Great Mogul, Akbar (d. 1602), here shown in a contemporary engraving.

MAN—G

a great southern continent. When the storm had vented its fury Drake anchored among islands in the vicinity of the Horn, and after going ashore "cast himself down upon the uttermost point, grovelling, and so reached out his body over it. Presently he embarked, and then recounted unto his people that he had been upon the southernmost known land in the world, and more farther to the southwards upon it than any of them, yea, or any man as yet known."

Drake's Round-the-World Voyage

Drake now sailed up the west coast, reaching the latitude of 48 deg. north, but no outlet into the Atlantic rewarded his efforts. The *Golden Hind* was scraped and repaired, watered and provisioned in an inlet near San Francisco. There Drake landed, took possession of the territory as New Albion, and again set sail with the intention of finding a passage north of the continent that would bring him into the Atlantic. Storms and "stinking fogs" thwarted him. He turned south and then west, sailing over two months until he came to the Moluccas. At Ternate he took four tons of cloves on board a ship already loaded with treasure and sailed for Java. The *Golden Hind* entered the harbour of Plymouth after an absence of nearly three years. She had sailed round the world.

Despite the Pope's line and Philip's fiat, there were plenty of Spaniards in the New World who raised not the slightest objection to trading with Englishmen. Their immediate need was a plentiful supply of labour, and they cared not who met it. The first Englishman to appreciate the demand was a sea trader named John Hawkins. His first expedition, financed by merchants of unblemished reputation, left Plymouth in the autumn of 1562, embarked some hundreds of poor wretches at Sierra Leone, West Africa, and duly delivered them at Hispaniola (Haiti) in exchange for pearls, hides, sugar and various other articles of commerce. Further voyages followed.

More American Discoveries

Much useful but unspectacular work was carried out elsewhere. John Davis, attempting to find the elusive North-West Passage, mapped the coast of south Greenland, Labrador and south-east Baffin Land. England, under the leadership of Sir Walter Raleigh, made its pioneer but unsubstantial settlement in Virginia in 1585. Bartholomew Gosnold, the discoverer of Cape Cod

and Buzzard's Bay, helped to found Jamestown, the first permanent settlement made by the English in America, in 1607.

Sir Walter Raleigh, interested in the finding of El Dorado, the fabled land of gold, navigated the Orinoco river in a fruitless search. In 1620, when the first shipload of slaves arrived in Virginia, the Pilgrim Fathers quietly left England for conscience sake, and giving the place of their arrival the name of the port of their departure, founded at Plymouth, Massachusetts, the first of the New England colonies.

The largest and most important of all the commercial undertakings that fathered the British Empire was incorporated on the last day of 1600 as The Governor and Company of Merchants of London trading into the East Indies. The finding of new routes was not included in their plan of operations. The hard-headed men who risked their cash preferred dividends to experiments. The early voyages were not undertaken by the company as a whole, but by individual members who shared profits and losses.

The East India Company

According to John Stow, the capture by Drake of a Portuguese trading ship returning from the East Indies heavily laden with pepper, spices and treasure had much to do with the origin of the venture. "By the papers found on board," he notes, "they so fully understood the rich value of the Indian merchandises and their manner of trading into the eastern world that they afterwards set up a gainful trade and traffic, and established a company of East India merchants."

The long and fascinating story of the East India Company covers from first to last over 250 years. Its charter was renewed or its terms amended again and again. It erected trading stations, built forts, waged wars, acquired land from the Great Mogul, ruled vast territories, lent huge sums of money to the State, secured the monopoly of the China trade, and finally in 1858 handed over a magnificent empire to the British Crown.

In 1616 William Baffin was sent by the Muscovy Company to find a north-west passage, and though he was no more successful than his many predecessors, he made valuable contributions to geographical knowledge. His farthest north (77° 45′) held the record for over 200 years.

A concern which still continues its many enterprises, although it was begun as a very modest affair so long ago as 1670, is the Governor and Company of Adventurers of England trading into Hudson Bay, usually called the Hudson's Bay Company. Its title is associated with the great navigator who gave his name not only to one of the most important rivers in the United States but also to the strait and bay which he came across in 1610. How Henry Hudson, his son, and seven others were set adrift in an open boat by a mutinous crew is a tale that will be told so long as one Britisher is left to repeat it to a listener.

It was not to the would-be-discoverer of a passage to China, however, that the great association of traders was due. For that England had to thank two French emigrants, Pierre Esprit Radisson and Chouart de Groseilliers. They sought Hudson Bay by the overland route from Montreal and returned with sixty canoe-loads of pelts. So bounteous a harvest should have whetted the commercial appetites of the fur-traders of New France. They fined the daring explorers for illicit trading and missed a golden opportunity of empire.

Radisson and Groseilliers crossed to England, where a joint stock concern was formed. To Prince Rupert and his seventeen fellow-adventurers were granted the fisheries, mineral wealth and control of what are now the provinces of Manitoba, Saskatchewan, Alberta, the North-West Territories and British Columbia. Their estate, equal in size to the whole of Europe, was named Rupert's Land. With certain exceptions this vast tract with its magnificent possibilities was sold to Canada for £300,000 in 1869.

Australia, lonely in its southern setting, was visited by Spanish, Dutch and perhaps Portuguese sea-dogs before William Dampier, in the service of buccaneers, landed in New Holland, "a very large tract" of territory, in 1688. This was a hundred years before the first British settlers arrived after its annexation by Captain James Cook. The colonists were convicts, victims of a harsh penal system that allowed a man to be sentenced to transportation for killing a sheep, or stealing a few pence, and they included eleven child "criminals."

WAR CANOES OF THE PACIFIC IN CAPTAIN COOK'S TIME

In 1776 Captain James Cook, who has been called the greatest of British explorers, was instructed by the Admiralty to discover a passage from the North Pacific to the North Atlantic. It was while he was on this voyage that he was murdered in Hawaii in 1779.

PICTURE WRITING OF THE MYSTERIOUS MAYAS

Only three native manuscripts survived the conquest of the Mayas by the Spaniards, whose priests destroyed every vestige of writing they could find. The writings are now treasured at Dresden, Paris and Madrid. Those shown above represent the Rain God pouring water on a seed and the Maize God being savagely attacked by birds and worms.

CHAPTER 17

AMERICA'S PUZZLING PEOPLES

Who were the Red Indians? Mayas and Toltecs. Chichen Itzá. Maya art and calendars. Coming of the Aztecs. Huitzilopochtli and his thousands of victims. Riches of Aztec culture. Peru and the Incas. State socialism in the Andes. Peru's Great Wall.

WHO were the peoples inhabiting the land that Columbus discovered and how did they live? Whether they were aboriginals or the descendants of immigrants from other parts of the globe, puzzled Columbus not at all. Believing he had reached Asia, he dubbed them Indians, and they have been referred to as Red or American Indians by the generality of people from that day to this.

A papal bull set doubt at rest on the vexed question of their humanity. Until that was issued none was sure that the natives were true men.

There were several distinctive features in the New World culture. The natives grew a food plant called maize (Indian corn) which was unknown to the Old World, as the cereals of the latter were unknown to America. They had tobacco, cotton, cacao and the potato. For them the potter's wheel and wheeled vehicles did not exist.

The central and southern parts of the continent furnished other types of civilization. Mexico was the home of the Mayas and of the ancestors of the Toltecs; each

had important influences on the other, until the Aztecs became the dominant people. In Peru lived the Incas. It has been suggested that there is a kind of parallel between the Mayas and the Greeks, the Toltecs and the Romans, and the Aztecs and the Etruscans.

Old Empire of the Mayas

The seat of the first phase of the Maya civilization, the Old Empire as it is called, was in Northern Guatemala. Among its chief sites, which were unfortified, were Uaxactum, Copan and Quirigua. These places were abandoned during the eighth century. Among many suggested alternative causes for this are the exhaustion of the soil, climatic change, earthquakes and outbreaks of yellow fever. The last mentioned seems the most probable.

The Mayas then established themselves mainly in Northern Yucatan, now forming part of Mexico, British Honduras and Guatemala. There they stayed until about the middle of the fifteenth century. The great and probably thickly populated city of Chichen Itzá, which means the Mouths of the Wells of the Itzá, the oldest city of the New Empire, was conquered in 1191 by the Toltecs, who developed an extensive trading empire which was dissolved between 1210 and 1220, perhaps owing to disease, famine or civil strife.

Chichen Itzá in all its grotesque and barbaric splendour was abandoned as a result of a war in the middle of the fifteenth century, when Tayasal, in Northern Guatemala, was founded. There the Mayas remained until 1679, when the city was conquered by the Spaniards.

The art of the Old Empire was superior to that of the New. Although the sculptors of the former had no knowledge of metals, they carved with their stone implements, figures in the block so cleverly that they looked almost in the round. The Mayas studied the stars, devised a unique calendar and chronological system, wrote books in hieroglyphics, and their dentists used metal fillings. They were the master builders of America, erecting stately temples, lofty pyramids and huge monasteries. This busy people dug canals for their trading canoes, and exchanged pottery and textiles for pearls and turquoises with the inhabitants of the territories now known as New Mexico and the republic of Colombia.

Coming of the Aztecs

There are definite traces of early Mayan and Toltec influence in the civilization of the Aztecs, who arrived in Mexico as a host of nomadic hunters, without arts or crafts, about the twelfth century of our era. But they brought bows and arrows with them, and were led, so they believed, by a mighty tribal god named Huitzilopochtli. Almost within the short span of a century the Aztecs had founded an empire that stretched from the Gulf of Mexico to the Cordilleran Mountains and south towards what is now Guatemala.

The Aztecs absorbed instead of dispossessing the gods of their neighbours. Gruesome human sacrifices were demanded,

FORTIFIED GREAT WALL OF PERU

The Great Wall of Peru, a huge Inca or pre-Inca fortification in the wilds of Peru. The Shippee-Johnson expedition traced it for a distance of thirty miles at an altitude of 11,000 feet. In the foreground can be seen the remains of the ground-plan of a ruined village.

FIFTY TONS OF SCULPTURE

The largest monolithic column at Quirigua. The great shaft was quarried and transported at least three miles. It is thirty-five feet high and weighs over fifty tons.

the drawing of blood sufficing on some occasions, the tearing out of hearts and decapitation on others. To capture prisoners for sacrifice and not to kill their enemies was the principal aim in Aztec warfare, and it contributed to their undoing when the Europeans came. Twenty thousand victims were sacrificed to Huitzilopochtli when his temple was dedicated. There were cannibal banquets, but also many wise laws, and a very strict code of individual

conduct and behaviour worthy of a Puritan.

When Cortes in 1519 reached the valley where Mexico City now stands and gazed on the shining Aztec lake cities of Tenochtitlan and Tlaltelolco, with their stone causeways to the mainland, the massive ten-mile dam and canals, he was amazed. "When we arrived at the great market place," writes the Spanish soldier Bernal Diaz del Castillo, "we were astounded at the number and quantity of merchandise that it contained, and at the good order and control that was maintained, for we had never seen such a thing before."

London's Oxford Street is scarcely more universal in attractions. Gold, silver, jewels, beads, cloth, garments, cotton, sandals, embroidered goods, skins tanned and untanned, vegetables and turkeys, ducks and game, eggs, fish, maize, bread, pastry, wines, honey, tobacco, medicinal herbs, salt, stone razors, knives, swords, and mirrors, metal axes, plumes, feathers, wood, lime and stone were displayed; "each object has its appointed place."

Wonders of Inca Civilization

The Incas of Peru were a pastoral people whose principal animals were the llama for carrying and food, and the alpaca for its fleece. Their crops were maize and quinoa (buckwheat), and they cultivated the potato. They erected stone aqueducts and employed huge blocks of stone, each cut to fit as required and not necessarily of the same size, without mortar. In the region of Truxillo, in Northern Peru, where suitable stone was not available, their structures were of sun-dried clay, and they delighted in pyramids and great carved figures.

The capital of the Chimu, or Yuncas, whose country was overrun by Incas just before the Spanish conquest, though now a mere geometric pattern of crumbled ruins in the sun-baked wastes of Truxillo, Peru, was laid out along straight and narrow streets in a way which recalls the blocks and avenues of a modern American city.

The capital of the Inca Empire, a domain stretching from Quito into Northern Chile and Argentina, and from the Pacific coast to beyond the Andes, was Cuzco, where settlement appears to have taken place in the beginning of the twelfth century. From Cuzco, guarded by the great fortress of Machu Picchu, roads marched for over 1,100 miles. The Incas were fine civil engineers, as stone cultivation terraces in the highland region testify. The government maintained a kind of state socialism. Idleness was a crime. Special attention was paid to military service and agriculture, which was regarded as divine labour; it was difficult to obtain exemption from either.

There were state granaries and stores of clothing and other necessaries ready for emergencies, postmen who delivered messages by word of mouth or knotted cords, for the Incas had no system of handwriting, and a highly organized Civil Service. If there was over-population in one place, superfluous folk were shifted to a district less well supplied. The Incas were sun-worshippers who believed in an un-known Creator, and they offered no wholesale human sacrifices, thus differing from the Aztecs of the northern continent.

The Shippee-Johnson Peruvian Expedition of 1931, undertaken mainly by aeroplane, discovered what is now known as the Great Wall of Peru, guarded by a series of fourteen forts. It is believed that in its original state it was some twelve or fifteen feet thick at the base and tapered upwards to a similar height. The length has not as yet been finally estimated.

Conquered by Pizarro, Peru was a dependency of the Spanish crown until 1821, when it proclaimed its freedom.

UNCOVERING AN ALTAR STONE IN QUIRIGUA

An altar slab nearly two feet thick and about twelve feet square in the ruins of Quirigua, an important centre of the Old Empire period of the Maya civilization. Its dominant design is a masked human figure in dancing posture wearing a large and complicated head-dress. The hieroglyphic inscription on the stone is interpreted to date it about A.D. 530.

CHAPTER 18

THE STANDARD OF REVOLT

Revolt of the Netherlands. The thirteen American colonies. Prussia's predatory war. Taxation without representation. Declaration of Independence. Louis XIV. Heralds of the French Revolution. Rights of Man. A king goes to execution. France becomes a republic. Napoleon bestrides the Continent. Beginnings of modern science.

RELIGION and trade have been dominating influences in the later chapters of the human story. They are the orb and sceptre of the race, things deemed by some worthy to fight and die for. Religion has been plentiful in martyrs; commerce has usually called upon substitutes to do the dying.

Attempts made by the fanatical Philip II of Spain to dragoon belief led to a revolt of the Netherlands. Philip had inherited the provinces, an immense empire and the projecting underlip of the Habsburgs from his equally intolerant father, the heretic-hunting Charles V. Precedent for the rising, had such been necessary, was furnished by Switzerland, already unloosened from the galling fetters of the Holy Roman Empire. It had become virtually independent as the sequel to a conspiracy hatched by three men in a meadow overlooking the placid waters of Lake Lucerne.

Birth of Dutch Republic

The struggle in the Netherlands, waged on land and sea, began in 1568; formal peace did not come for eighty years. The Dutch, glorying in the name of beggars bestowed on them by a sneering courtier, adopted the beggar's sack as their emblem. With a defiant bravery not excelled by the defenders of Warsaw in 1939, they resisted with stout heart a reign of terror, reckless in cruelty. Making breaches in the dykes that kept the North Sea out, they let it in, and sailing on the flooded low-lying land relieved besieged Leiden. Led by William the Silent, who was talkative but discreet, the seven northern and Protestant provinces united and won their freedom, to become Holland. The ten southern provinces, whose sympathies were with Philip's creed but not with him, remained under Spanish rule. As Belgium, the country became the cockpit of Europe.

In England, Cromwell struck a blow for religious and civic liberty that severed a king's head. He also entered into the first of a series of armed conflicts with Holland, despite the spiritual affinity of the contestants. It was mainly brought about by the hunger for trade. The sea beggars had become the world's maritime carriers, but England had enacted that cargoes destined for her ports must be carried in her ships or in those of the country of origin. When the three Dutch wars were over, the Hollanders had lost their proud position as "wagoners of all seas," and with it their American colony of New Netherland, whose capital, New Amsterdam, became New York.

Just over a century and a quarter separated the foundation of Virginia and Georgia, the first and last born respectively of Britain's thirteen colonial children on the Atlantic seaboard of North America. Why did brave men and braver women journey so far from the Motherland in search of homes? In some cases religious convictions that had neither scope nor fair play in the Old Country led them across the western ocean, but even there the spectre of intolerance was not unknown. Other venturesome spirits voyaged to the plantations intent on wooing the goddess of fortune, or anxious only to put 3,000 miles of turbulent water between themselves and an unhappy past whose miseries they would fain forget.

Pioneer Days in America

Conditions were not easy. The climate was less genial than had been anticipated. The cold was colder and the heat hotter. In winter the pioneers were often imprisoned by snow that blocked the land and ice that made the navigation of rivers and streams impossible. Behind them was the seemingly impassable barrier of the Appalachians and mystery; in front the grey, inhospitable rollers of the Atlantic.

The gallant company did not surrender. It subdued the wilderness and the forest, conquered the mountains and defied the weather. It sweated and froze, died and

200

IN THE FRENZIED DAYS OF THE FRENCH REVOLUTION

The people patrolling the streets of Paris on the night of July 12, 1789, two days before they stormed the Bastille, the grim fortress prison that was the symbol of tyranny and despotism. Some of them were armed with muskets obtained from the Invalides, where they had been stacked for the new militia. Many fashioned pikes and other weapons for themselves.

MAN—G*

went on living in its sons and daughters. Today there is none prouder in the United States of America than the man who has a pedigree which goes back to the pioneers.

To the north was land of unknown extent. England asserted that the territory was hers because it had been discovered by the Cabots. France objected because Jacques Cartier had annexed it in 1534. The seemingly endless wrangle, which had already drawn blood overseas, was brought to a head by the Seven Years War, which lasted from 1756 until 1763.

Prussia Begins her Career

It was begun by Frederick the Great's forestalling of the plan of Maria Theresa of Austria to recover Silesia, which the aggressive and unscrupulous King of Prussia had seized sixteen years before. Invading Saxony, he was damned as an arch-enemy by a council of the Holy Roman Empire. France, Russia and Sweden allied themselves to the queen: Great Britain bolstered up Frederick with gold.

In the end Prussia emerged a scarecrow state, her soldiers in tatters, her population decimated, many of her towns blackened ruins, but with the filched province intact and a prestige for military prowess that was to rank her among the leading Powers. A hint of the attitude afterwards adopted by Adolf Hitler, Chancellor of the Third Reich, is given in the predatory king's maxim: "Take what you can; you are never wrong unless you are obliged to give it back." France lost all her American possessions to Great Britain, and in India was worsted by Robert Clive and allowed to retain no more than a few factories.

With bitter irony the war, which had largely been waged on behalf of the colonists, was partly responsible for the final turn of the screw that caused them to rebel. Indirect taxation is a subtle form of raising money. Being out of sight, hidden in a lump of sugar or a cup of tea, it has not the blatant obviousness of the direct tax that stares at one from a demand note. Nevertheless it is a tax, and the colonists resented it.

There was a lack of sympathetic understanding on the part of Parliament and the Board of Trade and Plantations. Each colony had its own elected assembly, but the governor was usually sent by Great Britain, and could, and occasionally did, interfere. One or two statesmen, as distinct from politicians, scented the possibility of a breakaway and voiced their opinions. They were disregarded.

The colonists, on their part, did not fully appreciate England's difficulties. They had been triumphantly delivered from the French, but Britain had borne the main part of the burden that had attended the removal of the growing menace. She now had to shoulder the cost, a matter of 90 million pounds, whereas the annual revenue from the American customs totalled an almost negligible sum.

The British imperial idea was based on a strictly commercial foundation of golden guineas. There were many hearts that beat as one across the intervening ocean, but the official attitude was dictated by pedants who regarded a cash basis as the only possible policy.

Smuggling had been indulged in wholesale before and during the Seven Years' War. Contraband had passed to and from the enemy and Europe. The illicit trade continued to prosper. To put an end to it the Navy patrolled the high seas and the coast with increasing vigilance. Customs officials searched anywhere and everywhere. For the introduction of smuggling the Navigation Acts were in the main responsible. They virtually secured to Britain the monopoly of sea traffic. While various manufactures which competed with those of Great Britain were forbidden, others which did not were encouraged by stimulating bounties. What the daughter colonies desired was commercial life without parental interference. The venerable mother thought that they should contribute to the support of the family.

America's Revolution

The Stamp Act, passed in 1765, added fuel to fires already smouldering. Its purpose was to raise part of the money for "the necessary expenses of defending, protecting and securing the British colonies and plantations." The Americans objected that taxation without representation was altogether wrong, although in England the vast majority of the people were voteless. They argued that payment in silver for the stamped papers to be used for legal documents, ship's clearance papers, newspapers and so on would take money out of the country and play havoc with business.

There was a boycott of British goods. Insistent clamour, both in England and America, secured the repeal of the hated tax. Other concessions were made, but too

VICTIMS OF THE REIGN OF TERROR
During the French Revolution the absolutism of kings was succeeded by the absolutism of a democratic oligarchy and the tyranny of the few. The period September, 1793, to July, 1794, is known as the Reign of Terror, when the guillotine, familiarly called the National Razor, was busy. In a matter of a few weeks 2,085 victims were executed in Paris.

late. Parliament reaffirmed its supreme power over the colonies in matters of taxation and legislation, and by way of showing that it was master gave the East India Company a monopoly of the tea trade with the colonies. This was regarded as the thin end of a wedge of privilege that might be applied to other articles of merchandise and spell disaster to American importers.

The Declaration of Independence was signed in 1776, not on July 4 as is generally believed but on August 2; it was adopted by Congress on the earlier date. The militant intervention of France, Spain and Holland transformed the ensuing war into an international affray and had much to do with the ultimate triumph of the colonists, who were by no means united. The militia deserted in hundreds. The stalwarts who remained in the ill-disciplined ranks frequently went without boots, and sometimes waited months for their pay.

With her own oversea losses still ranking, the reason for the step taken by France was obvious. Spain saw an opportunity of regaining Gibraltar, the sentry-box of the Western Mediterranean, which she had lost in 1704. Holland joined in because of Britain's determination to uphold her right to search all neutral ships and to seize goods intended for the enemy that she might find in their holds.

In Paris, on September 3, 1783, Great Britain signed away her first colonial empire.

The echoes of the revolution reverberated in France, where an undertone of discontent had mumbled since the spendthrift days of Louis XIV, who reigned for seventy-three years and died in 1715. Virtually answerable to none, the Grand Monarch regarded his ministers as servants of the Crown in a very literal sense. He enforced his will on the *Parlement* of Paris, the supreme judicial court, whose duties included the registration of laws. The States-General, representing the nobility, the clergy, and the commons, never met. At the cost of hundreds of millions of francs he built an enormous palace at Versailles, where courtiers and courtezans preened their feathers and 36,000 workmen struggled to transform marsh into parkland.

For forty years he fought wars to the glory of Louis, and steadily sapped France. Corneille, Molière and Racine added brilliant pages to the literary annals of the age. A chaotic clutter of medieval traditions, laws, customs, tolls, dues and abuses made the ordinary man despair. It was said that if the peasant enjoyed the possession of his soul, it was simply because he could not put it up for sale.

Louis XV continued to sow the wind; Louis XVI reaped the whirlwind. Literary men, usurping the prerogative of Jove, hurled thunderbolts. The Baron de Montesquieu satirized the abuses of French society and government, and in his *Spirit of the Laws* attacked despotism in a book that was a best seller. The compilers of the United States Constitution took some of its findings to heart. Denis Diderot, seeking to give "a general picture of the efforts of the human spirit in every field, in every age," produced the *Encyclopédie*, assisted by some of the most brilliant intellects of France, including Jean le Rond d'Alembert, distinguished alike in letters, science and philosophy, and Jean Jacques Rousseau, generally acclaimed the torch-bearer of the revolution. The first volume of text appeared in 1750, the last fifteen years later.

Voltaire and Rousseau

François Marie Arouet de Voltaire ridiculed orthodox beliefs, mocked the doctrine that might is right, loathed cruelty and intolerance, and died, according to his own statement: "adoring God, loving my friends, not hating my enemies, and detesting superstition." Rousseau inveighed against what he termed stupid civil institutions "which only add the sanction of public authority to the oppression of the weak and the iniquity of the powerful." His writings became the Bible of the discontented.

"Man is born free," he wrote in his *Social Contract*, "and everywhere he is in chains." It was a pungent sentence that impressed itself on the memory without effort, and stated in black and white what multitudes wished to believe. Much of Rousseau's outpourings, often more than a little incoherent, was forgotten. This sentence remained. It stood out like the letters on the wall of Belshazzar's palace.

Paraphrased as "Men are born free and remain free and equal in rights," it was the first of the seventeen articles in the Declaration of the Rights of Man, voted and accepted by the representatives of the French people on August 27, 1789. The document, neither local nor national but universal in principle, became the creed of a crusade.

At long last, after an interval of 175 years, the Paris *Parlement* had compelled the calling of the States-General. The country faced bankruptcy, the aftermath of war and reckless extravagance; the people faced famine. The nobility, the clergy and the commons were ordered to meet and vote separately. The commons refused, and were joined by some of the nobles and many of the clergy, who swore in the Tennis Court of Versailles that they would not separate until they had given the country a constitution. The States-General became the National Assembly and the National Assembly the Constituent Assembly.

King and People in France

The king prepared a military counterstroke. The electors of Paris forestalled him. A National Guard was formed and armed, the Bastille prison, symbol of tyranny and despotism, was stormed, its governor murdered. Louis accepted the constitution. It robbed him of absolutism but left him with considerable power. Then he regretted his decision. Like many good-natured people, Louis made up his mind with diffidence and on second thoughts doubted the wisdom of his choice. He determined to flee.

The royal family might have escaped but for a trivial incident. To screen them from prying eyes the blinds of the carriage were drawn. But it was a hot day, and the little Dauphin asked for a breath of fresh air. Louis let down the windows and forgot to replace the blinds. At Sainte-Ménéhould, where fresh horses were harnessed, payment was made by paper money bearing a portrait of the king. The man to whom it was handed recognized Louis. The plot was foiled. A rising barometer, a child's wish and a man's forgetfulness changed the course of history.

Louis and his consort, beautiful but foolish Marie Antoinette, were guillotined; the fate of the Dauphin is unknown. France, already a republic, was then at war with Austria and Prussia. The former had refused to take action against the princes who had escaped from France and were organizing an army to invade their motherland.

WASHINGTON'S FIRST APPEARANCE AS PRESIDENT IN NEW YORK
On April 6, 1789, George Washington was unanimously elected as the first President of the United States, and on the last day of the month the oath was administered in Federal Hall, New York. The Vice-President was John Adams.

Revolution stirs up mud. The sediment takes time to settle. In October, 1795, renewed disorders in Paris were put down with a "whiff of grapeshot" by a young general named Napoleon Bonaparte, who four years later overthrew the government and in 1804 became Emperor of the French. From that moment until his final defeat at Waterloo in 1815, when having taken Europe prisoner he became Europe's prisoner, his armies stalked the Continent.

He distributed principalities and powers to his brothers and marshals, dissolved the thousand - year - old and spineless Holy Roman Empire, absorbed and adjusted. Napoleon the Genius, like Louis the Simple, forgot one thing. In extinguishing liberties he unwittingly aroused a spirit of nationalism in Prussia, Italy, Spain, Tyrol and elsewhere that was to have far-reaching consequences.

Other revolutions, significant if less spectacular, were taking place. They flamed from the mouths of retorts and not from the muzzles of guns, making little noise, and that only distinguished by the few. Wars

were fought with pen and paper in the quietude of the study, or with a spyglass in the loneliness of fields untrodden by devastating armies.

Antoine Laurent Lavoisier formulated new doctrines in chemistry, and, being told that "The republic has no need of scientists," had his head chopped off during the Reign of Terror. Joseph Black, Henry Cavendish, Daniel Rutherford, the discoverers of latent heat, the composition of water and nitrogen respectively, scoffed at Lavoisier's system but remained to praise. Joseph Priestley, who dabbled in everything from theology to economics, was a notable exception; he merely scoffed. Working independently, he was co-discoverer with Carl Wilhelm Scheele of oxygen, which he termed dephlogisticated air. The obscure Swedish apothecary gave it the simpler name of empyreal air.

Investigators such as Benjamin Franklin, Luigi Galvani and Alessandro Volta sought to understand something of the nature of electricity. With crude contraptions they helped to harness the force that was to give

SATIRICAL PHILOSOPHER

Voltaire (1694-1778), one of the most prominent literary heralds of the French Revolution. His writings were the Bible of the discontented throughout Europe.

light and relieve the world of much of its drudgery. None of them dreamed that the flickering candle of their day and generation was to be duplicated 800 million times in a searchlight.

Carl Linné (Linnæus) laid the foundation of modern botany and attempted to systematize the classification of animals, leaving as his successor Georges Cuvier, who went a step further and classified creatures according to their structure. Hitherto fossils had been studied in a perfunctory way; the French zoologist minutely examined the structure of extinct animals, but came to the conclusion that species remained unchanged. In this he was opposed by his contemporary Jean Baptiste Lamarck. He it was, to quote Charles Darwin, who "first did the eminent service of arousing attention to the probability of all change in the organic as well as in the inorganic world being the result of law and not of miraculous interposition."

James Hutton worked out a theory of the earth which later gave him the title of the father of modern geology. After being regarded as hostile to sacred history, the principles of probability and the dictates of rational philosophy, they were generally accepted, and formed the basis of Sir Charles Lyell's *Principles of Geology*, in which he attempted "to explain the former changes of the earth's surface by reference to causes now in operation."

The irascible John Hunter made surgery a science. He died of angina pectoris after having been contradicted. His most distinguished pupil was Edward Jenner, whose research in vaccination did much to rid the world of the dreadful scourge of smallpox. The discovery was actually a rediscovery, for twenty-two years before Jenner made his first experiment in 1796, a Dorset farmer named Benjamin Jesty had inoculated his wife and two sons.

Not all the discoveries of the time were of the earth, earthy. Pierre Simon Laplace worked out his nebular hypothesis of the development of the solar system, based on a theory put forward by Immanuel Kant, whose study of the human mind is set forth in *The Critique of Pure Reason*.

Gazing into the sky, with his devoted sister Caroline jotting down his observations, was William Herschel, an oboeist in the Hanoverian Guards turned astronomer and telescope-maker. He discovered the planet Uranus, and set about the colossal task of taking a census of the heavens.

BEHEADED AS UNWANTED

Antoine Laurent Lavoisier (1743-94) formulated new doctrines in chemistry and was guillotined with the taunt that "the republic has no need of scientists."

BARREL WHEELS TO AVOID RUTS

The roads were so appallingly bad in 1760 that the monthly stage coach which travelled between Edinburgh and London took sixteen days on the journey. Wagons built with wide treads that avoided adding to existing ruts were encouraged by the turnpike authorities and paid reduced tolls. John McAdam and Thomas Telford were the first modern road-makers.

CHAPTER 19

SPEEDING UP THE WORLD

Early textile inventions. The Spinning Jenny. Arkwright's frames and Cartwright's loom. Jacquard and Napoleon. First steam-engines. Watt's experiments. Extension of canals. McAdam and Telford build roads. Foreshadowings of the railway. Stephenson and the " Rocket." Steam transport on roads. Early motor-cars.

WHEN machines were introduced they were regarded by the majority of people as devices of the devil. They were held not to have a single redeeming feature. The fact that they reduced the almost intolerable burden of human effort was discounted by the belief that they would throw multitudes out of jobs.

Mankind is inherently conservative. The home-worker, though his fingers were sore with toil and his eyelids red with constant application, preferred that they should remain so rather than take a plunge into the dreaded unknown.

The transition of industry from the home to the large-scale factory was brought about during a series of years in which inventors were amazingly prolific in practicable ideas. In 1718 Sir Thomas Lombe, the son of a Norwich weaver, set up machines at Derby for the winding, spinning and twisting of silk thread. The yarn had previously been imported from Italy, whence his brother had brought drawings of the apparatus. When Lombe applied for

a renewal of his patent, which had considerably decreased the cost to the consumer, his appeal was disallowed because of the outcry of northern spinners. He was granted a solatium of £14,000.

The distaff gave place to the spinning-wheel in the reign of Henry VIII. In 1733 John Kay of Bury hit upon a mechanical means of throwing the shuttle across the web, and some thirty years later James Hargreaves of Blackburn invented the spinning jenny. It was regarded as a menace rather than a miracle, and when Hargreaves was absent from his cottage it was smashed to pieces by operatives who saw their means of livelihood taken away from them by a thing of wheels and wood. When Hargreaves and his partner Thomas James began to develop their business, the mill-owners promptly set about constructing spinning jennies for their own use.

A contemporary of Hargreaves was Richard Arkwright, "the subterraneous barber" who abandoned his penny shaves to invent a spinning frame. Two stocking manufacturers named Strutt and Need showed sufficient confidence in the machine to risk money on its development, and went into partnership with Arkwright. In 1771 they opened a mill in Derbyshire, the success of which exceeded all expectation.

Again jealousy got to work. Some of the Lancashire manufacturers encouraged Arkwright's workpeople to leave his employ, infringed his patents, and fought him in the courts. A mob wrecked one of his mills, but he went from strength to strength until he died as Sir Richard Arkwright in 1792.

A few years before, a studious little man who was rector of Goadby Marwood, in Leicestershire, happened to hear that Arkwright's spinning frames were producing such a quantity of yarn that difficulty was found in securing sufficient operatives to weave it. Being of a mechanical turn of mind, the Rev. Edmund Cartwright set to work, and in 1787 took out a patent for a weaving machine.

Misfortune dogged him at every turn. A mill in which he had erected some hundreds of his looms was razed to the ground by fire, and eventually he was compelled to hand over his own mill at Doncaster to his creditors. When his patent expired in 1804 his machine was widely copied. As some kind of return the government made Cartwright a grant of £10,000, mainly at the instance of certain mill-owners, who apparently had conscientious scruples against robbing a weaver who was a wearer of the clerical cloth.

Crompton's Spinning Mule

Samuel Crompton, a home-worker who spun yarn, annoyed by the clumsy mechanism of the machine he operated, invented the "mule," which he completed in 1779. He could not afford to take out a patent, and so, he tells us, "I gave it to the public." A little later he discovered that 311,000 spindles were in use on Arkwright machines, 156,000 on those of Hargreaves and 4,500,000 on his own. The precedent set in the case of Cartwright was followed by the government, but Crompton's award was only half that voted to the clergyman.

In 1789 Samuel Slater, who had worked for Arkwright, introduced his employer's machine into America. Another American who profited by the inventions of Arkwright and Crompton was Francis Lowell, who founded with his partner Paul Moody the first factory where all the various operations necessary for manufacturing cloth were

undertaken. A splendid impetus to the cotton industry was also given by Eli Whitney, who, in 1793, produced the first cotton gin for separating the fibre from the seed.

A machine that was lost to England for a time owing to lack of confidence on the part of its inventor was the loom for pattern weaving. Joseph Marie Jacquard, a Frenchman, happened to see an announcement that the Society of Arts was offering a prize for a lace-making machine. The son of poor silk weavers, he determined to compete, but when his apparatus was ready it looked so crude that he had not sufficient courage to send it in. A friend, however, took the matter up, and to the inventor's astonishment Jacquard was summoned to explain his invention to Napoleon.

Napoleon Meets an Inventor

"Are you the man who pretends to do what God Almighty cannot do—tie a knot in a stretched string?" asked General Lazare Carnot, who was at the interview. "I can only do what God has taught me to do," was the modest reply. Jacquard found in Napoleon, always anxious to strike a blow at British industries, a willing patron, but the inventor met with bitter opposition from both manufacturers and weavers.

Crossing to England, his loom was taken up with something approaching enthusiasm. Eventually Jacquard returned to France, and his apparatus proved so successful that it was declared public property. The inventor was granted a pension and a royalty on each machine that was made.

Hitherto all work in connexion with textiles had been carried on mainly in individual homes, though the methods of doing business were different. In Yorkshire, for the most part, the producer purchased his own wool, worked it and disposed of the finished article to a merchant. The domestic system, as it has been called, obtained in England, Belgium, Holland and Prussia.

"The manufacturer," to quote an official report issued in 1806, "carries it (the cloth) on the market day to a public hall or market where the merchants repair to purchase. Several thousands of these small master manufacturers attend the market at Leeds, where there are three halls for the exposure and sale of their cloths; and there are similar halls at Bradford, Halifax and Huddersfield."

In the West of England the workers were generally employed by a clothier or travelling merchant, who supplied the materials and paid wages for services rendered. It was the thin end of the wedge of the factory system, although perhaps in the hosiery industry, in which it was usual to provide the worker with a knitting-frame, more nearly approached it.

Actually it is impossible to give the starting point of the phase of labour which has gone on developing to the present day. Early in the sixteenth century, if tradition is not a lying jade, John Winchcombe had a hundred looms at work in his house at Newbury. His speciality was kersey, a coarse cloth, usually ribbed, woven from long-fibred wool. An Act of 1555 limited a weaver living outside a town to two looms,

The industrial revolution developed on the lines of the House that Jack Built. One thing led to another. Many attempts had been made to harness steam, but it took many centuries to overcome the initial difficulties. Once these were solved development proceeded apace.

Hero of Alexandria, who lived in the second century B.C., devised an apparatus worked by steam for pouring a libation on an altar. He also invented the earliest turbine. It took the form of a circular vessel fed by steam, which escaped from two nozzles and caused the globe to revolve. Giovanni Branca, an Italian, built a somewhat similar machine in 1629, but used

STEPHENSON'S "SUPERIOR LOCO MOTIVE TRAVELLING ENGINE"

"Locomotion No. 1" hauled the first public steam-train when George Stephenson drove it at the opening of the Stockton and Darlington Railway on September 27, 1825. The line is still in use as a section of the London and North Eastern Railway.

and thirty years later the weavers of Devonshire and Cornwall were precluded from housing more than three machines.

Sir Joseph Child, governor of the East India Company, although an ardent supporter of the monopolies of the concern which he ran so ably, stated in 1668 that he considered the laws "limiting the number of looms, or kind of servants, and times of working, to be certainly prejudicial to the clothing trade of the kingdom." In his judgment, "if we intend to have the trade of the world, we must imitate the Dutch, who make the worst as well as the best of all manufactures, that we may be in a capacity of serving all markets and all humours."

vanes against which the gas was directed. Edward Somerset, Marquis of Worcester, apparently succeeded in building a pump operated by steam in 1663.

Denis Papin, a French refugee who had helped Christiaan Huygens, an eminent Dutch mathematician, in his experiments with the air-pump, employed super-heated steam for what he called a digestor, and also invented a safety-valve for it, in 1679. Papin afterwards worked at an internal-combustion engine, using gunpowder at first and steam later to force the piston upwards. In 1707 it operated the paddle-wheel of a vessel on the Fulda river.

Thomas Savery in 1698 patented a steam

engine for draining mines. It is evident that Thomas Newcomen helped Savery, or was in partnership with him, or worked under his patent, for a print inscribed: "The Steam Engine, near Dudley Castle, Invented by Captain Savery and Mr. Newcomen. Erected by ye latter 1712," is the earliest known picture of the beam-engine.

Newcomen "used steam at or only slightly above atmospheric pressure, and his engine was really driven by the weight of the air above the piston, the steam being merely the agent by which, through condensation, a vacuum was produced in the cylinder." One of his engines "for raising water by fire" was used to pump water from the Thames; and another at Tanfield Moor Colliery, Durham, was kept in the mine for 120 years before it was dismantled.

Watt's Steam-engine

The steam-engine of James Watt, who completed his first engine in 1776, was a great improvement on that of Newcomen. Instead of cooling the cylinder he reasoned that it should be as hot as the steam within, and this led him to introduce a separate condenser. Dr. John Roebuck, of the Carron Iron Works, financed the preliminary experiments. Matthew Boulton followed as a partner, and spent £47,000 before he received any return.

The "fire-engine," as it was called, gave an impetus to coal-mining, which was rendered considerably less dangerous because the pump kept the water from flooding the lower workings, thereby making deeper shafts possible and increasing production. Iron was required in greater quantities for the making of machinery, although it was not until the middle of the nineteenth century that Henry Bessemer introduced his converter and produced high-grade steel at reasonable cost.

The anecdote of Watt and the kettle is a pretty story, but no more. When he was an instrument maker his mind was led in the direction of steam by his being asked to repair a model of a Newcomen engine. He did not invent the steam-engine, but as Professor Andrade says: "every economical engine of today, reciprocating or turbine, ends up with an engine on the Watt system, in which the steam, having been expanded to low pressure in other parts of the engine, does work by virtue of the partial vacuum created by a condenser."

As the condition of the majority of roads was deplorable, the necessity for improved methods of transport arose. James Brindley began the construction in 1758 of a canal from Worsley to Manchester for the third Duke of Bridgewater, who wished to convey coal on his estates to the growing centre of the cotton industry. Brindley's aqueduct over the River Irwell at Barton marked a real stage of progress in civil engineering, with the result that he was called upon to superintend the making of several hundred miles of artificial waterways.

Previous to the opening of the Bridgewater Canal the charge for sending goods by road from Manchester to Liverpool was £2 per ton. On its completion the cost by water was 12/- per ton. From 1758 to 1830 some 4,700 miles of canals were cut in England.

The roads were so appallingly bad in 1760 that the monthly stage coach which travelled between Edinburgh and London took sixteen days on the journey. It remained for a Scotsman named John Loudon McAdam to turn his attention to the study of road-making. "Macadamized roads" are familiar to all, but it took their inventor a long time to get his method of making them accepted. Provided that there was adequate drainage he contended that thin layers of hard stone fragments to the depth of ten inches would make a surface sufficiently solid for all ordinary vehicles.

Telford's Engineering Feats

Another busy engineer was Thomas Telford, the son of a Scottish shepherd, who began the construction of the Caledonian Canal in 1804. In addition to many other public works he made nearly 1,000 miles of roads, including the highway from Shrewsbury to Holyhead, with the gap of the Menai Strait spanned by a suspension bridge. His method differed from that of McAdam by paying special attention to the foundation, which was of large stones, on which smaller metal was spread. Telford also improved various harbours, and drained some 48,000 acres in the Fens.

John Rennie, also born north of the Tweed, must be mentioned. A natural gift for mechanics was quickened by surreptitious visits when a boy to the workshop of Andrew Meikle, the inventor of the threshing machine. On leaving school he became a millwright, then turned his attention to canals, the reclamation of waste land, and the building of bridges, his most famous effort in that direction being the structure which spanned the Thames and commemor-

NEW IN FASHION BUT CONSERVATIVE IN DESIGN

The first railway coaches retained the pattern of the old stage coaches, as the pioneer motor-cars followed the design of dog-carts. The " Experience " was built for the Liverpool and Manchester Railway Company in 1830. Note the step by which the door is reached.

ated Waterloo until it was demolished in 1934. Rennie planned the breakwater at Plymouth, the London and East India docks, many harbours, including those of Grimsby, Hull and Holyhead, and the Bell Rock lighthouse.

It was some years before the steam-engine was applied to traction. Horse-drawn trucks on wooden rails had been used in England for a century or more before the first primitive locomotive started on its panting and puffing journey. A marked improvement was introduced in 1767 at the Coalbrookdale Iron Works, when iron rails superseded the easily splintered timber scantlings.

Many independent workers were evolving a machine to take the place of the hard-worked horse. They included John Theophilus Cugnot, a Frenchman, whose engine showed a marked tendency to blow up or run away. William Murdock, in the employ of Boulton and Watt, constructed a model locomotive that in 1786 almost scared an unfortunate parson to death by making him believe that he was being chased by the Evil One when the inventor was making an experimental trial near Redruth. His employers dissuaded him from "wasting"

further time on the project, with the result that Murdock devoted his energy to the improvement of the stationary engine and the development of gas lighting.

France claims the honour for the latter invention by asserting that it was due to the experiments of Philippe Lebon, who secured a patent in 1799, but it seems that George Dixon of Cockfield, a Durham colliery proprietor, made inflammable coal gas nearly forty years earlier. In some of his experiments he used hemlock stems covered with clay as pipes.

At no considerable distance from the scene of the trial run of Murdock's ill-fated little contrivance Richard Trevithick, the inventor of the high-pressure steam-engine, was born in 1771. Yet again the good folk of Cornwall were to be scared. This time it was by a full-sized steam carriage, which Trevithick tried at Camborne on Christmas Eve, 1801. It was nicknamed the *Puffing Devil*.

The inventor next set about designing an engine for use on the plate rails for the horse tramway of an iron works at Penydaren, South Wales. In 1804 it hauled ten tons of minerals and seventy men at the rate of nearly five miles an hour. It also broke many of the tramplates, left the rails and was carted back to Penydaren by horses.

The next and last of Trevithick's locomotives, the *Catch-me-who-can*, was tried in 1812 on a circular track in London and received the blessing of Sir Humphry Davy, the inventor of the safety lamp which helped to rob the coal mine of its greatest peril.

Between 1813 and 1815 William Hedely, Jonathan Foster and Timothy Hackworth built *Puffing Billy* for Wylam Colliery. It drew nine wagons at four miles an hour.

Genius, like murder, will out. George Stephenson, the son of a colliery fireman, turned his attention from boot mending to pumping-engines, and by a natural transition to the problem of locomotion. Beginning with *My Lord*, built in 1814 for Killingsworth Colliery, Stephenson proceeded with a second and third engine.

The time was ripe for the development of the locomotive, for although the first Railway Bill introduced by Edward Pease, a Darlington mill-owner, for a line between Stockton and Darlington was thrown out by the House of Lords in 1818, Parliament was induced in the following year to approve the scheme. In the original proposal Pease had foolishly planned for the proposed route to cut through one of the fox-covers of Lord Darlington, later Duke of Cleveland. This was amended, the peer's sacrosanct covers were carefully dodged, and in 1821 the royal assent was granted.

First Railway Locomotive

Up to that time no suggestion had been made that any form of traction other than horses should be used. Stephenson saw his opportunity and seized it. He called on Pease, who was persuaded to see what a locomotive was capable of doing. An amended Act of Parliament allowing the use of locomotives under certain restrictions was obtained. Stephenson was appointed engineer of the railway.

At the opening ceremony on September 27, 1825, *Locomotion No. 1*, described on the note of invitation as "a superior Loco Motive Travelling Engine of the most improved construction," hauled a number of loaded wagons and a passenger coach called the *Experiment* with the directors and their friends. A horseman with a flag preceded the procession, but the rider was routed when the engine got going. "Such was its velocity that in some parts the speed was frequently twelve miles an hour."

When the Manchester and Liverpool Railway was proposed, fox-hunting squires were again in evidence to thwart the project, but the surveyors and others proceeded with their work. The man mainly responsible was William James, a London civil engineer. He employed Stephenson's son, Robert, as an assistant.

An Act giving powers to proceed was passed in 1826. The "quick and faithless depths" of Chat Moss were stabilized. Enormous quantities of material were dumped in the bog before plaited hurdles covered with brushwood and heather, sand and gravel, were sufficiently stable to allow of the sleepers being laid. A great tunnel had to be burrowed on the outskirts of Liverpool and a hundred bridges built.

" Rocket " Wins a Prize

Lengthy debates as to whether stationary engines or locomotives should be employed were indulged in by the directors. Finally they decided to offer a premium of £500 for an engine which should be "a decided improvement, as respects the consumption of smoke, increased speed, adequate power and moderate weight." The trials took place on October 6, 1829, at Rainhill. The *Rocket* with an average speed of a little over 15 miles an hour was adjudged the winner.

Meanwhile an Act for building the Canterbury and Whitstable Railway had received the Royal Assent in June, 1825. George Stephenson was appointed engineer in place of the enthusiastic projector William James, who had sadly miscalculated the cost. The railway was opened on May 3, 1830, and was the first to use steam for passenger traffic. From Canterbury the train was hauled by two stationary engines of twenty-four horse-power situated at Tyler Hill and Clowes Wood respectively. The carriages then descended by gravity to Bogshole. Thence the locomotive *Invicta* took the train to Whitstable Harbour, two miles distant. The veteran now stands on a pedestal at Canterbury. The Baltimore and Ohio Railway, U.S.A., with a route of fifteen miles, was opened on the twenty-second of the same month. The Manchester and Liverpool Railway started its career on September 15 following.

Even before the opening of the Stockton and Darlington Railway, enterprising merchants of Bristol had formed the London and Bristol Rail-Road Company, but the plan never came to fruition. The project was revived in 1832, and in the following year sufficient money was forthcoming to

STABILIZING THE " QUICK AND FAITHLESS DEPTHS " OF A BOG

George Stephenson, basing his plans on those of John Metcalf, familiarly known as Blind Jack of Knaresborough, constructed a railway track across Chat Moss by dumping into the treacherous morass plaited hurdles covered with brushwood, and heather, sand and gravel to give a stable foundation on which sleepers and metals might be laid.

enable preliminary surveys to be made. Isambard Kingdom Brunel was appointed engineer, and the title Great Western Railway chosen. The Paddington to Taplow section was opened in 1838, that to Bristol in 1841. The Box Tunnel, 1 mile 7 furlongs in length, cost £100 per yard and was then the longest railway tunnel. There are now over 750,000 miles of railway in the world.

While some inventors were experimenting with steam-driven machines operating on a specially laid rail-road, the question of a horseless vehicle for the common highway was puzzling the brains of others. In 1649 Johann Haustach of Nuremberg had built a clockwork coach which travelled at a speed of some 2,000 paces an hour. Newton conceived the notion of a carriage propelled by steam generated at the front and striking the air from a tube at the rear.

The first omnibus service was started in 1662 in Paris by Blaise Pascal, philosopher, mathematician, and physicist, whose *Thoughts* and *Provincial Letters* are included in the world's great books. London's pioneer buses were put on the road by Georges Shillibeer, also a Frenchman, in 1829. The first mechanically propelled omnibus in the metropolis started a public service in 1831 after its inventor, Walter Hancock of Stratford, had run it experimentally for about twelve months. He afterwards built another for the Paddington Steam-Carriage Company, which made its appearance on the streets on April 22, 1833. The engine and boiler were accommodated at the rear and operated by the driver, who sat on a seat on an open platform in front. The vehicle had room for fourteen passengers. On the opening day the *Enterprise* travelled some ten miles in fifty minutes.

Goldsworthy Gurney built steam vehicles between 1825 and 1832, fitting them with a water tube boiler and slide-valve engines. His coaches were used for a service between Gloucester and Cheltenham which started in 1831. During their existence 396 journeys were made covering a total mileage of 3,644. A steam-carriage ran between London and Birmingham in 1832, and in the early fifties one built by Richard Dudgeon was running in New York.

In 1863 Etienne Lenoir, a naturalized Frenchman who had been born in Belgium, fitted a gas-engine to a carriage which travelled six miles in an hour and a half. Ten years later a motor-car, the work of Siegfried Markers, a Mecklenburg mechanic, was shown at the Vienna Exhibition. A tricycle with the engine under the driver's seat and the steering wheel in front was built by Carl Benz in 1884 and travelled at eight miles an hour. Gottlieb Daimler fitted a vertical petrol-engine to a bicycle and thereby created the first motor-cycle. The trial took place in Stuttgart in 1886. In the following year he built his pioneer motor-car.

France took up motoring enthusiastically. Panhard and Levassor acquired Daimler's patents for France, and soon their names and those of Bouton and De Dion were as familiar in Paris as those of prominent politicians. Whereas De Dion's steam-car won the first of the long distance races from Paris to Rouen and back in 1894 at a speed of about thirteen miles an hour, the race to Bordeaux and back in the following year was won by Levassor with a petrol-driven car at an average of fifteen miles an hour for the 740 miles. In 1939 John Cobb set up a land speed record of 368·85 miles an hour, thus covering a distance of a mile in less than ten seconds.

As much ridicule was showered on the motor-car in its early days as was evident in the infancy of the locomotive, and in Great Britain vested interests raised unceasing protests. Until November 14, 1896, a man with a red flag had to precede the car, the speed of which was officially limited to four miles an hour.

The budding industry was greatly helped by the invention of the pneumatic tyre by John Boyd Dunlop. The first hollow tyres contained water and were bound to the wheels with surgical tape. Filling them with air in an inner tube came later.

RUNNING NON-STOP FOR NEARLY 300 MILES

It was recorded of " Locomotion No. 1 " in 1825 that " Such was its velocity that in some parts the speed was frequently twelve miles an hour." The " Coronation Scot " normally runs from London to Carlisle at an average speed of 63·4 miles for the 299·1 miles.

CHAPTER 20

SAIL SURRENDERS TO STEAM

Jouffroy's " Pyroscaphe." Man-power paddle vessels. The " Charlotte Dundas."
Fulton and Napoleon. World's first submarine. Atlantic crossed under steam. Origin
of Cunard Line. Wonders of modern steamships. Floating and graving docks.
Constructing Southampton's giant dock. From fishing village to premier port.

MANY minds had sought to solve the problem of navigation otherwise than by poles, paddles, oars and sails. Before experimenting with steam, Savery in 1696 had invented paddle-wheels turned by a capstan operated by man-power. In 1776 the Marquis de Jouffroy de la Pompe, working on the principle of Papin's engine, successfully tried a steam-driven "pyroscaphe." James Ramsay, of Virginia, made a model steamboat in 1784 which interested George Washington, and two years later John Fitch, also an American, launched a boat propelled by paddles driven by a steam-engine.

Patrick Miller, a large shareholder in the Carron Iron Company, revived the capstan method a century later, and had a ship with three hulls built and fitted with paddle-wheels operated on the same system as Savery's. He next tried a double vessel, two of which were built in 1787 and 1788 respectively. During a voyage to St. Petersburg (Leningrad) the timbers of one of these ships were so badly strained that on arriving in port she was abandoned.

In the seventies of last century twin steamers, the *Castalia* and the *Calais-Douvres*, ran on the Dover-Calais route. In rough weather they were steadier than the ordinary paddle-steamers, but they pitched badly when faced with a head sea.

Set-back to Steam

In 1787 William Symington had taken out a patent for a steam-engine, and James Taylor, at that time a tutor in the Miller family, suggested that the inventor be asked to design one for working paddle-wheels. It was fitted in a vessel constructed of tinned iron plates and proved a success. This was followed by the building of a larger engine for another boat, which attained a speed of seven miles an hour on the Forth and Clyde Canal. On an unfavourable report from James Watt, Miller abandoned the idea of using steam and reverted to the capstan.

Symington's next patron was Lord Dundas, the Governor of the Forth and Clyde Canal Company, and the inventor set about improving his engine. The tug-boat *Charlotte Dundas*, which began operations in 1802, may be regarded as the first practical attempt at steam navigation. It towed two loaded vessels nineteen miles in six hours against a strong wind. Unfortunately for the unhappy inventor, the authorities objected to the wash made by the paddle-wheel, which they said would damage the banks, and the vessel had to be abandoned.

Fulton's Steamboat

Better fortune attended the efforts in 1803 of Robert Fulton, an American, who had sailed on Symington's boat and taken notes, although he had also sent a sketch of a projected steamboat to Lord Stanhope in 1793. His vessel attained a speed of slightly over two miles an hour.

Napoleon was then concentrating on plans for the invasion of England, and Fulton offered his invention to him. He seized on the idea with avidity. "I have just read the project of Citizen Fulton, Engineer," he wrote to M. de Champagny, Minister of the Interior, "which you have sent me much too late, since it is one that may change the face of the world." He ordered its immediate examination by a commission of members chosen from among the different classes of the Institute. The report condemned the project.

Fulton returned to the United States, where he built the *Clermont*. With a twenty-four-horse-power engine and boiler supplied by Boulton and Watt, in August, 1807, the little steamer made a successful voyage on the Hudson of about 150 miles. The journey up river took thirty-two hours, and the return trip two hours less. In 1815, the year of his death, Fulton launched for the United States the pioneer steam war-ship, which was named after him. She was of thirty-eight tons; the tonnage of the

FLOWER-POT FORTRESS TO RESIST INVASION

A relic of the days when Great Britain was rearming in 1805, the year of Trafalgar. This Martello tower is one of seventy-four erected round the coast. The buildings are of two stories, the lower being used as a powder magazine and for stores. A swivel gun and two howitzers comprised the armament. The smaller type of tower cost £7,000.

British battle cruiser *Hood*, sunk in 1941, at the time the largest warship, was 41,200.

It was to the same erratic genius that the world owed its first submarine, the *Nautilus*, built in 1801. The motive power was supplied by two men, who revolved a pair of horizontal wings by means of cranks.

The first steamship to go to sea was the *Phœnix*, built by John and Robert L. Stevens, which sailed from New York to Philadelphia in 1809. On the other side of the Atlantic, Henry Bell, who, like Fulton, had watched the progress of the *Charlotte Dundas* with amazed interest, designed the *Comet*, which navigated the Clyde "by the power of air, wind and steam." Built in 1812, the vessel was of thirty tons, driven by a three-horse-power engine, and attained five knots. She carried passengers between Greenock and Glasgow, and was wrecked after a life of eight years.

In 1819 the *Savannah* (350 tons), using steam as an auxiliary to sails, crossed from Charleston to Liverpool, but her engine was only running for eighty hours. It was not until 1838 that the *Sirius* (703 tons) won for herself the glory of being the first steamship to cross the Atlantic solely under steam power, although a claim is also made on behalf of the *Royal William*, which completed the voyage from Quebec to London, after calling at Cowes, in twenty-five days. The *Sirius*, with ninety-four passengers, accomplished the voyage from London to New York in seventeen days. Both vessels were of wood and used paddles.

The propeller had been tried in various forms over a considerable period. In 1836 John Ericsson, a Swede, was given permission by the British Admiralty to display the merits of a twin-screw tug on the Thames. The vessel took charge of a naval barge at Somerset House, proceeded down the river and returned, whereupon one of the officials on the barge pronounced that "even if the propeller had the power of

propelling a vessel it would be found altogether useless in practice because, the
power being applied at the stern, it would
be absolutely impossible to make the vessel
steer." And yet the lie to the assertion had
already been given!

Ericsson was invited to the United States,
where he constructed the *Monitor*, victor in
a duel with the Confederate armoured
frigate the *Merrimac*. She contained the
first revolving turret mounting heavy guns.

The *Archimedes*, launched in 1838, was
the first steamship fitted with a screw to
weather the open sea. Her propeller was the
invention of Francis Pettit Smith, a farmer,
who was subsequently knighted.

The world owes its first regular line of
steamships running at definite intervals to
Samuel Cunard. His family, of Quaker
origin, had emigrated to America. Remaining on the side of the Old Country during
the War of Independence, his father started
life afresh in Canada and eventually founded

the firm of Abraham Cunard and Son.

The concern prospered; it bought and
built ships, and undertook a Government
contract for the conveyance of the mails
between Halifax and Newfoundland and
Boston and Bermuda, and became agent of
the East India Company. When the senior
partner died the name of the firm was
altered to S. Cunard and Company. Its
continued prosperity left no doubt as to the
chief force which had urged it forward.

Cunard had been watching the progress
of steam navigation with studied interest.
Should he follow the conservative principle
of the Black Ball and other lines and stick to
sail? Against it he set his own judgment and
held that "steamers properly built and
manned might start and arrive at their
destination with the punctuality of railway
trains on land."

An opportunity was afforded him of putting his faith to practical test. The Lords
Commissioners of the Admiralty, having

PERIL THAT MAN'S INGENUITY HAS NOT YET OVERCOME
*Despite the enormous advance made in the production of fire-resisting materials and fire-
fighting appliances, the danger of an outbreak remains a menace to safety. The picture
above shows blazing liner just before she heeled over and sank in dock. The fusing of
electric cables and leaky joints in oil pipes have been responsible for a number of disasters.*

snubbed and jeered at early efforts, now came to the conclusion that the Atlantic mails ought to be carried by steam packets instead of the ten-gun brigs, known to those who sailed in them as coffin ships.

Cunard packed a trunk and sailed for England. The required capital of £270,000 was raised, a seven years' contract for the conveyance of mails between Liverpool, Halifax and Boston was entered into at a subsidy of £3,295 for each round voyage, and the British and North American Royal Mail Steam Packet Company was founded.

First Cunarder

The Line began operations with the *Britannia*, a barque-rigged paddle steamer of 1,156 tons, which left Liverpool for Boston on July 4, 1840, with sixty-three passengers. Her horse power was 740, and on her maiden voyage she consumed thirty-eight tons of coal a day to achieve an average speed of 8·5 knots. The crossing took fourteen days eight hours. The last Cunarder to be constructed of wood was the *Arabia*, of 2,393 gross tons, launched in 1852. The *Scotia*, built in 1862 and wrecked in 1904, was the last Atlantic steamer to use paddles. The *Servia*, with a displacement of 12,300 tons, launched in 1881, was the first merchant vessel built throughout of Siemens' mild steel. Sir Samuel Cunard's largest vessel was of 2,243 tons; the *Queen Elizabeth*, which flies the Cunard White Star flag, is of 85,000 tons.

Progress in shipbuilding has brought about enormous elaboration. The requirements are constantly growing. There are mechanical refinements such as gyroscopic stabilizers and anti-rolling bilge keels. A great deal of research on the effect of wind and waves on speed is being undertaken. Fog remains a menace, but by means of Marconi's reflected beam system of short-wave transmission the pilots of ships get their bearings by radio signals from land.

Now let us think in terms of metal. In the *Queen Mary* there are twenty-seven boilers; fifty oil bunkers; 200 oil-fuel burners; seven turbo-generator sets for lighting, heating, cooking, and auxiliary work in connexion with pumps, lifts and ventilation; 257,000 turbine blades; 10,000,000 rivets; 3,000 feet of oil-fuel pipes; over 100 miles of electric cables. Each of the four manganese bronze propellers has four blades and weighs thirty-five tons. In terms of engineering history this means a total weight four times the tonnage of the *Comet*.

To launch this colossal vessel five and a half acres of the opposite bank of the Clyde had to be cut away so as to add 100 feet to the width of the river, which also had to be dredged to get sufficient depth. The removal of siltage is a necessary but costly process that has to be borne by port authorities. The greater part of the income of the Southampton Harbour Board goes in this way; £240,000 was recently spent on dredging the approaches to the great southern port.

In the days when ships were of relatively small tonnage, the tarring, painting, examination and repair of vessels did not usually present a very serious problem, particularly in or near port. If a hole were not too far below the water line, advantage was taken of a falling tide to load the craft heavily on the side that was undamaged so that the injury could be rectified.

Today major repairs and reconditioning necessitate the employment of either a floating or a graving dock. The world's largest floating dock, with an overall length of 960 feet, was built at Newcastle-on-Tyne. When the *Olympic* (46,439 tons), now broken up, entered it, 81,000 tons of water had to be pumped out of the tanks and sufficient air pumped into them to bring both liner and dock above the surface. This mammoth maritime lift, which was stationed at Southampton, became redundant in 1933 by the completion of the King George V Graving Dock at the same port.

Southampton's Giant Graving Dock

The graving dock is 1,200 feet long, 135 feet wide and 59 feet deep. No other dry dock could accommodate a vessel of 100,000 tons, if such a ship were built. At high-water level it holds 260,000 tons of water, which can be discharged in four hours. The total weight of the concrete bed and the walls is approximately 750,000 tons. The dock is virtually the northernmost portion of a reclaimed area that was formerly the bay of the River Test.

The quay wall that adjoins it extends for over one mile and a third, and against it eight of the largest liners can berth with ease. Behind this massive wall are 400 acres of land that required the shifting of 3,000,000 tons of mud and 7,000,000 tons of solid material before cranes, warehouses, railway lines and the paraphernalia of a great modern port could be placed in position. To construct the embankment 146 blocks of concrete, each forty-five feet square, were sunk on a base of gravel, sometimes at a depth of 100 feet. The quay was then built up by concrete.

Liverpool is compelled to wage an even more relentless war against siltage than her southern rival. Dredgers of the bucket, grab and suction types help to keep the sand at bay, aided by a revetment wall near the bar of the Mersey. For twenty years her citizens watched the growth of the Gladstone Docks, which cost £8,000,000 and in 1913 added over fifty-five acres of water, nearly three miles of quayage, and sixteen acres of sheds to her available accommodation as a port, making a total of forty miles of quays and 600 acres of water. Thus has the little fishing village developed since the time of dugouts and the collection of ferry tolls by the monks of Birkenhead Priory.

LARGEST LINER BUILT IN AN ENGLISH SHIPYARD

The " Mauretania," built at Birkenhead, had this proud distinction. The keel was laid in 1937, she was launched in 1938 and her trials took place in the Firth of Forth three months before the outbreak of the second World War. Her displacement was 34,000 tons.

CHAPTER 21

ALTERING THE MAP

After Waterloo. Trade unions. France's recovery. Germany unites. Making of Italy. Belgium parts from Holland. Norway and Sweden separate. Russia under the Tsars. Nationalism in the Balkans. American Civil War. European influence in China. Westernization of Japan. War of 1914-18. Post-war political movements. Hitler, Mussolini, Lenin. Totalitarianism and democracy.

THE world breathed a sigh of relief and of exhaustion when it learned of Napoleon's final defeat at Waterloo. Wellington, an admitted authority, who had enjoyed the best of opportunities for observation, called the result of the battle "a damned near thing."

Boatmen coined money conveying parties eager to catch a glimpse of the fallen emperor pacing the deck of his prison ship in Torbay. Some almost expected the beast with seven heads and ten horns mentioned in Scripture to appear. They saw instead a pale-faced, short-necked, dumpy man; the dictator who could no longer dictate but was dictated to. So that was the military genius who for over twenty years had kept Europe guessing, made war an industry and life a nightmare!

Soon the Corsican ogre would be at St. Helena; a spent force. Rather more than a tale that is told, however. From the facts and fancies of his career a legend was to be created. By means of it another adventurer was to rise to power and another French empire to be founded. But not yet.

Failure of Holy Alliance

There were to be no more wars, of course. Man always dreams happily after a blood-red sunset, envisaging the blissful dawn of the millennium. The rather vague Holy Alliance, based on "the precepts of justice, Christian charity and peace" and sponsored by Russia, proved to be the "loud-sounding nothing" that Prince Metternich, Chancellor of Austria, predicted.

Great Britain stood aside and looked dolefully at her balance sheet. The National Debt had increased by over £613,000,000, despite abundant trade and growing shipping, for at sea the navy had held the enemy as in a vice. The open field system had gradually disappeared, and given place to enclosures that had helped the farmer with capital but the smallholder and cottager

not at all. There had been a number of bad harvests, and the standard of living was low. Income tax had first reared its ugly head— on income above sixty-five pounds a year. Previous to 1815 the death of a miner by accident was regarded as of so little importance that no inquest was held.

Labour's Early Struggles

Those who were unable to make even a scanty living on the land were compelled to drift to the town or endeavour to begin life anew in the colonies. Combinations to demand higher wages were visited by severe penalties. These were rescinded in 1825, but attempts to restrain business, to leave work unfinished, or even to threaten to strike for better wages or improved conditions remained punishable offences.

Trade unionism is now so strong that it is difficult to realize that in 1834, only a little over a century ago, six farmhands of Tolpuddle, in Dorset, were sentenced to transportation to Botany Bay for seven years for having enrolled themselves by oath in the local branch of an agricultural union which existed primarily to secure a minimum wage of ten shillings a week. Public opinion ranged itself on the side of the men, and after two years of brutal hardships they were pardoned. The youngest of them survived until 1902.

Legislators enacted various measures for the relief of the hard conditions brought about by the industrial transition, but the organization that existed for their enforcement was totally inadequate. In 1809, an Act precluded the employment in cotton mills of children under nine years of age, and the toil of those under sixteen was limited to twelve hours a day, but time lost owing to the stoppage of machinery could be made up. It was not until 1842 that boys under ten and all females were forbidden to labour underground. Eight years later owners and managers of mines were made personally responsible for the proper conduct of operations performed in them.

By the terms of the peace France practically returned to her frontiers of 1790. She was no longer the dominant political factor in Europe but a country of tarnished glory, with an enormous indemnity to pay and an army of occupation to keep. The deluge which Louis XV had prophesied on his death-bed had come. It did not engulf her. Hundreds of thousands of men had been sacrificed, the long series of conflicts had dissipated her treasure, yet France was neither prostrate nor ruined. She turned her swords into ploughshares and machinery. Louis XVIII, younger brother of the ill-fated Louis XVI, was then placed on the throne by the Allies. He was fat and, wisely, inclined to be cautious.

Rapid Industrialization

France set to work with astounding energy. Farmers and smallholders sowed and reaped, roads were improved, making markets more accessible, and in 1832 the first railway was built. Among the industries that showed rapid development were coal-mining, silk and cotton manufactures, and the making of beet sugar, which had been introduced by Napoleon. High tariffs stimulated retaliation in countries with which France wished to trade. The excessive duties on British machinery which obtained until 1825 were a deterrent

to a country which had been left behind in the industrial race.

Of Charles X, who succeeded his brother, it was said that he had "learned nothing and forgotten nothing" in the great upset of the Revolution, in which he had played a reactionary part. That policy he continued, with the result that "the turbulent democracy" rose in rebellion, and in 1830 the monarch had no alternative but to abdicate.

Fall of French Monarchy

The vacant and insecure throne was filled by Louis Philippe, who had entertained sufficient liberal ideas in his earlier days to be admitted a member of the Jacobin Club and to join the National Guard. Under the Citizen King, as he was called, the country prospered, although there were serious insurrections at Lyons, the centre of the French silk industry. While the tendency of legislation was to favour the middle class, something was done to relieve the condition of the workers by the introduction of elementary education and the regulation of juvenile labour in factories. The corruption of the Government and a succession of bad harvests that increased the cost of living incited Paris to rebel. Once again a king of France abdicated, and in 1848 the Second Republic was proclaimed.

At the moment socialism, voiced by Louis Blanc, was rampant. National workshops were established and a commission

SPOIL OF ONE DAY'S BATTLE IN THE FRANCO-PRUSSIAN WAR
The Germans attacked the French Army under Marshal MacMahon on the morning of September 1, 1870. At the end of the day 17,000 Frenchmen had been killed and wounded and 104,000 taken prisoner. The number of guns captured by the Germans was 558.

for workers was opened in the Luxembourg Palace. The elections for the Constituent Assembly resulted in a substantial majority for the moderates, who imposed a new land tax and decreed that the experiment of the national workshops be discontinued and all workmen between the ages of eighteen and twenty-five employed in them be drafted into the army.

This proceeding acted like a match on tinder. For several days Paris was again ablaze with revolution. Then occurred the usual swing of the pendulum, and Louis

SHOWING PAGAN INFLUENCE

The old wooden church at Fantoft, Norway, showing pagan influence in its architecture, noticeably the dragon's-head terminals to the gables so suggestive of Burmese carving. It was probably built in the twelfth century.

Napoleon, nephew of the founder of the First Empire, was elected president. Within four years he was emperor, carried to the throne by the magic of a name.

Napoleon III did much to restore prosperity to France, despite his partiality for meddling with his neighbours' business and a firm belief in his destiny to right wrongs, particularly those of other nations. Banks were organized and co-operative societies created, new roads constructed, railways and canals developed, waste lands reclaimed, steamship lines inaugurated, and living con-

ditions vastly improved by the removal of slums. The right to strike was recognised; trade unions were established. France became the leading agricultural state in Europe.

People began to think that the emperor's axiom, "the empire is peace," was an ideal that had become a reality. When all went well his absolutism was counted for righteousness. He fought with Britain, Turkey and Piedmont against Russia in the Crimean War, but his conflict in Italy against Austria, from which he abruptly withdrew, was less popular, and his quixotic attempt to make Maximilian of Austria emperor of Mexico depreciated his "stock" even more. Napoleon sought to re-establish his waning power in France by the introduction of liberal measures. His next step was to fall headlong into a trap set by Prussia.

Germany Takes Shape

From the mosaic of hundreds of petty German principalities that had formed the Holy Roman Empire until its dissolution in 1806, a confederation of thirty-eight states, including parts of Austria and Prussia, was formed in 1815 with a diet at Frankfurt-on-the-Main. Twenty years later a Zollverein, or general customs union, abolished separate tariffs and drew a number of the states appreciably nearer by the silken cords of mutual commercial interest.

Austria remained conspicuously outside. It was soon evident that Prussia and Austria were both struggling for domination, though they joined in occupying the Danish provinces of Schleswig and Holstein.

Prussia's next move was to drive out the Austrians from Holstein, which was mainly German in population and sympathy, and occupy it. Austria, supported by various minor states, then declared war against her former ally. The decisive battle of Königgrätz, or Sadowa, fought in 1866, was won by Prussia, thanks to better generalship and breech-loading needle guns that poured out a more rapid fire than the muzzle-loaders of their adversaries.

Hanover, Hesse-Cassel, Nassau, Frankfurt, part of Hesse-Darmstadt, and Schleswig-Holstein were annexed by the victors. With these states as a substantial basis Prussia set about the formation of the North German Confederation. Bavaria, Baden, the remainder of Hesse-Darmstadt, Württemberg and Liechtenstein, theoretically independent but bound to Prussia by treaties, agreed to constitute by themselves the South German Confederation.

THE GLORY OF MODERN STOCKHOLM AND ITS CREATOR

Stockholm City Hall and its architect, Professor Ragnar Ostberg. The cost of the building, begun in 1911 and opened twelve years later, was over £1,000,000. The bricks used were modelled on those employed by Gustavus Vasa (1496-1560) in the building of the fortifications of the Three Crowns Castle. The walls of the Golden Chamber are entirely covered with mosaics of extremely bold design, including a colossal figure representing History.

OLD AND NEW COMBINED

Engelbrekt Church, Stockholm, features the typical Swedish roof and the most modern of campaniles. The main part of the beautiful interior is built in the form of four gigantic arches of white stone.

The Franco-Prussian War, eagerly sought by Otto von Bismarck, the Prussian minister president, owed its origin to disagreement over the acceptance of the Spanish throne by a distant relation of King William I of Prussia. France objected, seeing in the arrangement an attempt to alter the balance of power that would put her at a disadvantage. The candidature of Prince Leopold was withdrawn, but France, still more than a little suspicious, raised the question of guarantees. The King of Prussia, affronted by the suggestion that his word was not his bond, refused, and recorded his conversation with Count Benedetti, the French ambassador, in a telegram to Bismarck. This was skil-

fully adjusted by the wily statesman. "I boiled down those 200 words," he afterwards related, "to about twenty, but without otherwise altering or adding anything. It was the same telegram, yet different—shorter, more determined, less dubious."

When it appeared in the Press the French were furious. The cry went up "To Berlin!" No French soldier reached Berlin, but Paris fell six months later. On January 18, 1871, William I of Prussia was proclaimed German Emperor in the Hall of Mirrors at Versailles. The same apartment was used when the representatives of a German republic signed the Treaty of Versailles in 1919.

Bismarck became Imperial Chancellor. When the peace terms were discussed he did not forget for one solitary moment his own maxim that "people ought not to bring sentiment into politics." His policy of blood and iron exacted Alsace-Lorraine, Metz and Strassburg in territory and 200 million pounds in treasure.

In less than fifty years Germany, embryonic as regards unity, had closed her ranks and become a great power. She exchanged rôles with imperialistic France, and went steadily in pursuit of her aim to become predominant in Europe.

Austria Holds Down Italy

After the reactionary Congress of Vienna, which sought to put back the clock and to fashion a Europe much as it was before the French Revolution, Italy was nothing more than "a geographical expression," to quote the term used by the cynical Metternich. It was a collection of petty kingdoms, principalities and duchies. Austria, either by possession or alliance, dominated the peninsula with the exception of the Papal States and Sardinia, wielding what it was pleased to term "the sword of justice." Encouraged by an insurrection in Spain, Naples and Piedmont revolted and were sternly suppressed.

Greece was more fortunate. Aided by Great Britain, France and Russia, she secured her independence from Turkey in 1830. The powers concerned acted from no altruistic motives but to keep the Ottoman Empire "in her place."

In 1847 the first low rumblings of a storm were heard in Sicily that in the following year spread throughout Italy. Unfortunately for the cause of independence, the Patriots failed to show a united front, and in 1849 Austria regained her power except in Piedmont, which was included in the kingdom of Sardinia, ruled by Victor Emmanuel II and granted a constitution by his father twelve months before. Around that nucleus was built the foundation of the united Italy that was to come. "Italy shall be!" Such was the resolution.

Count Cavour, the Prime Minister, realized that without outside aid there was little likelihood of the consummation of this hope. He therefore concluded an offensive and defensive alliance with France and sent troops to help in the Crimean War. This led to an arrangement between Napoleon III and Cavour that if hostilities broke out between Austria and Sardinia the latter would cede Savoy and Nice to France in return for military support, aimed at recovering Lombardy and Venetia.

The clash came in 1859. The Emperor of the French fulfilled his promise, though the Piedmontese were bitterly disappointed when Napoleon consented to a truce that left Venetia still in the hands of the enemy. Parma, Modena, Tuscany and the Romagna asked to be annexed, but Francis II of the Two Sicilies would neither consent to an alliance with Sardinia nor grant a constitution to his people.

Giuseppe Garibaldi, who had already led an adventurous life fighting in Italy and South America and now commanded a gallant little band of Red Shirts, made himself master of Sicily in the name of Victor Emmanuel. Cavour next sent an army into the Papal States. The Marches and Umbria were annexed, although Pope Pius IX was left in possession of Rome and the surrounding region. The kingdom of the Two Sicilies was occupied, its people voting to be united to Sardinia, and in 1861 the first Italian parliament proclaimed Victor Emmanuel King of Italy. Venetia was added five years later, following Italian hostilities against Austria when the latter country was also at war with Prussia.

As the Pope refused to recognize the new order of things, and France was compelled by reason of her conflict with Prussia to withdraw the troops which guarded his remaining territory, Rome was occupied and annexed in 1871. This period is known as the *risorgimento*, or reawakening.

For over two centuries the Dutch Republic and Belgium went their separate ways. Then the latter was annexed by revolutionary France. The Congress of

MODERN SWEDEN DOES NOT FORGET HER PAST

Essentially modern in outlook, Sweden has preserved in the Open Air Museum at Skansen many ancient houses removed from various parts of the country and carefully rebuilt so that the past may not be forgotten. Old national dances in costumes long discarded for less picturesque clothing are performed there, to the accompaniment of venerable musical instruments.

Vienna brought about an unhappy union of the two countries, which ended in revolt and divorce at the instance of the Belgians. The decision of the Congress had been diametrically opposed to their wishes, for while they were Catholic with agricultural and industrial interests, their neighbours were Protestant and commercial.

With business acumen the Dutch visualized a substantial increase in prosperity, thanks to the raw materials of Belgium. Their capitalists invested heavily. They were less happy as to the future when it was found that the trade of Amsterdam and Rotterdam was slowly but steadily flowing to Antwerp and Ostend.

A period of depression followed the separation, but when the Belgians really settled down the result was entirely worthy of an industrious people that now claims the densest population in Europe. The iron works founded by John Cockerill near Liège went steadily ahead. The first railway on the Continent was laid down between Brussels and Malines. The coming of the iron road did not lead to the gradual neglect of canals, as in England. They were regarded as allies and not as competitors. Holland had the right to levy tolls on all vessels using the River Scheldt. With an eye to the future Belgium, in conjunction with other Powers, commuted this liability, with a view to the future prosperity of Antwerp.

Holland Overseas

The Netherlands Trading Company, founded in 1824, did much to revive the flagging mercantile interests of the Dutch. It awakened new enthusiasm as to the value of the colonies, the exports of which gradually increased. Holland is tiny when compared with the area of her overseas possessions, for while the former consists of some 12,500 square miles, the area of the latter is 783,000 square miles, for the most part in the Malay Archipelago.

In the economic progress of the country the Netherlands East Indies have played a conspicuous part. They include a section of Borneo as large as France; Sumatra, as big as Sweden; Celebes and Java, five and four times respectively the size of Holland; the Moluccas, or Spice Islands, and Western New Guinea. The Motherland is but a quarter the area of Surinam, or Dutch Guiana, in South America. Then there is Curaçao, in the Caribbean Sea.

The abolition of serfdom, of the negro slave trade, and of the duty on corn had stamped Denmark as a progressive country before the French Revolution and the Napoleonic wars plunged her into a sea of troubles. In 1814 Denmark suffered the loss of Norway, which was given to Sweden, and fifty years later she was compelled to cede the duchies of Schleswig and Holstein, as noted above. Part of the latter was returned to her following the war of 1914-18. She became the dairy of Northern Europe, with over 200,000 independent farms in addition to many thousands of State small-holdings. Yet it was not until 1864 that Denmark gave her serious attention to dairy farming.

Europe's Danish Dairy

Co-operative enterprises grew up in great numbers, taking the form of small-holders' associations, breeding, feeding-stuffs, manure supply, seed purchase and control societies, dairies and bacon factories. The exports included cheese, butter, condensed milk and cream, seeds, cattle, pigs, pork and bacon.

Many of the old cottage industries developed almost beyond recognition, notably those connected with clothing and leather. If cement, one of the most important of Danish exports, was severely utilitarian, it must be conceded that the exquisite productions of the Royal Porcelain Works at Copenhagen set an artistic standard unexcelled elsewhere.

Denmark is not the mother of a numerous family of colonies. Greenland is her only possession, though until 1940 Iceland, while a sovereign state, recognized the King of Denmark as her monarch.

The people of Norway, subordinate to Denmark since 1450 and dragged into the Napoleonic conflict by sheer force of circumstances, refused to acknowledge the treaty which had calmly made them subjects of Sweden. As the result of a week or two of armed conflict and of negotiations, the country was declared to be independent, though united with Sweden by the common bond of being subject to the one king. This arrangement, after many squabbles, came to an end in 1905, when Prince Charles of Denmark was unanimously elected to the throne as Haakon VII.

Although about seventy per cent of the land is sterile, practically every inch that can be used for agricultural purposes is employed, and of the registered holdings some ninety-four per cent are freehold farms. In the mountain districts the rearing of live stock is of prime importance. Oats

FOREST FURNACE OF THE CHARCOAL BURNER

Charcoal was formerly used for smelting purposes. For a time Sweden lost her supremacy in the iron industry because it was found that coal and coke could be used for the purpose and she was deficient in coal. The invention of the electric smelting furnace again placed the country in a favourable position. In the foreground, logs are being stacked in an English wood as a step towards preparing a heap of charcoal, like that seen burning behind.

and potatoes are grown extensively, but home crops are eked out by heavy imports.

The extensive lumbering operations give employment to many men who work their own farms during the summer and labour in the forests during the winter. Wood and wood products, such as pulp for newsprint, are important exports, and compete for supremacy with the fisheries. Whaling is also extensively carried on in the Antarctic.

Sweden, whose first parliament, or Riksdag, of nobles, clergy, burghers and peasants met in 1435, was once numbered among the Great Powers. Her Vikings founded colonies that formed the nucleus of Russia. Under Gustavus 'Adolphus the country dominated the Baltic, losing her position there by the reckless military adventures of Charles XII. During the Napoleonic Wars Finland and the Åland Islands were wrenched from her, but compensation was given by the union of Norway with Sweden under the same king, Charles XIV, formerly Marshal Bernadotte, who had deserted Napoleon. He was the founder of the present reigning house.

For a time Sweden produced more iron than any other country in the world. She gained that supremacy in the eighteenth century because the ore was good and not difficult to mine. The lead was lost when the ever-increasing demand compelled metallurgists to seek fresh sources of supply and to devise new processes of smelting, not the least important being the discovery that for ordinary purposes coal and coke could be used in place of charcoal. Deficient in coal, Sweden was unable to compete on equal terms with her rivals, but she continued to produce high quality iron and steel.

BUILDING A RAFT OF LOGS IN FINLAND

With territory larger than that of the United Kingdom and Eire, the people of Finland, numbering about 3,700,000, earn their living mainly by agriculture and industries dependent on the extensive coniferous forests, which cover nearly seventy-five per cent of the land area.

When the electric smelting furnace was introduced conditions were reversed, and the richness and purity of her ores, coupled with cheap water power, again placed the country in a favourable position. Probably the richest iron ore in the world is obtained from Kiruna, within the Arctic Circle. The passage of the mineral in German ships in Norwegian territorial waters from Narvik was the chief factor in drawing Norway into the second World War. Another great source of wealth is timber. Forests cover an area of approximately 58 million acres.

English Pope in Finland

Finland was first colonized by the Swedes, who sent Nicholas Breakspear, the only English Pope, to convert their eastern neighbours. For nearly 600 years, apart from a short interval during which she was plundered and bludgeoned by Peter the Great, she formed part of the Swedish realm. Without any formal declaration of war, Russian troops marched in and annexed the territory in 1809, and it was as a Grand Duchy that the country remained until the Russian Revolution of 1917 gave her an opportunity to unloose her shackles. Bolshevism broke out and flamed into a war for freedom which ended in the defeat of the Red Army.

With territory rather larger than that of the United Kingdom and Eire, the people of Finland, numbering about 3,700,000, earn their living mainly by agriculture and industries dependent on the coniferous forests, which cover over seventy-three per cent of the land area. All the professions, except the Church, are open to women.

The centralization of authority in Russia was begun by Ivan III, Grand Duke of Moscow, who steadily annexed territory, confiscated the goods of the Hanseatics and other foreign traders in Novgorod, issued a code of laws, and added much to the importance of Moscow. It remained for Peter the Great to give Russia, hitherto Asiatic in outlook and sympathies, "a window looking on Europe" in the Baltic.

Possessed of that touch of insanity said to be akin to genius, the burly savage organized an army on efficient lines, built factories, founded St. Petersburg (Leningrad), constructed roads and canals, encouraged trade, and paid a memorable visit to England to study shipbuilding and other crafts. Peter did not succeed in westernizing the masses, though he tried hard enough in his uncouth and barbaric way. His wish for an

ENTRANCE TO A WALLED CITY
The tiny gateway to the old walled city of Dubrovnik, formerly Ragusa, on the coast of Yugoslavia, which was colonized by refugees from a neighbouring Greco-Roman settlement in the sixth century.

outlet to the Black Sea was fulfilled by the iron-willed Catherine II, who began the conversion of a squalid Turkish village of fishermen into what is now Odessa.

It was not until 1861 that the gradual emancipation of the serfs was begun, a reform involving redemption payments that dragged on for over forty years and bred all manner of discontent which the calling of the Duma, or parliament, in 1906, following a disastrous war with Japan, did little or nothing to assuage. The operations of a trading corporation somewhat similar to the East India Company gradually spread eastward and led to the conquest of Siberia, to which the first batch of convicts was consigned in 1593. The officials of the concern explored, dealt in furs, and aided by the Cossacks penetrated and secured the possession of the Amur country.

It may be that the first inhabitants of Poland—the land of the *pole*, or field— were driven by the Romans from the vicinity of the Danube. For long the Hanseatics and other foreigners were the chief traders in a land that devoted what time it could spare from dissensions to the raising of cattle, the felling of timber, and the sowing and harvesting of wheat, oats, rye, flax and hemp. "One Pole a genius, two Poles a political party, three Poles a revolution," runs an old proverb.

Russia, Austria and Prussia mutilated the country by three partitions. The nation offered no resistance to the annexations of 1772, but when further territory was seized in 1793 the people under Thaddeus Kosciuszko put up a determined though hopeless fight, and in 1795 the kingdom came to an end. It was not until the downfall of Napoleon I, who had created a new Duchy of Warsaw, that Poland enjoyed a meed of prosperity. Like so many other European countries, Poland had its revolution in the thirties of the nineteenth century. It was suppressed with great cruelty. Some of the powers extended sympathy; none were willing to send help.

Balkan Chessboard

War has been the lot of the Balkans since the days of the ancient Greeks. Forming a rugged bridge between Europe and Asia, the peninsula has been a powder magazine and a melting pot. Feuds and territorial ambitions have set the countries ablaze from end to end; no other part of the world contains such a medley of peoples.

At the outbreak of the war of 1914-18 the comparatively small area of some 200,000 square miles was split up into Serbia, Montenegro, Albania, Greece, Bulgaria, Rumania and Turkey, with Bosnia, Herzegovina and Dalmatia subject to Austria. The Balkan countries, fearful that one should have greater influence than another, were the sport of the Powers. Great Britain preferred "the unspeakable Turk" at Constantinople to the "Russian bear."

The history of the Serbs has been mainly a record of repression and internecine strife since their entry into the peninsula They were subject for a time to the Byzantine Empire, till Stephan Dushan founded a short-lived state that fell under the crushing blows administered by the Turks at Kossovo in 1389. As a reminder of the battle, two big candles were placed in the monastery of Detchani. They were not to be lighted until Serbia was avenged. When the Turks were driven out in 1912, over five centuries later, wax and wicks radiated their pale and flickering light for the first time. Nor was this all. June 28 was set apart as a day of mourning. On that date in 1914 the pistol shots that killed Archduke Franz Ferdinand and his wife at Sarajevo started the First World War of 1914-18.

Under the Turkish Heel

The Balkans, with the exception of Montenegro, whose inhabitants maintained their independence in the fortresses of the Katunska Highlands for 500 years, became part of the Ottoman Empire after the stricken field of Kossovo. Serbia remained under the heel of the conqueror, with a brief period of subjection to Austria, until the nineteenth century, when revolts against the oppressor culminated in the withdrawal of the Turkish garrisons and a declaration of independence following the Russo–Turkish War of 1877–78. Conflicts ensued with Turkey and Bulgaria. The war of emancipation ended in 1918 with the proclamation of the kingdom of Yugoslavia. It incorporated Bosnia, Herzegovina, Montenegro and Serbia.

Bulgaria had been twice an empire before Dushan conquered the greater part of the territory. The Turks became its masters in 1396, and remained so until 1878. The country was useful for the provision of money in the form of taxes and of kind in the shape of stores and cattle. Boys were recruited for the restless Ottoman armies which frequently passed through the land and on occasion paid unpleasant attention to the inhabitants.

A rising in 1876 was followed by the burning of dozens of villages and the slaughter of thousands of Bulgars by the Turks. Gladstone pamphleteered against so wanton a punishment; Alexander II of Russia acted. He declared war. By the Treaty of San Stefano, a self-governing Bulgarian State was created—on paper. The Big Powers tore it up, and by the terms of the Treaty of Berlin, Bulgaria became a principality with the Sultan as

AMERICAN CITY WITHIN A CITY

Of all the cities of the civilized world, those of the United States of America have grown furthest away from the small towns of a century ago. The towering skyscrapers of today can house as many people as an old-time town. The great stone panel above, representing Wisdom, adorns one of the buildings of the Rockefeller Center in New York, which goes one stage further and contains several skyscrapers with offices and social centres of their own.

overlord. Macedonia, despite the object lesson in inhumanity so recently given, was handed over to the Turks. Southern Bulgaria was separated, became Eastern Rumelia, and in 1885 was united with Bulgaria. War broke out with Serbia, which was jealous of Bulgaria's growing importance. While the latter was victorious from a military point of view, she was compelled to call a halt owing to Austria's threat to take the field on behalf of Serbia.

Prince Alexander of Bulgaria, forced to abdicate at the instigation of Russia, gave place to Ferdinand, of the house of Saxe-Coburg-Gotha, later to be termed "the fox of the Balkans." In the autumn of 1908 Bulgaria announced her independence, and the prince was proclaimed Tsar of the Bulgars. Bosnia and Herzegovina, occupied by Austria since the Treaty of Berlin, were annexed by her with the connivance of Bulgaria and Germany.

Balkan League Overwhelms Turkey

Bulgaria, Greece, Serbia and Montenegro, with the approval of Russia, formed an alliance against Turkey. In 1912 hostilities began, ostensibly because of the failure of Turkey to fulfil her promise to introduce much-needed reforms in Macedonia. The allies were brilliantly successful, but under pressure of the Great Powers signed the Treaty of London. Although Turkey was left with scarcely more than Constantinople, none of the victors was satisfied with his share of plunder.

Bulgaria turned traitor and attacked her former allies. Taking advantage of the turn of events, Turkey recovered Adrianople. Rumania joined in and invaded Bulgaria. Of her former conquests Bulgaria retained only a portion of Western Thrace, with the port of Dede Agach. The others gained handsomely in territory. Albania became an independent principality under the German Prince William of Wied, with Durazzo as the capital. His unpopular rule was a matter of months.

In the south-west of Rumania are sturdy peasants who claim descent from Romans who colonized the country shortly after Trajan defeated the native king and made it a Roman province called Dacia. Turkey eventually got her grip on Wallachia, Moldavia and Transylvania, on which the hungry eyes of Russia and Austria were frequently turned.

For a few years following the Turko-Russian War of 1828, Russia occupied the two former territories, but after the Crimean War it was decided that they should be called the United Principalities of Moldavia and Wallachia and each have an individual ruler. This strange arrangement was brought about mainly to please Great Britain, then suffering from an attack of political nerves that visualized in the definite union of the principalities the making of a power that might shake the world.

The countries themselves settled the matter by electing the same ruler, Prince Alexander John I. In attempting to solve the land problem he created hundreds of thousands of peasant proprietors, who had to indemnify the previous holders by way of compensation for dues previously paid in kind and in labour. The scheme proved unworkable, and with loaded pistols pointed at his heart the unhappy ruler was compelled to sign his abdication. Prince Charles of Hohenzollern, backed by France and Prussia, succeeded him.

The independence of Rumania was recognized in 1878 by the Treaty of San Stefano, which wound up the Russo-Turkish War, in which Charles and his troops had played a valiant part against the Ottoman Power. When he became king in 1881 as Charles I he had a simple crown fashioned from the metal of captured Turkish cannon. "Out of the very steel that once cost so many Rumanian lives," he said, "our crown shall be made, in token of its having been won upon the field of battle, and bought and paid for with our own blood."

Modern Switzerland Takes Shape

Not until the end of the Napoleonic wars were all the cantons of Switzerland brought together, to quarrel on occasion about religion and politics until 1874, when the constitution was revised and took its present form. Associated in the popular mind with the export of dairy produce and the import of tourists, this mountainous oasis bordered by jangling nations has been the home of many political hopes, disappointments and experiments. Geneva is at once the city of Calvin, Rousseau, Voltaire, the International Red Cross Society and the League of Nations.

In the early stages of its independence the United States had the usual maladies that afflict political childhood. History has no record of civilized lands that have managed to escape the measles of disaffection, the scarlet fever of revolt and similar ailments.

PLANT THAT CLOTHES THE WORLD'S PEOPLES
The downy fibre that envelops the cotton seeds is one of the most valuable products of the vegetable world. Even the seed is crushed for the oil it contains. In normal times raw cotton is the principal single export of the U.S.A. The divergence of interests between the cotton-growing South and the industrial North was a part cause of the American Civil War (1861-65).

There was but partial co-operation between the States previous to 1789, when the first Congress met and elected George Washington as president, but even then Rhode Island and North Carolina preferred to remain outside the new federation. In 1803 Louisiana was bought from France; an area larger than the original Thirteen Colonies was sold for 1¼d. an acre. By annexation, powder and shot and purchase, forty-eight states between ocean and ocean, were eventually included in the Union.

When the Quadruple Alliance of Austria, Russia, Prussia and France threatened the new republics born out of the revolt of the Spanish colonies of Latin America, George Canning suggested that Great Britain and the United States should issue a joint declaration that they would not tolerate such intervention. Although President James Monroe did not fall in with the idea, the action of the British Foreign Secretary made an excellent impression in America. What is now known as the Monroe Doc-

trine was defined in the president's speech to Congress in 1823, when he declared that "the American continents, by the free and independent condition which they have assumed and maintained, are not to be considered as subjects for future colonization by any European Power."

While railroads and canals were developing, enterprising settlers and many thousands of immigrants from Europe made their toilsome way to the fertile west, which was rendered even more attractive by the discovery of gold in California in 1848. During the nineteenth century no fewer than 100 million people crossed the Atlantic to begin life anew in the United States.

The bitter struggle of the civil war was not caused entirely by disagreement about slavery, nor even by the breaking away of various Southern States to form the Confederate States of America. Threats to secede had been made before; three such had come from the north. It was a quarrel concerning business interests as well.

GARMENTS BY THE YARD

An Eskimo tailor preparing part of the intestine of a whale for making into a waterproof garment, a much-needed article for dwellers in the ice-bound regions of Alaska.

The south, where cotton was king, was undergoing a period of depression, for which it stoutly maintained that the high tariff was responsible. In the north manufactures flourished and expanded. It had undergone an industrial revolution such as had obtained in England, and profited by it. Hatred, malice and all uncharitableness bred the war long before the first soldier was mobilized.

Following the victory of Grant and Sherman, the United States prospered in a

way that was the envy of less favoured nations. Circumstances compelled her to fling back the curtains of her splendid isolation and to take an active part in affairs often staged many thousands of miles across the seas.

By the enforcement of the Monroe Doctrine she compelled France to withdraw from Mexico, and she acquired territory by the purchase of Alaska from Russia, of the Virgin Islands—formerly known as the Danish West Indies—from Denmark, and the Panama Canal Zone from the republic of Panama. Hawaii was annexed during the Spanish-American War of 1898, brought about by outrages in Cuba and the sinking of the United States battleship *Maine*, and Puerto Rico and Guam were gained as a consequence of it. Part of Samoa was obtained by treaty. Cuba, "the gem of the Antilles," while nominally an independent republic is in effect a protectorate.

War for a Flower

No country has been more widely or wildly exploited than "the unwieldy colossus" of China. External pressure was brought to bear on internal weakness. In 1840 Great Britain waged war for a flower. The white poppy which is the source of opium had been grown in China for centuries, but some years before this the native product was prohibited and its importation forbidden. Whether the action of the emperor was for the good of his subjects or to prevent the heavy drain of silver from the country to pay for the drug is open to question; the right of a foreign land to break an edict for gain is not.

Opium began to reach China from India. Insults and outrages to British subjects resulted. Over 20,000 chests of the stuff, valued at two million pounds, were surrendered, but a guarantee not to repeat the offence was refused. Britain declared war and won the fight. She was indemnified by the payment of six million pounds, the opening of the ports of Canton, Amoy, Foochow, Ningpo and Shanghai to her subjects, and the cession of Hong Kong. The gradual suppression of opium was agreed upon by the two countries in 1911.

Great Britain having forced the door ajar and placed a substantial foot in the opening, other countries arrived like importunate tramps. Barriers were removed from many other ports following further action on the part of Great Britain and France. Customs regulations were revised and treaties concluded with those countries, the United States and Russia. Kowloon, on the mainland opposite to Hong Kong, was ceded to Great Britain, and Russia gained 360,000 square miles of territory, building on a suitable site the port of Vladivostok, that gave her an exit to the Pacific and afforded an eastern terminus for the Trans-Siberian railway. Trouble over the Burmese frontier led to Burma becoming British. Russia demanded and secured additional territory. Annam and Tongking became French possessions.

After China's defeat in a war with Japan over the control of Korea, of which the Emperor of China was overlord, the Pescadores Islands and Formosa passed to the victor and the Hermit Kingdom was declared independent. The Liaotung peninsula was also included in Japan's demands, but Russia obtained its return to China and was rewarded by being allowed to continue the Trans-Siberian railway across Northern Manchuria. Germany secured Kiaochow for a term of ninety-nine years as a peace-offering for the murder of one of her subjects in a riot.

China and Europe

Concession after concession was granted: to Russia the lease of Port Arthur, to Great Britain Wei-hai-wei, to France Kwang-chow-wan. Commercial and other privileges in "spheres of influence" were secured.

Whether an individual country has a moral right to keep her natural wealth buried in the earth or only partially worked when it is a necessity to mankind is an ethical problem that we are not called upon to discuss. Selfishness is of stubborn growth and less easy to conquer than a country.

"China for the Chinese" was the battle-cry of a patriotic and bloodthirsty society known as the Boxers. It led to the dispatch of an international expeditionary force to China in 1900, and incidentally gave the German Emperor an opportunity to make one of those fiery speeches which would have warned the chancellories of Europe of future possibilities, had his utterances been regarded as anything more than bluster.

"When you meet the foe," he told his troops, "you will defeat him. No quarter will be given, no prisoners will be taken. Let all who fall into your hands be at your mercy. Just as the Huns a thousand years ago, under the leadership of Attila, gained a reputation in virtue of which they

still live in historical tradition, so may the name of Germany become known in such a manner in China that no Chinese will ever dare to look askance at a German." Hitler was to use similar flamboyant talk. The indemnity was 64 million pounds.

Russia's activities in Manchuria, which she had undertaken to evacuate, and more especially in Korea, led to war with Japan. It ended in 1905 in disaster to the Russian Army and the annihilation of her fleet. Russia's rights in the Liaotung peninsula

PROVIDED BY NATURE

A native of Annam, one of the native kingdoms in French Indo-China, wearing a palm leaf hat and a palm leaf raincoat.

and half the island of Sakhalin went to the victors, who annexed Korea.

For the first time in modern history a great European Power had been defeated by an Asiatic nation. The repercussion startled even the sleepy giant on whose territory the conflict had been waged. China blinked a little, sat up and began to take a more than perfunctory notice of the outside world. An era of reform set in; soldiering became a fashionable profession. Collections were made by Navy Leagues to provide money for the building of a fleet. A parliament was promised—in nine years' time—and provincial councils were inaugurated. A start was made in the gradual suppression of opium smoking. The value of western education was recognized. The death of the ultra-conservative and masterful Dowager Empress was regarded as the removal of a stumbling block. In 1912 the Yellow Kingdom became the Chinese Republic.

Amazing Story of Japan

The Japanese are firmly convinced of three things: their country was the first land to be created; they are descended from the gods; their nation is destined to become the greatest in the world. These are the pillars of their abiding faith.

From 1639 to 1853 Japan's doors were bolted and barred; no western hawkers were allowed. In the latter year a small United States squadron appeared off Uraga, and for a time caused pandemonium in the city. But neither Commodore M. C. Perry in command of the four vessels, nor his guns, spoke in anger. The officer merely showed his credentials and handed President Millard Fillmore's demands to the commissioners of the Shogun. He would call for the reply after a decent interval for consideration had elapsed.

In the following year the courteous officer again put in an appearance, supported by a more formidable armament. Whereupon the ports of Simoda, Hakodate and Yokohama were opened to American trade. Commercial treaties were also signed with Great Britain, France, Russia, Portugal and the Netherlands.

When Japan really got going she showed that she was in a hurry. French military and British naval instructors were appointed, feudalism was abolished, conscription was established, and foreigners were welcomed. She took a leaf or two out of the history books of other nations; fought China, added to her empire, took part with Euro-

peans in the suppression of the Boxer insurrection. The anchorite had become a man of the world.

In 1902 Japan entered into a defensive alliance with Great Britain. Its objects were, to quote Baron Koto, "the consolidation and maintenance of general peace in Eastern Asia and the maintenance of the independence and integrity of China, as well as the principle of equal opportunities for commerce and industry for all nations in that country, and the maintenance and defence respectively of territorial rights and special interests of the contracting parties in Eastern Asia." The alliance was dissolved in 1922, but the above is interesting in the light of subsequent events.

Germany and Austria-Hungary launched the war of 1914-18. For years the German people had been stimulated by propaganda telling them that the earth's destiny was in their hands. "The modern world owes to us Germans pretty well everything in the way of great achievements that it has to show. Ours is the future, for we are young." Thus Professor Fritz Bley. General Friedrich von Bernhardi trumpeted the gospel of force in books that had as their basis the fixed belief that war was a "necessary element in the life of nations and an indispensable factor of culture." "France must be crushed so utterly that she can never again obstruct our path," he wrote.

Bernhardi and Britain

Bernhardi also fostered hatred of Great Britain: "There can be no doubt that England seriously contemplates attacking Germany should the occasion arise." The hallucination of German encirclement, afterwards to become an obsession with the Third Reich, was as evident in his writings as is a halo in the painted representation of a saint. The next war was to be "fought for the highest interests of our country and of mankind. 'World power or downfall!' will be our rallying cry." Bernhardi died in 1930, but his inhuman philosophy, like John Brown's soul, went marching on.

Physical hostilities ceased at the eleventh hour of the eleventh day of the eleventh month of 1918. To many the alliterative figures took on a mystical meaning. They fixed themselves in the memory more readily than other statistics: 65 million men mobilized and eight million men dead, for instance. When peace was signed in 1919, people of goodwill regarded the formation of the League of Nations much as the cloud

JAPANESE VERSION OF ST. GEORGE AND THE DRAGON

According to tradition, a giant snake with eight heads was slain by a Japanese St. George in remote times. A festival in honour of the deliverance is still held in Osaka. In the course of the ceremonies the reptile, which is represented by an enormous rope, is hacked by a young girl, while the assembled witnesses sing a song of thanksgiving.

that gave light by night to the Israelites and darkness to the pursuing Egyptians. The specific covenants and mutual guarantees were to afford humanity a means of escape from legalized murder.

The gleam of the first of Woodrow Wilson's fourteen points, announced by the autocratic president of a democratic republic to the United States Congress before the cessation of hostilities, took on added brilliance and flamed as a pillar of fire: "Open covenants of peace openly arrived at, after which there shall be no private international understandings of any kind, but diplomacy shall proceed always frankly and in the public view." Ideal and idea became no more than vague shadows. Wilson was to be repudiated by his own people, as the League repudiated itself and the world repudiated the League. An era of social and economic experiments began.

Austria-Hungary was rent in twain; Alsace-Lorraine was returned to France, the greater part of Upper Silesia, Posen and West Prussia to a restored Poland;

Danzig blossomed as a free city under the jurisdiction of the League; certain Rhineland territory was occupied for a term of years; all German colonies and overseas possessions passed to the victorious powers, who were granted mandates for their government. In Europe about 29,000 square miles of territory were surrendered by Germany. The sum to be paid as compensation to the Allies was not stated in the treaty. It was afterwards assessed at 132,000 million gold marks (about £6,000 millions).

The first president of the German republic was Friedrich Ebert, socialist and one-time apprentice to a saddler; the second was stolid Field-Marshal Paul von Hindenburg. His achievements during the war of 1914-18, swollen by legend, had made him an idol of colossal proportions. Despite this adulation he was elected only by a narrow majority. When he heard the result he merely remarked: "As God wills. Now let me sleep two hours more."

Reparation payments, extravagant expenditure on the social services and

PROPAGANDA BY MAPS OF MARBLE

In 1932 four marble maps showing the growth of Rome from a tiny village to the seat of a far-extending Roman Empire were erected in the Eternal City by Mussolini's orders. They were calculated to inspire Italian youth with the idea that what had been might be again.

municipal enterprises, general financial instability and unemployment helped to swell the ranks of discontent, though the policy of Gustav Stresemann, who as Foreign Minister strove for the friendship of his country's late enemies and secured her entry into the League of Nations, did something to steady the ship of State.

Rise of the Nazis

In 1923 Adolf Hitler, General Erich von Ludendorff and a number of armed National Socialists—called Nazis for short—attempted to establish a military dictatorship. Hitler was an Austrian misanthrope and neurasthenic with an overweening belief in his own abilities; Ludendorff had been mainly responsible for the victory of Tannenberg. Tried and imprisoned in the fortress of Landsberg-am-Lech, Hitler was released after serving only six months of his five years' sentence. He left jail with part of the manuscript of *Mein Kampf* ("My Struggle"), a Bible of hatred, under his arm, and after lying low for a time renewed his tirades against the Versailles Treaty, Jews,

pacifists, profiteers, capitalists, landowners and the existing government.

Hitler's private army of Brown Shirts grew formidable. Nine Nazis were returned to the Reichstag, a helpless but not hopeless minority, but in 1930 the National Socialists had gained 107 seats, and two years later were the strongest single party. In January, 1933, Hindenburg yielded to pressure and offered the chancellorship to Hitler, who thus assumed the mantle of Bismarck. An alleged plot against the régime was defeated with ruthless severity in June, 1934, when General von Schleicher, Hitler's predecessor in the chancellorship, and his wife were shot dead and hundreds more silenced for ever.

When, in the fullness of years, Hindenburg died, Hitler as president, chancellor and commander-in-chief paid a glowing tribute in the Reichstag to his predecessor's memory, in which he made this pious appeal: " May the Almighty in His mercy let us ever find the right way for securing the boon of peace for our people and sheltering it from the misfortune of war, just as the great dead leader has ever wanted it honestly and wholeheartedly."

A cunning sentence in the light of after events. Germany had built up her former prosperity by peaceful penetration, by commercial travellers. The new leader continued the policy but also developed the technique of political penetration by armed forces that did not fight.

It answered amazingly well for a time. Germany left the League, marched into the demilitarized zone of the Rhineland, invaded Austria, fooled Mr. Neville Chamberlain and the British Empire with a paper promise, crushed Czechoslovakia and seized Memel from Lithuania. Then she marched on the city-state of Danzig.

Here the new technique broke down. The German people were no longer sheltered from the misfortune of conflict. Poland resisted the invaders to exhaustion. Great Britain and France shook off their apathy. The second World War began.

Poorly equipped and badly organized, victims of muddle and corruption, the armies of Russia had fought against Germany and desperate odds from 1914 to the revolution of 1917. The first phase of the revolt was accomplished with little bloodshed, but extremists quickly gained the upper hand, sparing neither friend nor foe in their ruthless determination to set up the Russian Socialist Federated Republic of Soviets (councils). In destroying one despotism they erected another.

Maker of Modern Russia

The dominating personality of those who sought to build a new Russia on proletarian lines was Vladimir Ilyich Uliánov, otherwise Nikolai Lenin, formerly a political prisoner in Siberia and exile in London, where he had fondly awaited the rising of the masses. It was at a congress in that city that the word bolsheviki, or majority, was first used to denote those who agreed with Lenin's idea that the capitalist system could be rooted out only by violent measures.

FAR-FLUNG FRONTIERS OF ANCIENT ROME

A close-up of the marble map of the Roman Empire when it had reached its greatest extent under Trajan, who died in 117. The maps are on the walls of the basilica of Maxentius, near the Colosseum. The Fasces, representing the bundles of rods carried as signs of authority by the lictors of Ancient Rome, and now insignia of the Fascists, are in the bottom corner.

Those who preferred evolution to revolution were the mensheviki, or minority.

Lenin, an earnest disciple of Karl Marx and exponent of the materialist conception of history, chose as his chief of staff Leon Bronstein, alias Leon Trotsky, who formed the Red Army of 1,500,000 men which fought in the exhausting civil war that followed. Not all were enamoured of Lenin's communist State, and an ill-starred counter-revolution of the Whites was backed by the Allies.

The frail little Mongolian-looking man who lived in the servants' quarters of the Kremlin then set about the colossal task of industrializing a land of peasants and making it self-supporting. The first Five-Year Plan was inaugurated. Some of the communist principles were dropped; science was brought to the rescue of the starving. The worship of the machine began.

PETER OF YUGOSLAVIA

Peter, king of Serbia, who became ruler of Yugoslavia following the war of 1914-18, as represented by Ivan Mestrović, the most famous modern Yugoslav sculptor.

ing it self-supporting. The first Five-Year Plan was inaugurated. Some of the communist principles were dropped; science was brought to the rescue of the starving. The worship of the machine began.

When Lenin, worn out by overwork, closed his steely eyes for ever, his body was embalmed, placed in a coffin with a glass lid and taken to a massive red mausoleum suggestive of the pyramid tombs of ancient Pharaohs. There it is gazed at by the idle, the curious and the devout. The dictatorship of the proletariat had been the dictatorship of one man.

The mantle of Lenin fell on the son of a Georgian cobbler, Joseph Djugashvili, now called Stalin, which means steel. Trotsky, Stalin's relentless critic, was deposed from his high estate, bundled off out of the way, and met his death in Mexico in 1940. Whereas Lenin had aimed at world revolution, the man of steel devoted himself to internal problems that he regarded as of more practical and immediate importance to the 160 million people who looked to him for guidance. He has been termed "the queen bee of the communist hive," an unfortunate simile in that the insect is of feminine gender, but none the less suggestive. Industrial production has increased sixfold since the revolution, the standard of living is higher, and illiteracy is gradually dying.

Vehemently cursed by Hitler as the cause of most of the trouble in Europe, Russia co-operated with Germany when she invaded Poland in 1939—and divided the spoils. Estonia, Latvia and Lithuania, Russian provinces until they broke away following the war of 1914-18, again came under the old sphere of influence. Their geographical position, small size and inability to fight a giant left them with no alternative but to sign "pacts of mutual assistance." Russia's long-sightedness in thus strengthening her frontiers was justified when, in June, 1941, Hitler let loose his armies, without a moment's warning, on his erstwhile friend.

Blacksmith's Son becomes Duce

Benito Mussolini, born into a revolutionary household, was named after Juarez, the Mexican president who succeeded the Emperor Maximilian. His father was a blacksmith, a freethinker and one of the first Internationalists. When Benito shook the dust of his native village near Forli from his feet, it was rather glad to get rid of him; later Forli subscribed to give him the medieval castle at Rocca della Caminate.

In his early story there is much that reminds one of Hitler's struggles as a young man, days of vagabondage and such like, but whereas the latter had only one taste of prison, the former was in jail eleven times. On one occasion he also emerged with a wad of material he had written, appropriately enough on John Huss.

Appointed editor of the Socialist daily newspaper *Avanti* in 1913, he resigned in the following year because he was in favour of Italy's entry into the war on the side of the Allies, and was thrown out of the party. "You may expel me," he shouted, "but not my ideas." Founding *Il Popolo d'Italia*, in which he advocated his policy of intervention, he volunteered for the army, and after some opposition by the authorities was accepted. Rising to the rank of corporal—as did Hitler—Mussolini was blown up and badly battered. He again took up the weapon that is alleged to be mightier than the sword, and fought with that.

Founding of the Blackshirts

Inflamed by the weakness of the government, inspired also, it may well be, by personal ambition, he founded in March, 1919, in a back street in Milan, the first fascio. The movement spread, and the Black Shirts, based on the model of the legions of ancient Rome, became a vast private army comparable with their imitators, the Brown Shirts of Germany. To put down strikes, stamp out corruption, to bring some sort of unity into a country sadly disillusioned, such was its business. It met violence with violence, murder with murder.

With extravagant rhetoric, the Duce promised order for chaos, stability for insecurity. The fruits of victory had been withheld from Italy. Pledges made by her fighting partners had been disregarded. Not a solitary overseas mandate had come her way. It was a slight that could not be forgiven. He and they must dismiss lethargy, become the servants of the State and redeem Italy. They remained servants; he became master of them and of Italy.

The movement entered party politics in 1921 at a time of grave civil disorder and ineffectual government. In the following year a general strike was declared and Mussolini ordered columns of the Fascisti to march on Rome. He travelled by railway sleeping-car. The king refused to decree martial law and asked Mussolini to form a cabinet. Action was constitutional enough for a time, but gradually the supreme power passed to the Grand Council. Free institutions were suppressed.

In less than twelve months Mussolini showed that in foreign affairs he was not disposed to ask "By your leave" at a conference table. His high-handed methods revealed that the principles of the League of Nations were not his unless they suited his purpose. Three Italian members of the Greco–Albanian Boundary Commission holding meetings in Corfu were murdered. The capital of the island was bombarded and occupied by Italian troops, although there was no proof that the assassins were Greeks. It cost Greece an indemnity of 50 million lire to bring about evacuation.

RECLAIMING 200,000 ACRES OF FEVER-RIDDEN SWAMP

One of the giant excavators which helped to drain the pestilential swamps in Italy and transform bogs into arable soil. Several towns, including Littoria and Sabaudia, have also been built on the land reclaimed from the marshes. The first attempt was made in 442 B.C.

When Dr. Engelbert Dollfuss, the Austrian Federal Chancellor, was murdered by Nazi terrorists in Vienna in 1934, Mussolini sent 40,000 men and an air force to the Brenner Pass to warn Hitler that he would tolerate no interference with the independence of Austria. Four years later the Duce took no action when the Germans seized the country. One surmises that the price of his silence was help to make the Mediterranean a Roman lake.

Italy Conquers Abyssinia

Even then he was brooding over the projected seizure of Abyssinia. It was carried out with the loss, so it is said, of no more than 2,313 soldiers, and at a cost of 120 million pounds. When the decree of annexation was proclaimed in 1936 and Victor Emmanuel III assumed the title of Emperor of Abyssinia, the Chamber of Deputies agreed that a bronze tablet should be put up with this inscription: "On May 9, in the fourteenth year of Fascism, Benito Mussolini founded the Empire."

It is only reasonable to assume that it was in pursuance of his ambition to establish paramount influence in the Mediterranean that he and Hitler, having formed what was known as the Rome–Berlin axis, went to the help of General Francisco Franco during his rebellion against the Spanish republic. The Spanish civil war which followed lasted from July, 1936 to February, 1939, in which month Franco was recognized by Great Britain.

Albania, with an army of 12,000 men—one for each square mile of territory—was invaded by Italy in April, 1939, with the approval of Germany. The conquest not only strengthened Mussolini's control over the Adriatic but also gravely menaced Yugoslavia, Greece, Rumania and Turkey.

"Democracy," according to Mussolini, "is the form of government which gives or tries to give the people the illusion that they are sovereign," and he has suggested that this will be the century of universal Fascism. Corporations representing both employers and employed control the economic life of the country. They are, according to their originator, the instruments "which, under the aegis of the State, discipline the productive forces with a view to the development of the wealth, of the political power, and of the well-being of the Italian people." What they decide is submitted to the National Council of Corporation for approval. Mussolini is president of

this body and also Minister of Corporations. He is therefore the court of last resort.

Material progress has been made under the authoritarian régime. Large tracts of land that harboured mosquitoes and malaria have been reclaimed and towns built on sites that were formerly pestilential swamps. A great deal of social work, such as maternity aid and the organizing of child welfare centres, has been done, sport has been fostered, and education considerably improved, although all subjects are given a Fascist bias if capable of such treatment.

One of the reasons why Turkey entered into the war of 1914-18 was "to free the Mohammedan world from the power of the unbeliever and to give independence to the followers of Mohammed." When the conflict was over she had ceased to be an empire. The remaining vestige of her once mighty power was Anatolia, or Asia Minor, for the Allies controlled Constantinople and the Dardanelles, and Syria, Palestine and Mesopotamia had been conquered by force of arms. The landing of Greek soldiers in Smyrna (Izmir) in 1919, with the approval of Great Britain and France, aroused the ire of the Turks, and of Mustapha Kemal in particular. Disregarding the Sultan, whom he loathed with a consuming hatred, the general who had prevented the capture of the Gallipoli peninsula set up a government at Angora, now Ankara, and defied the world.

Turkey Comes to Life

It was anything but a walk-over for Kemal, but he fought and won. Smyrna was burned to the ground, and Turkey recognized as an independent sovereign state by the subsequent Treaty of Lausanne, signed in 1923. In Europe she recovered some 9,500 square miles of territory. The Sultan was deposed, and Kemal elected president of the republic by the People's Party which he had brought into being. The Caliphate was abolished. The name Atatürk, or Chief Turk, was conferred on Kemal by the Grand National Assembly.

The high cheek-boned, thin-lipped, hard-drinking dictator carried out the process of westernization with the ruthlessness of Peter the Great, but with more success. He compelled his followers to adopt the European calendar, the Latin alphabet, the metric system; abolished the veil for women and the fez for men; gave the country a new civil code and transformed Ankara; opened opportunities to women never enjoyed by them before. "History will say of me," he remarked before he died in 1938, "that in spite of being hampered by a lot of rascals, poor Kemal did his best."

The rivalry between Russia and Great Britain in Iran (Persia), for long the subject of jealousy between these two powers, was more or less settled in 1907 by an agreement regarding spheres of influence. Russia secured a privileged position in some 300,000 square miles of the northern part of the country. Great Britain was satisfied with considerably less, including the outlet of the Persian Gulf and the frontier of Baluchistan. The defence of India and the control of the oilfields were the main objects.

In 1909 the Anglo–Persian Oil Company was formed, and in 1914 every citizen of the British Empire became a shareholder by reason of the Government's financial holdings in it. The oilfield in question covers nearly 500,000 square miles, or more than three-quarters of the total area of the country. Five years later an Anglo–Persian treaty was signed that further strengthened British interests.

In 1925, the Kajâi dynasty, which came to the throne in 1795, was dismissed. The King of Kings, after having spent years in pursuit of pleasure in Paris and elsewhere beyond the confines of his kingdom, was told that his continued absence must be permanent. Riza Khan Pahlevi, once a private soldier, donned the crown of Darius. Four years before, as a senior officer of the Cossack Division, he had captured Teheran, the capital, and had assumed the rôles of Commander-in-Chief and Prime Minister. The rich and lawless feudal chiefs were deprived of their power, religious toleration was fostered, and nationals were placed in control of the various civil services, hitherto under

FROM CHURCH TO MOSQUE AND FROM MOSQUE TO MUSEUM

Among the many reforms introduced by Kemal Atatürk, the first President of the Turkish Republic, were the adoption of the European calendar, the Latin alphabet, the metric system, and the abolition of the veil for women and the fez for men. On his instructions many of the mosaics in Santa Sophia at Istanbul (Constantinople), built as a Christian Church and converted by the conquering Turks who took the city in 1453 into a Mohammedan mosque, were uncovered, and the building maintained as a museum of Byzantine art.

foreign advisers. The construction of a railway from the Persian Gulf to the Caspian Sea was begun. The official name of the country is Iran, "the land of the Aryans."

Among the results of the Washington Conference of 1921–22 was the decision that a number of naval vessels should be scrapped, and that the total tonnage of capital ships should be restricted to 525,000 each for the British Empire and the United States, and 315,000 for Japan. Another attempt to limit the power of Mars was made by the Geneva Disarmament Conference, which first met in 1932. It should have been called the Geneva Disagreement Conference, for after discussing and haggling for nearly three years it adjourned indefinitely. The president, Mr. Arthur Henderson, received a Nobel Prize, but the failure of the nations to arrive at an understanding broke his heart.

Japan announced that she intended to build a navy as powerful as that of any other Power. She had already gone some way to becoming overlord of Asia and to enforce a kind of Monroe Doctrine of the Far East. In 1931 her soldiers had seized Manchuria in flagrant violation of her agreement to respect China's integrity. Three years later a puppet ruler was enthroned there in the person of Henry Pu Yi, who enjoyed the distinction of having been Emperor of China from 1909 until the country became a republic in 1912, and again for a fortnight following a rising in 1917. The new monarch, whose subjects numbered over 32,240,000, was named Kang Teh, literally "tranquillity" and "virtue," the new state Manchukuo, and Changchun, selected as the chief city, became Hsinking, which means New Capital.

Japan takes to Imperialism

Forty-two nations unhesitatingly condemned Japan's action in Manchuria. She left the League, but refused to surrender the mandated territories of the Marianne, Caroline and Marshall Islands in the Pacific, her "first line of marine defence" according to Admiral Suyetsugu.

The Germany of the Far East pushed her aggressive way into China proper, then the plaything of quarrelling and ambitious warlords. It caused the Chinese to rally round Chiang Kai-shek and to offer something approaching a unified resistance. Japan flooded the world with cheap goods —cotton that undercut Lancashire, bicycles at less than one pound each, fountain pens at threepence—the products of cheap labour. At one big cotton-spinning mill at Osaka, the chief manufacturing centre, girls between the ages of thirteen and twenty contract for five years to live, work and sleep in the factory at less than one penny an hour for a nine-hour day. Such is the way of Japan's industrial revolution.

Great Slump in America

In 1933, the year of Japan's withdrawal from the League, Franklin Delano Roosevelt became President of the United States. The country had plunged from the peak of prosperity into the abyss of depression. Hundreds of banks had closed their doors, millions of people were out of work, and many of them were homeless. Roosevelt proposed to mobilize for human needs. "We must face our responsibility for human service, broader in conception, deeper in sympathy and understanding."

With dogged courage and a smile, the president sought to help the "forgotten man" of the masses and bring about a better social order. Under the National Recovery Administration production and distribution, wages and hours of labour were regulated. In one year the cost of public works to assist the unemployed was assessed at 800 million pounds. Roosevelt's New Deal, notes Mr. H. G. Wells, "involves such collective controls of the national business that it would be absurd to call it anything but socialism, were it not for a prejudice lingering on from the old individualist days against that word."

Despite the noisy opposition of isolationists, a Neutrality Bill enabling Americans to sell munitions to the belligerents in the second World War became law in 1939. This was benevolent neutrality in that Germany, by reason of the British blockade, was unable to send transport, the use of United States vessels being forbidden.

In the quiet cemetery of the little Normandy village of Cocherel is a slab of roughly hewn stone. It bears the name of Aristide Briand, twenty-five times a minister of France. Briand's most valued possession was a book containing signatures of over three million folk, the silent applause of those who appreciated his efforts for peace and conciliation. As co-author of the Kellogg-Briand Peace Pact to outlaw war, and protagonist of the idea of a United States of Europe, the scoffers called him a butterfly-chaser and a rainbow-builder. The Pact failed; the U.S.E. is yet untried.

FIGHTING DROUGHT IN AFRICA

Bush women filling empty ostrich eggs with water at a stream. The holes are afterwards covered with dry grass and the eggs put in a safe place for emergence in time of drought. If water is plentiful the eggs are brought out and replenished from time to time.

CHAPTER 22

BREAKING DOWN THE BARRIERS

Living near the poles. England annexes the Cape. Explorers of Africa. Death of Mungo Park. Goldie and Nigeria. Hedin and Stein in Asia. Unconquerable Everest. Algerian pirates. Morocco and the Riffs. Lyautey's work in Africa. Redistributing the Dark Continent. Opening-up of Canada.

MAN'S quest for knowledge and wealth has led him to the icy fastnesses of the poles, the fever-haunted forests of the equator, and the less hazardous intervening spaces. But for this relentless urge, this must-force, he would have perished before the last retreat of the glaciers. Man must be doing something, even if it is no more than making himself a nuisance to his fellows.

The earth's frigid extremities were the last to surrender their secrets. Both were discovered without the refinements that latter-day science has placed at the disposal of explorers. The mystery of millions of years was unveiled, and the endeavour of centuries consummated, when farthest north and remotest south were discovered within a little over two and a half years of each other. Robert Edwin Peary and Roald Amundsen trudged their way to goals now reached in the cockpits of aircraft.

There are possibilities in the Arctic; the Antarctic seems to be a geographical Old Mother Hubbard's cupboard—five million square miles of barrenness. The peoples of Arctic Russia have had culture thrust upon them. Some tribes, for fear of such scourges of civilization as tuberculosis and pneumonia, are allowed by the Soviet Government to continue to eat uncooked food and to live in tents, though they go to school in wooden buildings. Towns are springing up.

Port Igarka, on the lower Yenisei river, a tiny settlement of nondescript shacks in 1930, now numbers 14,000 people. Most of the adult inhabitants are engaged in lumbering, but some are equally busy raising vegetables on indoor farms, often buried deep in snow and stiff with ice. Electricity furnishes light and heat. The wind, sometimes blowing at gale force, supplies power

245

for the motors. Port Igarka is but one of a number of centres under the control of the Northern Sea Route authority.

Russia is intent on developing her Arctic estate. Her attack in 1939 on Petsamo, in the extreme north of Finland, was not unconnected with this ambition.

For months, Ivan Papanin and four companions drifted from the North Pole on an ice-floe that constituted the Soviet polar station, plumbing the depths of the sea, analysing the water, examining its organic life and the flow of its currents. Their devotion was in pursuit of facts for future service.

Had Columbus turned tail and America remained unknown for a generation or two, Africa would doubtless have received the attention that was so liberally bestowed on the New World. Half a dozen years before

THIRTY-SIX YEARS' WORK

This imposing column at Hammerfest, Norway, commemorates the completion of the work of measuring the degrees of the earth's surface. The task, which was begun in 1816, was not completed until 1852.

the Genoese adventurer weighed anchor from Palos, Bartholomew Diaz had discovered the Cape of Storms, now the Cape of Good Hope, and had bundled ashore at different points three wretched black women, charged with the task of taking messages to the legendary Prester John.

Commodore Humphrey Fitzherbert annexed Table Bay for England in 1620. His gift was spurned. The Dutch came later, built a fort, founded a settlement, and sent an expedition to seek a fabled empire that proved as elusive as the mythical Christian hero whose address was no more explicit than "somewhere in Africa." In the flux of events the colony passed to Great Britain, and now, as the Union of South Africa, covers 472,347 square miles of territory.

The Dark Continent, six times larger than Europe, remained true to its sinister name until the nineteenth century, when the "scramble for Africa" took place and explorers began to fill in the map. Even so late as 1891, Henry Morton Stanley complained that "it is time that its lands were explored and exploited for the benefit of civilization." In that year a German periodical caricatured a map of Africa as a grinning human skull.

Seeking the Nile Sources

Blazers of trails in Africa furnish a long Roll of Honour. Early in the list is James Bruce, who made his way across Abyssinia to Gondar, its capital, despite shortage of supplies, torrential rain, intense heat and the suspicions of the natives. From Gondar he set out in 1770 to find the source of the Nile. He came across it, as he fondly believed, at Geesh.

Bruce received a rude awakening. It was proved that he had discovered the source of the Blue Nile and not of the main stream; moreover that Pedro Paez, a Jesuit missionary, had visited Geesh over a century and a half earlier. When the explorer returned to Europe, many of his stories were so amazing that he was stigmatized as an impostor, but time proved the truth of many of his claims. Within an ace of death on many occasions during his hazardous wanderings, Bruce lost his life by falling down the stairs of his Scottish home.

The passing of Mungo Park, who made two unsuccessful attempts to find the source of the Niger, was more in keeping with his adventurous career. He was attacked by natives and drowned in the river of his heart's desire in 1805.

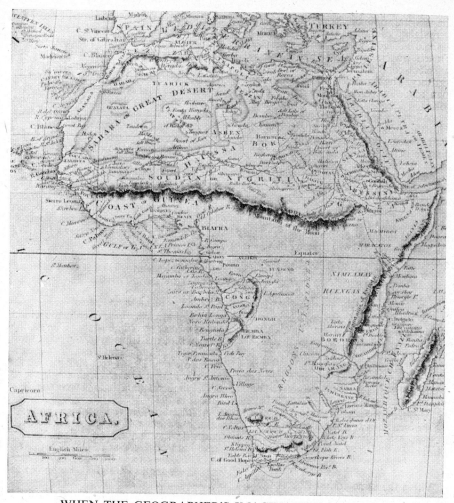

WHEN THE GEOGRAPHER'S IMAGINATION RAN RIOT

A map of Africa published in 1816. It shows the vast extent of the interior then unexplored and various geographic features that existed only in the cartographer's imagination. Notice in particular the great range of completely imaginary mountains that was supposed to extend almost across the whole width of the continent from east to west.

Park's failure was retrieved in 1822 by Alexander Gordon Laing, who also reached Timbuktu, and was murdered as a sequel. The first white man to return alive from the forbidden city was René Auguste Caillié. Disguised as an Egyptian Moslem, he accomplished his purpose, and continuing his dangerous journey across the Sahara, eventually reached Fez and Tangier. Today one may visit the city, which was occupied by the French in 1894, by motor-car.

Floating hulks that did duty as British trading posts were established in Nigeria about 1870. There was fierce competition, a lack of unity and a general tangle of interests and privileges. A young Manxman named George Taubman Goldie discerned that the only means of overcoming the difficulties of the situation was by amalgamating the various concerns. When everything was ready for the formation of the National African Company the Government refused to grant a charter. There was a slump in the imperial idea at the moment.

the general opinion being that colonies were liabilities rather than assets.

Goldie bided his time. The appearance of French traders on the Lower Niger was sufficient confirmation of the value of the territory. The far-seeing and tactful Manxman made overtures to the native chiefs, collected treaties with the avidity of a schoolboy swapping foreign stamps, and with these in his pockets approached the rival traders, who were usually willing to dispose of their interests on the generous terms offered. The coveted charter was obtained in 1885 and retained until 1899, when the British Government took over the administration of the territory. The colony and protectorate of Nigeria was formed in 1914, and with the English portion of the mandated territory of the Cameroons has an area of over 372,670 square miles.

Between 1849 and 1887, less than forty years, explorers gained a stack of information that was a godsend to cartographers, who had hitherto pictured elephants on certain parts of their maps of Africa to cloak ignorance of geographical details. David Livingstone discovered Lakes Ngami, Shirwa, Nyasa and Bangweulu and the Victoria Falls, and when he was lost Stanley discovered him. John Hanning Speke and Sir Richard Burton found Lake Tanganyika, and Speke the Ripon Falls and Victoria Nyanza, covering 26,000 square miles of fresh water. Sir Samuel Baker and his devoted wife were the first white folk to gaze at Albert Nyanza and the turbulent Murchison Falls.

Crossing Australia

Within the same period Robert O'Hara Burke and William John Wills crossed Australia from south to north but died on the return journey, Ernest Giles explored from Fowler's Bay to Perth, and other hardy adventurers investigated the terrain of the great southern continent.

In 1885, the year of General Charles Gordon's death at Khartoum and Great Britain's evacuation of the Sudan, to be reconquered later, Dr. Sven Anders Hedin began the first of a long series of arduous journeys in the interior of unknown Asia. He travelled from Stockholm to unknown Tibet, discovering in the wilderness of the Gobi desert, once an inland sea, a Mongolian city that had been abandoned many centuries before, probably by reason of overwhelming sandstorms. When within five days' march of the sacred city of Lhasa

the Swedish explorer was turned back by a Tibetan guard. Hedin tried another ruse, and was stopped by a formidable band of 500 soldiers, with whom he thought it unwise to argue. "Asia," in the opinion of Hedin, "is to at least as great an extent as America the land of great possibilities, and one can be certain that within a short time events will take place in the heart of Asia that have not been dreamed of."

In innermost Asia Sir Aurel Stein unearthed the buried civilizations of the Taklamakan desert, and thought lightly of a march of 11,000 miles. An expedition led by Georges-Marie Haardt made its way from Beirut to Peking in caterpillar track cars, encountering snow twelve feet deep in crossing the Himalayas and reaching the record altitude for a motor-car of 13,775 feet. Attacked by unfriendly tribes, scorching at 120 deg. in the shade and shivering at 29 deg. below zero, Haardt died after an arduous journey of 7,500 miles.

Attacks on Everest

Several attempts have been made within living memory to climb Mount Everest, the monarch of the Himalayas, the great rampart between India and Tibet. The mountain, towering 29,141 feet above sea-level and the loftiest in the world, continues to defy climbers, though an aeroplane flew over it in 1933.

Animals on Everest at high altitudes furnish evidence of the persistence of life under the most adverse conditions. Spiders have been observed at 22,000 feet, finches at 21,000, the mouse-hare at 20,100, sheep at 20,000, moths at 18,000, butterflies at 17,000, beetles at 16,500 and wingless grasshoppers at 10,000. Plants struggle hard for existence, but willows, gentians, primulas and blue poppies flourish despite exposure to blustering wind and heavy snow.

The first white man to gaze on Kilimanjaro, the tallest mountain in Africa although a dwarf of 19,321 feet compared to Everest, was Johannes Rebmann in 1848. It was not until 1889 that the first ascent was made, after the mountain had been included in German East Africa by what Dr. Robert Brown refers to as "a deliberate deflection of the straight boundary line." It is now in Tanganyika territory.

One reason why no philosophy of history is entirely satisfying is because so many apparently trivial incidents have led to big events. The case of the little Dauphin and the stuffy carriage has been cited. Had the

IN THE LAND OF A THOUSAND MONASTERIES

A Tibetan priest, or Lama, robed to take part in a religious dance. The mask is intended to scare everything that is evil. The Potala, the residence of the Dalai Lama, spiritual ruler of Tibet, is at once monastery, palace and fortress. The Jo-Kang, in the heart of Lhasa, contains a golden statue of the Buddha seated on a throne covered with jewels and wearing a crown in which is a flawless turquoise reputed to be the largest in the world.

PYGMIES OF THE CONGO

The great Ituri forest in the Belgian Congo is the home of the pygmies. The height of the old man being measured is 4 ft. 6 in.

Archduke Ferdinand's chauffeur not taken the wrong turning at Sarajevo, the heir apparent of Austria would probably have escaped assassination and the world been spared the fiery furnace of 1914–18 and its sequel of 1939. The French colonial empire in North Africa had its genesis in a fit of temper. The Dey of Algiers struck the French consul-general in the face with a fly-flap. The act cost him his territory.

Once the grim and sinister strongholds of the bloodthirsty Barbary pirates, the ports of Algeria now shelter ships that load iron, lead, copper and phosphate. Thousands of acres of vines, cork forests and plantations of date palms flourish. Hundreds of towns and villages have been built, dams for irrigation and hydraulic power constructed, swamps drained, and strips of desert redeemed. Many of the ancient tracks along which heavily burdened camels and asses made their laboured passage have been converted into roads and railways.

Algeria was one of the most important granaries of ancient Rome, supplying nearly 350,000 tons of corn in a good harvest. Now wheat, barley and oats grow anew. The French freedom from colour prejudice has had much to do with the success of the administration.

Morocco, the Mauretania of earlier times, is divided into three spheres of influence: the small international zone of Tangier, which Spain "took over" in 1940, the larger Spanish zone, and the French protectorate of 200,000 square miles. It was in the Spanish zone that Abd-el-Krim in 1921 claimed the right to establish an independent Riff State. The affair is cited here because similar problems are likely to arise in the future, and also because it throws a ray of half-diffused light on the workings of the native mind, which is apt to appreciate the sinister side of western culture while disregarding the dark side of its own.

Riff Leader on Civilization

"We believed in European civilization before the World War began in 1914," Abd-el-Krim declared, "but we can no longer respect that civilization, with its rage for destruction, its poison gases, bombardment of undefended towns and liquid fire. It is not the possession of a civilization such as that which can entitle one nation to say that because a neighbouring people has not evolved quite as far as it has, it can intervene in its internal affairs and dominate it by force."

A perfectly logical statement, but the defence must also have its say. Thousands of Spanish men, women and children were butchered by the turbulent tribesmen, who in 1925 also attacked the French. Spain and France then made common cause, and in the following year Abd-el-Krim surrendered after many of his followers had deserted his cause.

Of Marshal Lyautey it was said that he subordinated the use of war to the work of peace. He conquered the country, and during the war of 1914-18 held it with no more than a skeleton of an army. Commanded to evacuate the interior and withdraw his handful of soldiers towards the coast, he refused to do so and maintained perfect order. Through fear? On the contrary; through sympathy. When, at the beginning of his administration, rebels attacked Fez, Lyautey created a special medical service to tend the enemy's sick and wounded. Years later, when he was ill, special prayers were said for the great proconsul in every mosque. Lyautey set about the development of the territory, and a turbulent, bandit-ridden country was re-generated and transformed.

Mussolini, intent on making a new Roman Empire in Africa, was less successful with his colonial projects than other Powers. Libya, annexed in 1912 after a short war with Turkey and sandwiched between French colonial Africa and Egypt, is mostly gravel desert that scorches under a glaring sun. Once cereals grew plentifully, and an attempt was made to restore its ancient fertility. Following the traditions of their great Roman predecessors, the Italians constructed a coastal highway that ran 1,250 miles from the frontier of Tunisia to that of Egypt. Peasants and smallholders were sent from Italy en masse: in 1938, on the seventeenth anniversary of the Fascist march on Rome, nearly 20,000 embarked at Italian ports to begin life anew as colonists in the old Roman provinces of Tripoli and Cyrenaica, into which Libya's 636,000 square miles are divided.

In 1938 Eritrea, Abyssinia and Italian Somaliland became Italian East Africa.

Eritrea, the oldest colony, of little value on account of its climate, was the scene of the unflagging zeal of Prince Luigi, Duke of the Abruzzi, who explored the headwaters of the Webi-Shebeli and found at one place a stupendous gorge several miles wide and from three-quarters of a mile to one mile deep. It was inhabited entirely by monkeys.

About 43,000 square miles of the British province of Jubaland, forming part of Kenya, was handed over to Italy in 1925 in fulfilment of the Treaty of London, signed ten years before, that she should have equitable compensation if Great Britain and France gained territory in Africa as a result of the war of 1914-18, into which Italy had not then entered.

Scarcely more than two generations ago the Belgian Congo was known in Great Britain as Murderland. It was primarily associated with Leopold II of Belgium, a greedy and cynical business man, who was execrated because of the atrocities perpetrated on the wretched natives by a system of forced labour.

The territory, some 900,000 square miles

GROTESQUE GODS OF THE CHASE

These curious fetishes, half man and half beast, represent the idea of a primitive tribe in the Belgian Congo regarding the divinities who are supposed to control the chase. Hunters perform dances before these images and offer them portions of the flesh of their prey.

in extent, was transferred to Belgium in 1909. It has now over 25,000 miles of motoring roads, nearly 3,000 miles of railways and regular air services. Today the administration of the Belgian Congo is humane, and the natives are no longer exploited. The Albert National Park of 450,000 acres not only shelters the Pygmies but wild animals which would otherwise have been exterminated.

Alexander Mackenzie, Simon Fraser and David Thompson rendered yeoman service in discovering many of the topographical secrets of Canada. That there was a golden future for the Dominion of tomorrow admitted of no doubt, provided it had adequate transport facilities. The completion of an ocean-to-ocean link was mainly due to the patience, genius and indomitable pluck and energy of George Stephen, later Lord Mount Stephen, and his cousin Donald Smith, afterwards Lord Strathcona. In November 1885 the rails of the Canadian Pacific Railway which had been laid down from the east met those of the west. Now the system controls over 20,000 miles and operates liners and smaller vessels on both the Atlantic and Pacific Oceans as well as the railways.

There can be no last word in human effort until the sole survivor of the race surrenders to the implacable enemy and the miracle of man is no more than a tale that is told. Humanity now shares its triumphs with contrivances of its own making, but the greater includes the less, and the creator is mightier than the created. With increasing wisdom man has learned to multiply his activities, to fashion limbs and muscles of steel that do his bidding, to construct ears and tongues that listen and speak round the world, and to mould eyes that peer into the remote realms of outer space. Thus he breaks down the barriers.

HUMAN ENERGY TRANSFERRED TO STEEL MUSCLES

An electric crane capable of lifting a large type Canadian locomotive and transferring it from one side of the erecting shop to the other. The two great land transport systems of the Dominion are the Canadian Pacific Railway and Canadian National Railways. An ocean-to-ocean track across the American continent was completed by the former in 1885.

CHAPTER 23

PIONEERS OF MODERN THOUGHT

Origins of German state-worship. Gobineau's race theory. Carlyle and " Great Men." Prussian glorification of war. Optimism in Victorian literature. Heralds of world planning. A philosopher's plea for a democracy of trained minds.

THE proof of the pudding is not in the eating, as the proverb has it, but in the digestion. Vicious theories are not necessarily unpalatable, though their after-effects may be acutely distressing to the body politic. A typical instance is the doctrine that might is right and that necessity knows no law—which are in effect just two ways of expressing the same thing.

" God's Chosen People "

The assertion is as old as civilization; its practical application almost as ancient. Yet it was not until the twentieth century, when humanitarianism was beginning to flower, that the belief was backed by so considerable a body of public opinion that it became the everyday philosophy of a great European nation. " Remember the German people are the chosen of God," said Kaiser William II; "on me, as German Emperor, the spirit of God has descended."

A consequence of this code of morality and of the arrogance associated with it was the first World War. Theobald von Bethmann-Hollweg, Imperial Chancellor, explaining to the Reichstag why German troops had invaded Belgium, said: "We are now in a state of necessity, and necessity knows no law. We are compelled to override the just protest of the Luxemburg and Belgian Governments. The wrong—I speak openly—that we are committing we will endeavour to make good as soon as our military goal has been reached. Anybody who is threatened, as we are threatened, and is fighting for his highest possessions, can have only one thought—how he is to hack his way through." The doctrine had not then been pushed to its logical extremity. It remained for Hitler and his colleagues to dragoon the whole nation into the belief and to make it a complete war machine.

Bethmann-Hollweg's remarks had about them something of an apologetic nature. They suggested that he was just a little ashamed of himself and of his country and was acting against the dictates of his conscience. The protests of the neutrals were "just"; the invasion of their countries was definitely "wrong." Nevertheless they embodied the Prussian philosophy that the end justifies the means. "I begin by taking," said Frederick the Great. "I can always find pedants to justify my rights afterwards." "Who minds or keeps guarantees in this age?" avowed the same highwayman.

Now see how Hitler intensified this doctrine of brutality in *Mein Kampf.* "Nobody can doubt that this world will one day be the scene of dreadful struggles for existence on the part of mankind. In the end the instinct of self-preservation alone will triumph. Before its consuming fire this so-called humanitarianism, which connotes only a mixture of fatuous timidity and conceit, will melt away like snow under the March sunshine. Man has become great in perpetual struggle. In perpetual peace he will go to destruction." And again he writes: "In might alone lies right."

Heine, Soldier of Liberation

The divinity of the German race was no new theme. Heinrich Heine, a Jew born in Hamburg in 1797, poet, satirist and journalist, who described himself as "a brave soldier in the war of liberation of humanity," foresaw the consequence of the assumption. An admirer of Napoleon because he had given the Jews more freedom than they had hitherto enjoyed, he left Germany when the petty sovereigns and princelings began to break their promises after the fall of the Emperor of the French. "Paris is the new Jerusalem," he clarioned, and in the year following the July Revolution of 1830 he crossed the Rhine, "the Jordan which divides the consecrated land of freedom from the land of the Philistines."

With prophetic insight Heine wrote of the ideology that was to be brought to fruition by the Nazis: "I had the opportunity of admiring the precision with which my friends the 'ancient Teutons' prepared the lists of those who would be proscribed by them as soon as they arrived in power. Any one who was descended, even seven

EMBLEMS OF THE DOCTRINE THAT MIGHT IS RIGHT

Count von Bethmann-Hollweg, Imperial Chancellor, excused the invasion of Belgium by Germany at the beginning of the first World War by stating that " necessity knows no law." It remained for Adolf Hitler and his fellow adventurers to dragoon the whole people into the belief that might is right, and to make the nation a complete war machine.

generations back, from a Frenchman, a Jew, or a Slav, was to be condemned to exile. Anybody who had ever written anything against Jahn or the absurdities of the old Germans might expect the death penalty, carried out, of course, with the axe and not by that French invention, the guillotine."

Heine diagnosed the mental make-up of the Germans with almost uncanny insight. "Christianity," he wrote, "has to a certain extent softened the brutal and warlike ardour of the Germans, but it has never been able to destroy it entirely. A day will come when the Cross, that talisman which still holds the nation in bondage, will be broken, and then the ferocity of the old fighters will once more break out and the frenetical exultation of the Berserkers will flow over, that exaltation which the Nordic

poets are even today chanting in their songs. Alas, the day will come when Thor will arise, brandishing his gigantic hammer, and demolish the Gothic cathedrals. On that day, when you hear this tremendous noise and tumult, be on your guard, our dear French neighbours, and do not interfere, for it may cost you dearly. Do not laugh at the advice of a fantastic dreamer.

"Whatever happens in Germany, whether a royal prince of Prussia or a German doctor becomes dictator, be always armed, our French neighbours, remain quietly at your post, weapons in hand. I harbour only friendly sentiments for you, and I was frightened the other day when your ministers were planning the disarmament of France. Among the joyous divinities on Olympus and feasting on nectar and ambrosia there is one goddess who always walks about armed in the midst of the merry crowd, helmet on head and lance in hand. She is the goddess of wisdom."

The alleged racial supremacy of the Germans was expounded by a French nobleman, Alexandre de Gobineau, who published his *Inequality of the Human Races* in 1853 and 1855. Superiority was retained by pure blood, and the Nordic races were undoubtedly the finest representatives of *homo sapiens*. The theory was developed later by Houston Stewart Chamberlain, an Englishman who married Richard Wagner's daughter.

"Nothing," says this apostle of Teutonism, "is so convincing as the consciousness of the possession of race. The man who belongs to a distinct, pure race never loses the sense of it. The guardian angel of his lineage is ever at his side, supporting him where he loses his foothold, warning him like the Socratic dæmon where he is in danger of going astray, compelling obedience, and forcing him to undertakings which, deeming them impossible, he would never have dared to attempt."

First published in 1899 in German, Chamberlain's *Foundations of the Nineteenth Century* was widely read in influential circles, perhaps because it attracted the favourable attention of the Emperor William II. Regarding history as "that past which still lives actively in the consciousness of man and helps to mould him," Chamberlain taught that the story of mankind resolved itself into a struggle for supremacy between the Teutonic and Semitic races, and that it was the mission of the Germans to dominate all others.

It is rather curious that a trinity of foreigners helped to mould the belief that the Germans were so immensely important in shaping the destiny of the human race. To the two writers already cited has to be added a third, Thomas Carlyle. For fourteen years, aided by an unpaid Bavarian who dug out dry-as-dust documents, he toiled and moiled erecting a voluminous literary monument to Frederick the Great, who has been characterized by a scholar of opposite opinion to Carlyle as "the human embodiment of might without right."

The sage of Chelsea, or of Ecclefechan if you happen to be a Scotsman, believed in the gospel of force, and always held the man of action in highest regard. He maintained with passionate fervour that "Universal history, the history of what man has accomplished in this world, is at bottom the history of the great men who have worked here." He expounded this belief in a series of lectures entitled *On Heroes, Heroworship and the Heroic in History*, which was first printed in 1841. His sentences teem with ungainly Germanisms. It was not

MAKING THE YOUTH OF ITALY WAR-MINDED

Under the Mussolini régime hundreds of thousands of Italian boys between eight and eighteen years of age went through military drill. They were called the Balilla, the nickname of a youth who, in 1746, hurled a stone at an Austrian patrol and started an uprising that drove the Austrians from Genoa and Liguria. The various sections were under the command of Fascist officers. There was also an organization of a similar type for training girls.

without a certain significance that while Carlyle declined the Grand Cross of the Bath, he accepted the Prussian Order Pour le Mérite offered through Bismarck, and that the German Emperor sent a wreath to be placed on the grave at Ecclefechan on the centenary of Carlyle's birth.

"Find me the true *Köning*, king, or able-man, and he *has* a divine right over me." The purport of that single sentence has been worth many army corps to Hitler and Mussolini, for whereas Carlyle is almost, if not quite, as dead as the dodo in Britain, he has had a mighty resurrection in Germany and Italy. He is also one of the most widely known and studied English writers in Japan.

Great Men in History

There is much to be said for the Great Man theory of history, and the belief that the hour makes the man has as many up-holders as that the man makes the hour. Perhaps it is something of each. The exact shade of meaning of the adjective "great" also comes into the question. It cannot be denied to Jesus, James Watt and Napoleon, all great men in a very varying sense.

It must be admitted that an outstanding individual, good or evil, is usually conspicu-ous in connexion with outstanding events. These leaders Sir Charles Oman terms "cataclysmic personalities," and adds that they are strewn at intervals along the course of history, which they deflected in ways that could not have been foreseen. The same eminent authority submits that "to believe in the 'inevitable logic of events' is as dangerous as to leave things to luck. Do not believe in determinism," in other words, the doctrine that man's will is not free, and that our actions are determined by our previous history or causes outside our-selves. "History," said Lord Tweedsmuir, "is full of pregnant trifles."

Hero-worship is not confined to the rank and file. Earthly gods, beneficent or other-wise, have their graven images. The Nazi leaders who were primarily responsible for the second World War had their idols. Hitler was a fervent admirer of Frederick the Great. Goering's adoration was divided. He had a triad of celebrities deemed worthy of devotion, including the same cynical King of Prussia, the elder von Moltke, and Napoleon, each a militant maker of misery and none too scrupulous.

The double preference for Frederick the Great is not surprising. He made war a trade, and helped himself liberally to other people's possessions, including a slice of Poland, thus setting a precedent. The crafty monarch, who loved only his dogs, was referred to in German newspapers as "the Führer's illustrious predecessor."

In three of his dislikes Hitler emulated both Frederick and Napoleon. He hated tobacco, heavy eating and drinking. In 1924, when he began *Mein Kampf*, he had his hair brushed back; later he saw fit to let a tuft fall over his forehead as did Napoleon, who also started writing in prison, though he earned no extravagant royalties.

Napoleon also was a fervent admirer of Frederick, whose tomb at Potsdam he visited. As a memento he took his hero's sword and sent it to Paris for safe keeping in the Invalides. Incidentally he paid a back-handed compliment to the bandit king's troops. "I always admired Frederick II," he remarked, "but I admire him twice as much since I have seen what kind of men they were with which he resisted Austrians, French and Russians."

When Friedrich Ebert, the sometime saddler, was President of the German Re-public, a film featuring Frederick's career, under the title *Fridericus Rex*, was shown in Berlin. It drew such frenzied crowds that police reserves had to be called out to keep would-be patrons from storming the box-office. At Leipzig a short play called *The School of the World*, written by Frederick, was also an astonishing success. Hitler noted these things and profited by them. In 1940 one of the slogans of the Nazi Party was: "Remember Frederick the Great!"

Glorifying the German State

G. W. F. Hegel, in contradiction to Kant, who sought perpetual peace, taught that the State was everything and the individual nothing, and that "the conflicts arising between the interests of several States, each an absolute power, not only necessitate but justify wars, States being above treaties when their respective interests are at stake." The highest manifestation of his "World Spirit" was the German nation.

Heinrich von Treitschke, whose *History of Germany in the Nineteenth Century* had a strong anti-British bias, drilled into his devotees that "It has always been the weary, spiritless, and exhausted ages which have played with the dream of perpetual peace." According to him: "The State is the highest thing in the external society of man: above it there is nothing at all in the history of the world." Moreover, "one must know

IN THE PALACE WHICH FREDERICK CALLED "FREE FROM CARE"
Frederick the Great and Voltaire discussing affairs at the Potsdam palace of Sans Souci.
"I soon felt attracted to him," wrote the French philosopher, "the more that he was a king
—always a very attractive circumstance to human weakness. In general, it is we literary
people who flatter kings, while this one applauded me from tip to toe."

how to break laws when the good of the State requires it."

His disciple Friedrich von Bernhardi maintained the thesis in his *Germany and the Next War*, published in 1912, admittedly written to "strengthen the national purpose." He glorified conflict, believing with Nietzsche that "war and courage have achieved more great things than the love of your neighbour."

Bernhardi declaimed that Providence had set great tasks before the Germans "as the greatest civilized people known to history." It was in this book that he insisted that war was "a biological necessity of the first importance, a regulative element in the life of mankind which cannot be dispensed with, since without it an unhealthy development will follow, which excludes every advancement of the race, and therefore all real civilization . . . The inevitableness, idealism, and blessing of war, as an indispensable and stimulating law of development, must be repeatedly emphasized."

In Bernhardi's opinion history confirmed the view "that wars which have been deliberately provoked by far-seeing statesmen have had the happiest results." All of which had been summed up in a sentence by Luther, who asserted that war "is a business, divine in itself, and as needful and necessary to the world as eating or drinking, or any other work."

Friedrich Nietzsche's conceptions of the Superman and the Will to Power also played important parts in the formation of the spiritual life of Germany. His philosophy of aristocracy and exclusiveness, which he shared with Goethe, made a special appeal to the Prussians, despite his hatred of all things German. Pity and humility were qualities of the weak, whom he called slaves. It was only by becoming hard that men strong in intellect, will and physique could be raised. Christianity, democracy, equality, socialism and what he termed herd-morality were anathema to him.

Nietzsche prophesied that the twentieth century would witness wars for the dominion of the world. "What means life?" he asks, and answers: "To thrust away from us everything that wants to die; to be cruel and inexorable towards everything that grows old and weak; to be murderers all the time." According to him each age and race develops a conscience to suit its own requirements; there is no such thing as a fixed and permanent morality.

A book which had considerable influence on modern German youth was Oswald Spengler's *Decline of the West*, the first volume of which was published in 1918 and the second in 1922. Only by racial strength could a better world come into being. Every culture has its spring, summer, autumn and winter. The Western or Faustian culture grew up in the German forests. Man is a beast of prey. War is the creator of all great things. Cæsarism is the last stage of civilization. In *Man and Technics*, which was a summary of his philosophy, he held that the Western nations had made an insuperable blunder in spreading their technical knowledge in the Far East and elsewhere.

When, after thirty-six years of thought, ill health and drudgery, Herbert Spencer dictated the last words of his *System of Synthetic Philosophy*, he said: "I have finished the task I have lived for." That task was to formulate "a general theory of evolution as exhibited through all orders of existence." To him we owe the phrase "the survival of the fittest," which Darwin accepted as better than his own "natural selection." In his vast and rambling work he foresaw the passing of the military stage of existence and the dawn of a constructive rather than a destructive epoch. He held that "the ultimate development of the ideal man is logically certain." Yet in 1893 Spencer admitted that a wave of barbarism was approaching. "I have for a long time past," he wrote, "seen the inevitableness of the tremendous disasters that are coming."

Poets of Progress

Carlyle preached the gospel of labour in prose, his contemporary Robert Browning in poetry, both in a craggy diction not too readily understood. Tennyson wrote in melodious verse, but whereas Browning was a sturdy optimist, the faith of the Poet Laureate was tinged by uncertainty. He believed that "There lives more faith in honest doubt . . . than in half the creeds," yet the line "I doubt not through the ages one unceasing purpose runs" would suggest that he held to the inevitability of progress.

Both Algernon Charles Swinburne, one of the most famous of lyrical poets, and George Meredith, poet and novelist,

rejected Christianity. The philosophy of Thomas Hardy, called the last of the great Victorians, was tinged with pessimism; with what Meredith called a "twilight view of life." He wrote as chief mourner for humanity. To Hardy the universe was profoundly indifferent to man. Tragedy was humanity's lot from cradle to coffin. The immanent Will worked blindly. Men and women were but cogs in the mechanism of Nature, of which he was a superb portrayer.

Hardy certainly did not agree with Browning that "God's in His heaven— All's right with the world!" He believed in the potential nobility of man, despite the dice being loaded against him. In Browning the children of earth suffer for a purpose; in Hardy there is no apparent purpose but a very obvious irony.

Novelist Looks at Politics

Meredith believed that the universe ultimately makes for good. Perhaps his guiding philosophy may be summed up in the quotation from his *Vittoria*, dealing with the Italian revolt against Austria in 1848-49, which is on his tombstone:

> Life is but a little holding
> Sent to do a mighty labour.

One of Meredith's excursions into politics may be cited here as affording an interesting light on subsequent happenings. It was written in 1903, when the Emperor William II was dreaming of a mighty battle-fleet and a world empire: "The trident must be in our fist." Meredith evidently thought that the Kaiser's subjects would be unable and unwilling to stand the strain. He did not fully appreciate the bloated nature of Pan-Germanism.

"We should be grateful to the Germans," declared Meredith, "for their crusty candour in telling us of their designs upon us. They stir a somnolent people, and, without stooping to regard them as enemies, we can accept them as urgently stimulating rivals, whose aim is to be the first of the world Powers, chiefly at our expense."

John Ruskin, of the same distinguished Victorian company, touched on many phases of life. Art, economics, science, politics, religion, social reform, the holiness of beauty, the tyranny of oppression, the abuse of wealth, the destruction of loveliness by industrialism, and much else were prey to his facile pen. To Ruskin's inspiration the pioneers of garden cities and suburbs owed a great deal. Much subsequent legislation followed the principles pu

HITLER SPEAKS IN THE MUNICH BEER CELLAR

The annual meeting in the beer cellar on November 8 celebrated the anniversary of the unsuccessful Putsch in 1923, the beginning of Hitler's rise in the Nazi Party. An important part of Nazi propaganda was the exploitation, with spectacular theatrical effects, of the sentimental appeal of Hitler's early struggles. In 1941, when the R.A.F. bombed Munich, they scored a hit on the beer cellar, it is said only a short while after Hitler had left it.

SOUGHT PERPETUAL PEACE

Immanuel Kant (1724-1804), who believed in the reality of man's moral freedom. Criticism and reverence, it has been well said, were the two poles of his philosophy.

forward in *Unto this Last.* The organization of labour, old age pensions, and the provision of decent homes for the working classes were mooted by him in a series of magazine articles. They had to be brought to an end hurriedly because the ideas were too advanced for the readers.

Another remarkable man who worshipped at the shrine of Art, and through her sought to make human conditions more tolerable, was William Morris. During his volcanic life, which lasted from 1834 to 1896, he was poet, architect, artist, weaver, dyer, decorator, upholsterer, carpenter, printer, bookbinder and socialist. A wholehearted admirer of the crafts and guilds of the Middle Ages, he sought to revive them. He wanted "a system of co-operation where there shall be no masters or slaves, but where every one will live and work jollily together as neighbours and comrades for the equal good of all."

Delighting in paradox, George Bernard Shaw tilted his lance at many an accepted convention. Often prancing in cap and bells, he sometimes castigated society with a slapstick and sometimes with an axe. No literary man better appreciated the significant but important truth that the British people hate to face unpleasant facts, which he proceeded to bring to their attention in a

way that could not be dodged. Shaw mocked at pomp and circumstance and the worship of "the thing." As he saw him, modern man "instead of pursuing a free activity which he understands, and carrying out a process which he can carry out completely is entangled in a monstrous routine, a monstrous machine. He has no control of it whatever."

The works of H. G. Wells form a library in themselves. They range from the fantastic to the factual. The universe was his literary parish. *The World of William Clissold,* declared by the author to be "a novel, that and nothing more," was actually a dissertation on a multiplicity of topics rather than a story. *Tono Bungay* shows that people can be ruined by the possession of too much money as easily as by poverty. *Mr. Britling Sees It Through* will be valued by future generations for its diagnosis of a middle-class Englishman on the Home Front during the first World War. When history was the Cinderella of literature Wells set all the world reading a subject neglected by the general public since Macaulay.

DEIFIED THE STATE

G. W. F. Hegel (1770-1831), German philosopher, taught that the State was everything and the individual nothing. The highest manifestation of what he called the World Spirit was, he declared, the German nation.

HITLER YOUTH IN A MARCH PAST AT NUREMBERG

The Young Folk, the Hitler Youth and the German Girls Federation, all played conspicuous parts in the training of the children and youth of Nazi Germany. A book which had much influence on senior members was Spengler's "Decline of the West," which taught that man is a beast of prey, and only by racial strength could a better world come into being.

In a spate of literary works, Wells urged humanity to surrender its complacency and tidy up its inheritance. If on occasion it seemed that the social theorist led his disciples into a jungle of ideas and left them there, it is only just to add that Wells was a philosopher in a hurry because he regarded the federated government of the world as of prime and urgent importance. He would build a new heaven and a new earth before it became too late to have either.

In his urge for a planned instead of a haphazard world, Wells conceived a great encyclopædia, a World Brain, where facts could be co-ordinated by permanent boards charged with keeping it up-to-date. He would "bring all the scattered and in-effective mental wealth of our world into something like common understanding and into effective reaction upon our political, social and economic life."

That there is much need for closer co-operation in every walk of human activity cannot be gainsaid, but the average man is by no means enamoured of the notion that science is a cure for all ills. He cannot over-look the fact that total war—in which every man, woman and child is potentially a participant—was made possible by science.

Love of power in one form or another is an ingredient of human nature. It may be applied to human betterment or debase-ment. Bertrand Russell, seeking ideal types that, instead of enslaving others, sought to set them free, found them in such leaders as Christ and Buddha, in Pythagoras and Galileo, believing that "It is not ultimately by violence that men are ruled, but by the wisdom of those who appeal to the com-mon desires of mankind, for happiness, for inward peace, and for the understanding of the world in which we have to live."

In his opinion the abuse of power, whether by kings or priests, industrialists or dictators, is only to be overcome by a reorientation of the repressive education which has created both bully and slave. He would have a democracy of trained minds.

CHAPTER 24

PATHWAYS OF THE SKIES

Early myths of flight. A flying monk. First balloon. Steam-driven airships.
Zeppelins and gliders. Atlantic crossed by air. Flying in the first World War.
Altering the character of combat at sea and on land. Air survey and exploration.

MAN'S attempt to conquer the air is so long a story that it goes back to Greek mythology. Icarus, imprisoned by King Minos, made waxen wings and escaped, only to be drowned because he flew so high that the sun melted the material of which they were made.

On the authority of Geoffrey of Monmouth, Bladud was killed while attempting to fly in 852 B.C. William of Malmesbury asserts that Elmer, a monk of the monastery, about the year 1060 fitted wings to his hands and feet, and launching himself from a lofty tower, "was borne upon the air for the space of a furlong; but owing to the violence of the wind, or his own fear, he then fell to the ground and broke both his legs." Clem John, an American bird-man who jumped from aeroplanes and used "wings," crashed to death in 1937.

Roger Bacon, the inquisitive thirteenth-century friar, prophesied with uncanny foresight, but probably not without close reasoning, that flying machines would move "with incalculable speed. . . . For the things which have been done in our days prevent anybody from smiling or being surprised." Nearer our own times Jules Verne conceived in his novels the submarine, the aeroplane, the motor-car, the cinematograph, wireless telephony and television. "Whatever one may have been able to imagine," he wrote in one book, "you may be sure that another man will be able to do."

Montgolfier's Balloon

The first practicable flying machine was the balloon, the invention of Joseph and Jacques Montgolfier, although a balloon is said to have ascended at Peiping (Peking) in the first decade of the fourteenth century. In 1783 the brothers built a globe of linen, 105 feet in circumference, and filled it with smoke and hot air by means of a fire of chopped straw. It ascended to a considerable height, travelled a mile and a half, and came down after an aerial journey lasting ten minutes. A balloon of gummed silk, filled with hydrogen, was next tried. It rose to a height of 3,000 feet, remained afloat nearly an hour, and fell fifteen miles away from the Champ de Mars, Paris, whence it had been released.

A sheep, a cockerel and a duck were the first living balloonists. Their ascent was witnessed by Louis XVI, Queen Marie Antoinette and a crowd of lesser notabilities in 1783. In the same year Jean François de Rozier went up several times in a captive balloon and later in a free balloon. The first balloon released in England made its trial trip from Chelsea in 1783. It was constructed by an Italian, Count Francesco Zambeccari. In 1784 Vincent Lunardi used oars for steering and assisting in the movement of the aircraft, as did Jean Pierre Blanchard about the same time. In these devices we have the germ of the propeller.

Steam-driven Airships

From balloon to airship was an obvious step. Henri Giffard constructed an airship driven by a steam-engine in 1852, and Wolfert and Baumgarten built the first dirigible to be fitted with an internal combustion engine in 1879.

The pioneer Zeppelin, named after its builder, was launched in June 1900, two years after Alberto Santos-Dumont took to the air in a miniature non-rigid dirigible that was 82½ feet long, held 6,354 cubic feet of gas, and was operated by an engine that developed 3½ horse-power. Count Ferdinand Zeppelin's vessel was 420 feet long, was divided into seventeen sections holding 400,000 cubic feet of gas, and carried two sixteen-horse-power Daimler motors. The first airship to be used for passenger service was the *Deutschland*, which in 1910 made a trip of over 300 miles. The *Graf Zeppelin*, built following the first World war, was about 700 feet long and 100 feet wide. It circumnavigated the globe and crossed to South America many times. The framework of *Zeppelin I* was of aluminium, but duralumin, an alloy of aluminium, was used in later types, including the *Hindenburg*, which was destroyed by fire in 1937.

During the first World War the aircraft sponsored by Count Zeppelin raided England fifty-one times.

The initial experiments that led to the heavier-than-air machine were made with box kites and gliders. Among the many pioneers were Captain Le Bris of France, who used a glider in 1855; Otto Lilienthal of Germany, who crashed to death in 1896 after many successful glider flights; and Octave Chanute of the United States, who made over 2,000 trials following his first glide in 1896.

In that year Professor Samuel Pierpont Langley built two model "aerodromes" driven by steam-engines of $1\frac{1}{2}$ horse-power.

and began to build their little four-cylinder engine. Then they bedded it on the lower wing, fashioned two six-bladed propellers, and connected them with the engine shaft by means of chain drivers. The biplane looked a very ramshackle affair. Even when they had proved their case it was five years before they received the recognition and support that were their due.

It may be added as a pathetic postscript that in 1914 Langley's old machine, adjusted and fitted with floats, rose from the Potomac and flew with Glenn Curtis, one of the professor's former pupils, as pilot. Langley had died in 1906.

The internal combustion engine was the

MODERN GODS IN AN EAST INDIES TEMPLE

A strange blend of ancient and modern in a temple on the island of Bali. The native sculptor has sought to represent aeroplanes in flight and scared people below, including a man seeking refuge by climbing a tree, and a cyclist. At the top right of the carving is depicted an imp grinning maliciously at man's dismay as he watches the results of his own achievements.

Both were successful, and the inventor set about constructing a full-sized machine. This he launched from the top of a house-boat on the Potomac river in 1903. It failed to rise and tumbled into the stream.

A little over a week later the first aero-plane to fly by power remained in the air for twelve seconds. The builders were Wilbur and Orville Wright, the date December 17, 1903, the scene Kitty Hawk, North Carolina, U.S.A.

Beginning their experiments in 1896, these young cycle makers and repairers made repeated experiments with gliders before they achieved the type they required

one essential that several men who almost solved the problem lacked. The *Ariel*, projected in 1843 by W. S. Henson and John Stringfellow, seemed to offer such possibilities of success that a Bill was introduced in the British Parliament for the formation of the Aerial Steam Transit Company. A monoplane built by Stringfellow in 1878 flew a distance of 120 feet, and a model triplane constructed by him twenty years later lifted the wire to which it was attached for safety purposes and travelled about 300 feet before it had to land.

Hiram Maxim, the inventor of the Maxim gun, constructed a steam flying machine that for the purpose of experiment ran along a kind of railway track having guide rails that enabled it to rise but not to fly away. In July, 1894, when it was travelling with Maxim and two mechanics at the rate of about forty-five miles an hour, it rose from the safety rails, and after covering some 400 feet was brought to a standstill after damaging one of its two enormous propellers. The fuel employed was naphtha.

The first aviator to design and fly a power-driven aeroplane in Europe was the indefatigable Brazilian investigator Alberto Santos-Dumont. This achievement took place in France in 1906. S. F. Cody, an American inventor employed by the British War Office, made the pioneer flight in an aeroplane in England in 1909, in which year J. T. B. Moore-Brabazon achieved the distinction of becoming the first British-born pilot, and Louis Blériot, a Frenchman, crossed the English Channel in a monoplane. Sighting a number of submarines, Blériot realized the immense possibilities of the machine in future wars. Great Britain's insularity was destroyed.

Ten years later Capt. John Alcock and Lieut. Arthur Whitten Brown succeeded in flying the Atlantic from Newfoundland to Ireland, a distance of 1,960 miles, in sixteen hours twelve minutes. In 1939 an American air-liner carrying twenty-six passengers and a crew of twelve spanned the same ocean in eleven hours thirty-five minutes.

The first World War had much to do with the rapid development of the aeroplane, which played no small part in altering the character of warfare. Aircraft "spotted" for the guns, and from a high altitude observed the passage of submerged submarines, just as they bombed enemy trenches and convoys by flying low. They reported movements of troops, and waged aerial combat with machine guns.

Aeroplanes aided Germany in her rapid conquests of 1939–40. Troops were carried in them and dropped from them by parachutes, and they acted as winged artillery in co-operation with mechanized vehicles.

The seaplane is an aeroplane with floats for taking off and landing in place of wheels. In such a machine Flight Lieut. G. H.

TRAIN, PLANE AND MOTOR-BUS IN FRIENDLY RIVALRY

The Union Limited, the most noted express of South African Railways. It covers the journey from Cape Town to Johannesburg, a distance of 956 miles that includes much mountainous country, in just over 28 hours. The original line, built in 1860, covered only two miles.

BIRDS VERSUS MEN IN FLIGHT

Apart from the balloon, man's first attempts to fly were centred on the mechanical imitation of wings, and much attention was paid to birds and insects as they made their way through the air. None of the many experiments made with apparatus that flapped like wings succeeded, though Otto Lilienthal, the German aviator, used a rigid glider that utilized air currents the shape of which was based on the membranes that enable a bat to fly.

Stainforth, of the Royal Air Force, travelled at the rate of 415·2 miles an hour, the highest speed ever reached by man, bird or beast. The helicopter rises and descends vertically by means of horizontal rotating wings above the engine.

Aircraft are now valuable allies of the explorer and the surveyor. In 1926 Admiral Richard E. Byrd, an American, reached the North Pole by aeroplane, and three years later visited the South Pole by the same means. Roald Amundsen, discoverer of the South Pole, flew over the North Pole in the airship *Norge* in 1926, voyaging from

King's Bay, Spitsbergen, to Teller, Alaska, a distance of 2,700 miles, in 71 hours.

A great deal of survey work in northern Canada and Alaska has been done by aviators. Forests are patrolled by aircraft carrying observers who watch for fire and also fight it, and poison dust is diffused for the purpose of killing harmful caterpillars.

"The conquest of the air," wrote John Galsworthy, "so jubilantly hailed by public opinion, may yet turn out the most sinister event that ever befell us." History, since these words were written, has made its own comment on the shrewd remark.

CHAPTER 25

MAN DISCOVERS HIMSELF

Progress of psychology. Heredity and eugenics. Glands and sunshine. Public health and feeding. Vitamins. Progress in industrial welfare. Education and propaganda.

AFTER thousands of years of striving man has succeeded in bursting many of his bonds asunder. Other shackles, strong as steel, remain in plenty. Some of the swaddling bands of earlier ages still bind him. Fallacies, passed on from generation to generation, continue to cobweb and darken the mind.

Fear of this, that and the other, from policemen to dandelion picking, is instilled in children "for their good" by parents and others. They just pass on the treatment that was meted out to them when they were youngsters, totally unaware of the mischief perpetrated and perpetuated. Frequent scolding, for instance, upsets breathing and is not unconnected with the growth of adenoids in children.

According to Dr. Ernest Jones, the building of character is over at the early age of four. "Nothing that happens after that age," he states, "will change the character, which will show itself in different ways at different times, but fundamentally it will be the same through life as it was at the age of four."

Man Studies Himself

Despite intensive research, the cause of many dire diseases remains undiscovered, setting at nought probe, ray, retort and microscope. At the same time it is evident that an ever-increasing number of people are becoming more responsive to the urgent demands of science for clear thinking as a beginning to a general spring-cleaning of the world. Man is more conscious of his evolutionary history, more interested in the working and care of his body and mind than ever before. The boundaries of knowledge on these matters are constantly enlarging. Side by side with the expansion of human needs and wants, there is an ever-growing organization for their supply, whatever the needs may be.

The materialistic and mechanical conception of nature, so popular in the nineteenth century, is clearly on the wane. Professor J. B. S. Haldane, for instance, avows that there may be "a core in religion which is independent of scientific criticism." Dr. C. E. M. Joad is much of the same opinion, admitting that "Science is competent to tell us something about everything, but it is not in a position to tell us everything about anything, and in regard to some things—for example the human mind—the information which it gives is often found not to be the kind of information which is important."

Can Science Explain Everything?

He adds that "we must admit the possibility that we are as likely, perhaps more likely, to be receiving information as to the real nature of things during an æsthetic and ethical experience as when we are studying the stores of evidence which science accumulates, and mapping the world which science explores."

Lord Horder, one of the most famous of diagnosticians, adjudged that "The art of healing is based upon deep-seated law, and it is impossible to separate the moral from the physical law. To break either leads to disease or pain, and recovery or relief can only be achieved by a renewal of obedience and loyalty."

While a great deal of valuable work has been done regarding the operations of the mind, some thinkers are of the opinion that exaggerated importance is attached to conditioned reflexes, behaviour, sex, inferiority, correlations and so on. There are essential differences in the various schools of psychology and psycho-analysis, and until these can be reconciled it cannot be said that the study is in any way an exact science like chemistry and physics. Much of it will have to be de-bunked.

Whereas Dr. Sigmund Freud held that most mental disorders were due to sex repressions, and sought to parse and analyse the language of dreams, Dr. C. G. Jung looked for what he termed the ancient man—"the fear of ancient man crouching at the ford is in our unconscious mind, as well as all other fears and speculations born of man's experience through the ages. The mind is immortal."

Dr. Alfred Adler, who broke away from the findings of Freud, believed that certain mental troubles were due to "the effect of over-compensation for the feeling of inadequacy resulting from the 'inferiority complex'," of which much abused term he was the originator. Adolf Hitler, acquisitive and amoral, was probably a victim of this state of mind.

The insane, once treated worse than criminals of the deepest dye, are now cared for with sympathy and skill. Writing in 1807, Sir G. O. Paul had this to say of pauper lunatics in the United Kingdom: "I believe there is hardly a parish of considerable extent in which there may not be found some unfortunate creature of this description, who, if his ill treatment has made him phrenetic, is chained in the cellar or garret of a workhouse, fastened to the leg of a table, tied to a post in an outhouse, or perhaps shut up in an uninhabited ruin, or, if his lunacy be inoffensive, left to ramble half naked or starved through the streets or highways, teased by the scoff and jest of all that is vulgar, ignorant and unfeeling."

Over a period of twenty-three recent years it was ascertained that mental defectives in the United Kingdom had increased from 4·6 per 1,000 to 8·4. This would be alarming but for the fact that there is no common standard of measurement. As Dr. Julian Huxley points out, "reliable general conclusions cannot be drawn from observations on material from different environments until it is possible to allow scientifically for the effect of environment."

Insanity and mental deficiency are not bound to be inherited, according to Sir Robert Armstrong-Jones, the eminent alienist. Of 100 typical cases of mental deficiency, forty were definitely transmissible, thirty were due to causes other than hereditary, and the genesis of the remainder could not be ascertained. Stress and strain are factors frequently responsible for mental instability. The operation for the removal of tumours from the brain is now an everyday affair.

Sterilization and birth control have been advocated by some students of genetics, or the science of heredity, to prevent the

PHOTOGRAPHING THE INTERIOR THROUGH THE EXTERIOR

The enormous strides made by medical science are admirably attested by the ever-widening scope of radiography. The presence of diseased tissue often reveals itself to the piercing artificial eye of the X-ray. Radiography is also extremely valuable in industry.

multiplication of the unfit. In 1934 a law came into force in Germany whereby persons suffering from transmissible diseases and mental defects became liable to be brought before a special court, consisting of a judge and two doctors, for examination. If it was found highly probable that the defects would be passed on to the children of the "defendants," compulsory sterilization could be ordered.

The diseases included imbecility, St. Vitus's dance, inherited epilepsy, blindness and deafness, chronic alcoholism and serious deformity. The consent of the man or woman primarily concerned was not necessary. It was estimated that about 400,000 persons were implicated and that the cost to the nation for the care of the congenitally unfit amounted to nearly £2,000,000 a year.

According to a statement published twelve months later, when the Supreme Court decided that foreigners were not exempt, between 180,000 and 200,000 operations were ordered during the first year. The law was to be regarded as "an act of neighbourly love and of provision for coming generations." A State law of Oklahoma, U.S.A., enacted in 1934, made the sterilization of third-term sexual offenders compulsory.

Dr. Eugene L. Fisk, of the Life Extension Institute, says that during the last four centuries thirty-seven years have been added to the average lifetime. So great has been the advance of science that thirteen of these years have been added during the last three decades or so. Not only have preventive and curative medicine and surgery advanced, but hygiene and what may be termed general knowledge on matters pertaining to health have made the strides of a Gulliver. While it would appear to remain true that ancestry is still the most important ingredient in the recipe for longevity, the fact that a child born today has an expectation of twelve years more life than his grandfather had is striking and significant.

Progress in Public Health

Medical supervision at schools, clinics, the clearance of slums, better sanitation and many other things have contributed their quota to human betterment. Perhaps even more important, the old dread of "seeing the doctor" has almost disappeared. This highly desirable state of affairs has been helped in Great Britain by the passing of the National Health Insurance Act in 1911 and by the establishment in 1919 of the Ministry of Health.

One of the most remarkable of modern discoveries was that the ductless glands influence mind and body. Previously it was believed that everything was adjusted by the nervous system. Each gland manufactures chemical substances called hormones unique to that gland. The thyroid gland, situated in the neck, produces thyroxin. If it does not function properly in babyhood and too little is produced a child grows up as a cretin, with stunted growth and mental deficiency. When it is lacking in an adult he becomes melancholy; if there is too much, then he becomes excitable.

A very daring operation was carried out in France. The thyroid gland of a man who had been guillotined for murder was grafted on a child which was backward both mentally and physically. Some months later it was announced that the little patient was normal. According to Professor R. G. Hoskins, the body uses about one-hundredth of a grain of thyroxin a day, the amount representing the difference between mental normality and imbecility.

Glands and Character

If the two-lobed pituitary gland, in the base of the skull, is over-developed it produces a giant; if it is not sufficiently active a dwarf. Sometimes obesity and sluggishness result, Dickens's Fat Boy being cited as an example. Disorders of this gland, says Professor W. Langdon Brown, may make for boastfulness, thieving, lying and a craving for the limelight. The posterior lobe produces a secretion that affects blood pressure.

The pineal gland, once believed to be the seat of the soul, influences the development of the reproductive organs. The secretions of the adrenal glands keep up blood pressure. Their deficiency can now be supplied by a synthetic substance called adrenalin, which has proved valuable in relieving asthma and checking hæmorrhage. A research worker discovered that women burst into tears in circumstances where men fly into a rage because there is a more active secretion by the gland in a man than there is in a woman.

As a sequel to many experiments it was found that when the pancreas gland within the abdomen was not functioning correctly diabetes ensued. It remained for Dr. (later Sir) Frederick Banting, of the University of Toronto, to discover that certain globules in the parts of the pancreas known as the

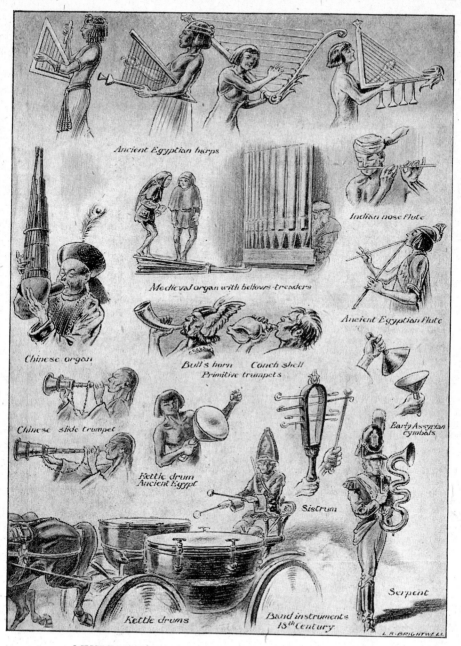

Ancient Egyptian harps

Indian nose flute

Medieval organ with bellows-treaders

Chinese organ

Bull's horn   Conch shell
Primitive trumpets

Ancient Egyptian flute

Chinese slide trumpet

Kettle drum
Ancient Egypt

Sistrum

Early Assyrian
cymbals

Serpent

Kettle drums

Band instruments
18th Century

L.R.BRIGHTWELL

MUSIC-MAKERS OF MANY PEOPLES AND EPOCHS

Music is noise carefully blended so that it is pleasing and not offensive to the ear. The injurious character of the inharmonious variety has been proved by a multitude of experiments carried out by individual researches and learned bodies. Its effect on the nervous system is to increase fatigue in adults and prevent normal physical development in the young.

islets of Langerhans were the secreters of the substance. After many failures he succeeded in obtaining insulin—a name derived from the Latin word *insula*, meaning island—from animals. Administered at correct intervals the treatment makes good the deficiency but does not cure the disease. In 1923 Dr. Banting and Professor J. J. R. Macleod, in whose laboratory the experiments were carried out, were awarded the Nobel Prize for medicine, which they generously shared with Dr. J. B. Collip and Dr. Best, who were associated with them in their research work.

In the popular mind glands are intimately associated with attempts to stave off old age. Before the glandular theory was fully developed Professor Elie Metchnikoff, who proved that the phagocytes or white corpuscles of the blood are troops which fight against dangerous invaders and not agents of destruction, as was formerly believed, sought to increase their power and thus offer a greater force of resistance. He thought he found the elixir of life in an organism abundant in yagourt, a form of sour milk drunk by Bulgarian peasants. As he died at the comparatively early age of seventy-two after taking yagourt for years, the belief was somewhat discredited.

The search was taken up by various practitioners, including Dr. Serge Voronoff, who became an exponent of rejuvenation by gland grafting. The sexual gland of a healthy monkey was used for the purpose, and according to the experimenter many of the operations were successful. The first operation was performed in France in 1921, and the patient apparently kept wonderfully fit until 1932, when he died suddenly. This type of surgical operation is, however, not recognized in Great Britain.

The Miracle of X-rays

The enormous strides made by medical science are admirably attested by the ever-widening scope of radiography. When in 1896 it was known that Professor Wilhelm Konrad von Röntgen, a German physicist, had found a ray which enabled him to see the bones of his hand through the flesh, the world was suspicious. The discovery of X-rays—X standing for unknown—was really due to Sir William Crookes, with whose vacuum tubes Röntgen was experimenting at the time. Crookes accidentally photographed a leather case containing instruments that by some mischance had got between the rays and the sensitized plate.

He put the print aside to attend to more urgent matters. Röntgen's discovery was announced shortly afterwards.

In time it was all too obvious that indiscriminate exposure to X-rays had disastrous effects on those who worked with them. Several notable experimenters lost their lives; others had to have their hands amputated. Precautions now taken have eliminated a danger of which early investigators were unaware, and the rays are used to treat various diseases. The exploratory operation is rapidly becoming a thing of the past, for the presence of diseased tissue often reveals itself to the artificial eye of the X-ray where the real eye would be useless.

X-rays and Industry

To engineers, X-rays are invaluable. At Woolwich Arsenal it was discovered that of 140 gun-carriages radiographed some ten per cent had serious flaws. Imperfect welds, air bubbles in cordite, hidden defects in castings, the presence of slate in coal, contraband disguised in innocent-looking packages, all these things and many more are revealed by this wonderful scientific detective. It has been found invaluable for inspecting the assemblage of the component parts of delicate apparatus.

The curative effects of carefully selected rays of light on the human body were suggested by Roger Bacon in the thirteenth century, although it was not until the present century that ultra-violet sun rays were employed in treating disease. This was thanks to Niels Ryberg Finsen, a Danish physician, whose name is perpetuated in a lamp he invented for the cure of various skin afflictions, including lupus. Sunlight, in the opinion of Sir Bruce Bruce-Porter, is the greatest preventive of disease. That notable authority instanced a slum area in London where there were no rickets because the poor kiddies of necessity wore few clothes, and thus the sunlight was able to get to their bodies.

An experiment with 233 chicks was undertaken. They were divided into three groups. One group was kept in natural sunlight, another in natural sunlight passing through window-glass, and a third in natural sunlight but exposed at intervals to ultra-violet rays from lamps of fused quartz. The results were astonishing. Group one grew normally, group two developed rickets, and at the end of twelve weeks group three was two weeks ahead in physical development over group one. The reason

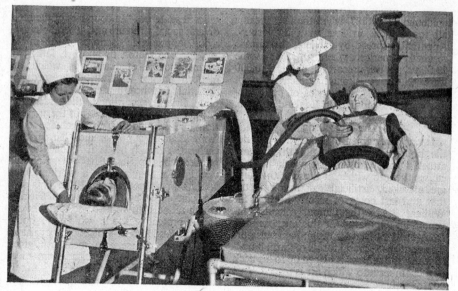

TO ENABLE SUFFERERS TO BREATHE

One of the several types of iron lung (left) and Professor Burstall's jacket, used for the treatment of infantile paralysis. In 1938 Lord Nuffield announced that he would give an iron lung to each hospital in Great Britain and the Empire in need of the apparatus.

why group two was afflicted was because ordinary glass keeps out the beneficial ultra-violet rays. Other experiments proved that the rays also stimulated the growth of plants and the ripening of fruit. Frozen strawberry plants subjected to ultra-violet rays flowered within three weeks and bore delicious fruit in a little over six weeks.

The first clinic for the treatment of surgical tuberculosis was opened in the Alpine village of Leysin in 1903 by Dr. A. Rollier, with such notable results that helio-therapy soon became recognized as an important branch of the science of healing. The increasing popularity of sun-bathing, with its bracing effects so long as it is carried out under proper conditions and not carried to excess, is in the right direction.

In manipulative surgery the medical profession was pig-headedly unprogressive. It took Mr. (later Sir) Herbert Barker over forty years to overcome professional prejudice, and his anæsthetist, Dr. F. W. Axham, was struck off the medical register for assisting him. Sir Herbert's work was vindicated in a report on a demonstration he gave to orthopædic surgeons at St. Thomas's Hospital, London.

By means of local anæsthetics shock and after-sickness have been overcome. Many a

disfiguring facial injury has been obliterated by skilful skin-grafting, so that plastic surgery has been added to the ever-growing list of wonders of the age.

Blood transfusion was first tried, so far as we can trace evidence, when the blood of three boys was administered to Pope Innocent VIII in 1490. The experiment was fatal to patient and donors. Late in the nineteenth century Dr. James Blundell had more success, although he also registered a number of failures, and it was not until the first World War that the practice became frequent. Of 1,150 cases 56 per cent gave good, very good, or excellent results, 21 per cent showed satisfactory improvement, 18 per cent of the patients responded to the treatment but died, and 5 per cent gave no appreciable result.

An example of how long a disease may defy medical skill is afforded by polio-myelitis, commonly called infantile paralysis. A stele picturing an Egyptian prince of the time of Abraham, and the story in the Gospels of the man with the withered hand are sufficiently indicative of the antiquity of the trouble. All recent photographs of President Franklin Roosevelt representing him standing show him unable to do so without support, for he is a victim of the same fell malady. It was not known to be epidemic until 1887, when the fact became all too evident in Sweden and Norway. Apparently spread by carriers, the disease reached America, where in 1916 some 29,000 cases were recorded, of which 6,000 were fatal. A similar epidemic swept America in 1937, and cases of poliomyelitis were even notified in England at Eton.

The Iron Lung

It was ascertained that the virus invades the body via the nose and throat, and attacking nerve cells that work muscles causes them to wither. If those of the lungs are attacked, artificial respiration is the first and last court of resort. In 1932 Sir William Bragg, the famous scientist, invented an apparatus for this purpose, and from it was evolved the Bragg-Paul pulsator. There are also several forms of "iron lung," in which the sufferer is placed up to his neck in a chamber into which air is forced. This contracts his chest and expels air from the lungs; when the pressure is reduced the chest expands and the patient breathes.

There was a time, and that well within the memory of many adults, when food was regarded mainly as "something to eat." So long as it was palatable it was supposed to do one good. Taste wielded the sceptre. People stuffed themselves until they felt full; "satisfied" was the correct term used in the best circles. The question of the nutritive value of what they consumed never entered their heads. For the most part medical practitioners put food in two categories: that which was digestible and that which was indigestible. This haphazard way of assessment has been altered by the science of dietetics, although much remains to be done to make its findings known to the layman. For example, the outer leaves of the lettuce, a plant of considerable food value, are usually thrown away; actually they are the most useful.

"Life," as a well-known scientist avowed, "would seem to be balanced upon a set of chemical pin-points." He did not get into trouble for making this remark, yet in the fifties of last century Jakob Moleschott was dismissed from his professorial chair at Heidelberg for merely stating that "Man is what he eats." It was felt that he had undermined morality. Now we know that man is the sum total of many factors, of which food is one of great importance.

The final report of the Mixed Committee of the League of Nations on the problem of nutrition, issued in 1937, contains this significant sentence: "In countries of the most diverse social structure and general plane of living, appreciable sections of the public are, for one reason or another, failing to secure enough of the foods which the modern science of nutrition regards as essential for health and efficiency." In Great Britain, according to the evidence of one authority, 13·7 per cent of the population had incomes which precluded them from securing a proper diet. Three years earlier the British Medical Association expressed the opinion that the minimum weekly diet required by a working man could be obtained for 5s. 10½d. This sum was challenged by the Ministry of Health, which reduced the bill to 4s. 10d. The so-called protective foods, which are body-building and health-protecting, consist of milk, butter, cheese, eggs, meat, fish, green vegetables and fresh fruit, and are more expensive to purchase than the purely energy-giving eatables such as cereals and sugar.

Before Nazism cast not only its ugly shadow but its substance over Norway, children in the capital of that peace-loving and democratic country who arrived at school thirty minutes before the official opening were provided gratis with what came to be known as the Oslo breakfast. This was a standard meal consisting of whole wheat bread and butter with grated cheese, half an apple or carrot, half an orange, and a little over half a pint of milk. The result was a marked improvement in the physique and condition of the children.

Milk and Health

The provision of free or cheap milk at the public expense must be regarded as a credit and not a debit on the national balance sheet. The value of pure milk can scarcely be over-estimated. Mortality among artificially fed babies is considerably higher than among breast-fed infants. Improvements in weight and height are not the only good results produced by the school child's daily "dose of cow's juice," as one toddler termed it. Rheumatic and catarrhal conditions have been reduced, and even the liability of bones to fracture when a rough kick is encountered on the playground. The addition of one pint of milk a day to the diet of growing boys resulted in an average annual gain in weight among them of 6·98 pounds, and an average increase in height of no less than 2·63 inches.

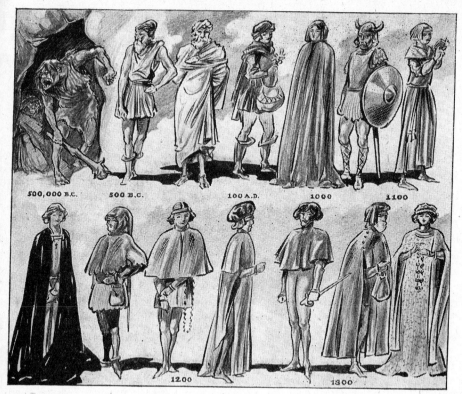

500,000 B.C.   500 B.C.   100 A.D.   1000   1100

1200   1300

FASHION FANCIES THROUGH THE CENTURIES

Thomas Carlyle wrote a book on the philosophy of clothes. Almost until the present time woman's wear seemed to alternate between the drab, the picturesque and the grotesque. The day of heavy petticoats and an excessive abundance of underclothing has been relegated to limbo. A woman's skin is able to breathe in light modern clothes, with beneficial results.

Dr. H. N. Bundensen, President of the Chicago Board of Health, was so convinced of the value of milk that he undertook a remarkable experiment to prove the amount of energy it contained. He compressed two tons of dried sour milk into briquettes, which were loaded into the tender of a locomotive attached to eleven coaches. This was the only fuel used by the engine, which hauled the train a distance of over twenty-five miles.

Milk may be a source of infection. Fortunately there is a means whereby disease germs in it may be killed. The process, known as pasteurization, consists in heating the liquid to 145 deg. Fahrenheit, and keeping it at that temperature for thirty minutes, after which it is immediately cooled and bottled in sterilized containers and adequately sealed for delivery to the customer. This represents a tremendous advance on the time-honoured but essentially harmful practice of leaving a jug on the doorstep to be filled from a metal can, exposed to dust and other injurious elements whenever the lid was opened.

We owe the germ-destroying process that robs milk of its possible and probable terrors to Louis Pasteur, a patient French chemist who discovered many things that made for the betterment and happiness of mankind. Damned as a quack by the Academy of Medicine because he dabbled in biology, he was to live to hear that learned body make an honourable apology to him years later.

The investigator discovered that the cause of certain harmful fermentations in wine and beer, and of milk going sour, was living microscopic bodies called bacteria.

What was of greater practical importance, he indicated methods by which the lowly organisms could be combated.

When he studied the incidence of rabies those who did not see eye to eye with Pasteur dubbed him a murderer. Fifty years later his first patient to be inoculated against hydrophobia was still living.

Jupille, his second patient, was for long the concierge at the Pasteur Institute in Paris, which was endowed by world-wide public subscriptions and a French banker who had originally intended to leave his money for the building of a battleship. It was at the opening of this home for the study and prevention of disease that the man whose name it bears uttered these noble words:

"Two opposing laws seem to me now in contrast. The one, a law of blood and death, opening out each day new modes of destruction, forces the nations to be always ready for battle. The other is a law of peace, work and health, whose only aim is to deliver man from the calamities which beset him. The one seeks violent conquests, the other the relief of mankind. The one places a single life above all victories, the other sacrifices hundreds of thousands of lives to the ambition of a single individual. The law of which we are the instruments strives even in the midst of carnage to cure the wounds due to the law of war. Treatment by our antiseptic methods may well preserve the lives of thousands of soldiers. Which of the two will prevail? God only knows. But of this we may be sure, that science, in obeying the laws of humanity, will always labour to enlarge the frontiers of life."

FOUR HUNDRED YEARS OF CLOTHING

From the fifteenth to the eighteenth century men's garments had about them certain feminine characteristics unless they happened to be suits of armour. Feathers, ruffs and brightly coloured silks were the rule, and some of the footwear reached such extremes in length that the unwieldy toes were supported from the knee, as shown in the seventh figure in the top row.

WORN WHEN VICTORIA WAS QUEEN

The era of the crinoline, a framework of steel hoops or unpliable material, began about 1860 and was perhaps the most inconvenient of the dictates of fashion. It met with the approval of the Empress Eugénie and had a fairly extensive life. The dress of many flounces followed. Heavy cloaks for women and voluminous ulsters for men saw the nineteenth century out.

Faulty or deficient nutrition, due to lack of certain substances necessary to human diet known as vitamins, is the subject of intensive study. The vital importance of this phase of biochemistry is accentuated by the statement of Sir Frank Smith that the absence of five-millionths of a grain of a vitamin appreciably shortens life.

What exactly is a vitamin other than a term which has been fashionable and bandied about in book and newspaper during recent years? Vitamins are necessary for the maintenance of life, and are therefore / not altogether unimportant. Sir Frederick Gowland Hopkins, their co-discoverer, originally termed them "accessory food factors." Then Casimir Funk, a Polish investigator, called a substance he found in yeast vitamine, from the Latin *vita,* meaning life, and *amine,* the name of certain groups of compounds containing nitrogen. When it was doubted whether this was a correct description because it was by no means certain that the substance was an amine the "e" was struck off and the word applied to the whole group of food factors. Each was accorded a letter for identification purposes, namely vitamin A, B, C, D, E, K and so forth.

Attention was first drawn to the subject in 1897, when Professor C. Eijkman, studying the disease of beriberi in Java, noticed that a number of hens belonging to the pathological institution of which he was the director became paralysed and died. He investigated their diet and found that they had been fed on boiled rice, in other words on polished rice from which the bran and germ had been removed. The scientist then tried giving a number of hens whole rice. As they thrived it was inferred that there was something in the bran of the rice that was essential.

There the matter remained until Sir Frederick Gowland Hopkins found that young rats raised on pure proteins, carbohydrates, fats and mineral salts fell victims to malnutrition, but others raised on a similar diet plus fresh milk flourished. There was evidently a necessary growth-promoting body in the milk which the other foodstuffs lacked, although they were supposed to be the essentials. That unseen "something" was labelled vitamin A.

In 1929 the Nobel Prize for chemistry was divided between Professor Eijkman and Sir Frederick. The latter described a vitamin as an indispensable need fulfilled by an amount so infinitesimal as to be no more than a minute fraction of a grain. An ounce of the pure vitamin C, according to the same authority, would protect at least 5,000 human beings from scurvy for a year, whatever their food.

The alphabet of the vitamins is apparently incomplete. Fresh letters are added from time to time as biochemists enlarge their knowledge.

Sources of vitamin A, which promotes growth and helps in resistance to disease, are milk and milk products, cod-liver oil halibut-liver oil, the liver fats of calves,

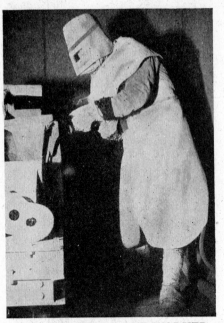

SAFEGUARDING THE WORKER

Shot blasting a steel casting to remove sand and dirt from the surface. The operator wears protective clothing and is supplied with pure air in the same way as a diver.

oxen and sheep, and vegetables, notably carrots. What was formerly called vitamin B is now known to be really a group of vitamins, B1, B2 and so on, which protect from beriberi and neuritis and help to nourish the nervous system. They are found in seed germs, nuts, yeast, egg yolk and many vegetables, hence the desirability of including wholemeal bread, fresh vegetables and orange juice in one's diet. Vitamin C, the anti-scurvy vitamin, is also present in the juice of the orange, the tomato and the lemon. It guards against general lassitude and anæmia, and helps to form sound teeth.

The liver of fish, such as eels, is the richest source of vitamin D, the preventive of rickets, and this vitamin is also obtained artificially by the action of ultra-violet light upon ergosterol, a complex chemical, present in the ergot of rye and elsewhere. A daily dose of no more than two milligrammes of this preparation has been known to cure obstinate cases of rickets, which is in many countries one of the most prevalent of diseases.

Vitamin E, which comes mainly from lettuce and the germ of wheat, helps to pre-vent sterility. Meats, milk, eggs, yeast and certain fruits and vegetables contain vitamin G, an aid to the nerves and digestion.

In many countries the civilizing of the factory has helped to atone for the appalling conditions that were a legacy of the early and cruel days of the Industrial Revolution. Tots of five years of age are no longer employed in cotton mills working shifts of twelve hours so that the commodious beds were never aired because they were always fully occupied. In peace time humanity is at least human and humane.

Much valuable work, carried out by private and individual initiative, has been done to improve conditions in factory and office, quite apart from enforced results brought about by legislation. Happy employees are healthier and do a better job.

During the first World War, when there was an imperative call for a redoubled effort to increase the supply of munitions, owing to losses on the Western Front, a continuous seven-day week of two shifts a day was attempted in the cartridge-filling shops of Woolwich Arsenal. It proved satisfactory for a time, but gradually an increasing number of workers fell sick and the output decreased accordingly. It was found imperative to make a break, and the so-called "danger buildings" where the operations took place were therefore closed every Sunday from 7 a.m., when one night shift finished, until 7 p.m., when another began. In 1940 the output of a continuous night shift in a munitions factory was from five to ten per cent less than that of day workers. When a weekly change of shift was made output in the factory was brought to the maximum.

For over twelve months expert psychologists watched ten girls wrapping, unwrapping, weighing and packing toffee. Their ages were between fifteen and sixteen years. According to a report issued by the Medical Research Council: "Efficiency, loss of time and behaviour were found to be dependent on the girls' likes and dislikes of the different processes. Complex and varied work was liked best, because it occupied the mind and helped time to pass quickly. Next in favour were mechanized and rhythmical operations which could be 'carried on with a swing'." When time-rate payment was made the slower workers set the pace, and boredom was evident, but there was little or no unfriendliness. A competition bonus scheme increased output but unfortunately gave rise to bickerings.

The manner in which work is presented has an important effect on the mind. At a jam factory it was shown that if a stone of currants was presented to a worker for picking and sorting the mountainous mass had a most depressing effect. The reaction was: "How on earth am I going to get through this lot?" When only half the weight was placed on the bench at a time the output was exactly doubled. At a factory which employed about 1,000 workers, improved lighting reduced the number of accidents from about 400 to 150. The introduction of music broadcast by loud-speakers increased production in a canning factory by nearly one-third, and dissipated all signs of boredom among the workers.

Music is noise carefully blended so that it is pleasing and not offensive to the ear. The injurious character of the inharmonious variety has been proved by a multitude of experiments carried out by individual researchers and learned bodies in many parts of the world. Its effect on the nervous system is to increase fatigue in adults and prevent normal development in the young. Noise increases the blood pressure, and it has been proved that a sudden report such as that caused by the bursting of a motor-tyre or a blown-up paper bag, raises the pressure higher than an injection of morphine. A recent discovery is that double windows increase noise unless they are properly spaced, otherwise they add insult to injury by setting up sympathetic vibrations which are more irritating than the noise they were designed to keep out.

The unit for the acoustic standard of measurement is the phon. A pneumatic drill has a loudness of 100 phons, which is forty phons above what certain authorities hold to be good for the nervous system.

SWEAT AND GRIME IN THE UNDERWORLD OF COAL

Coal is the basis of the world's great industries, and coal-mining is one of the most dangerous of employments. Carbon dioxide may cause suffocation. Methane when mixed with air may cause an explosion. Both these gases are given off by the mineral. The dust is responsible for a great deal of ill-health. Accidents caused by falls and in haulage operations are many.

Occupational deafness has increased of late years, thanks to the plague of noise and despite the considerable attention given to making the world quieter for democracy.

Colour may be helpful or harmful to health. Experiments carried out in a motor works proved that a combination of light green and white was most favoured. Stone colour was appreciated by workers not engaged in mechanical operations. A physician who had his consultation room painted in buttercup yellow and the furniture upholstered a cheerful blue found that the effect had a marked influence for good on his patients. Red helps to lift depression, blue tends to soothe restlessness. Light green, pink and what are usually referred to as autumn tints have been found beneficial to some sufferers from shell-shock.

Revolution in Dress

The philosophy of clothes is so fully appreciated that it requires no more than brief mention. The day of heavy petticoats and an excessive abundance of underclothing has been relegated to limbo. A woman's skin is able to breathe, with beneficial results. A man's clothes are little better than sponges.

Air and temperature have at last come into their own as fundamental factors in the upkeep of health. Investigations extending over a considerable period show that a temperature of 60 deg. to 62 deg. Fahrenheit is best for places where light manual work is carried on; of 58 deg. Fahrenheit where hard manual work is done, and of between 62 deg. and 66 deg. Fahrenheit for clerical work. Cross-ventilation, such as can be carried out by windows open at the top on opposite walls, is considered excellent for ordinary purposes.

By means of air conditioning it is possible to get air of absolute purity and the correct temperature and humidity. The air is drawn from outside the building by electric fans. It then passes through a filter which eliminates dust, soot and other injurious materials, is given a bath, shaken into spray and, if necessary, warmed. It is then sent on its mission of mercy and health by tube. As it enters a room the used air is drawn off at the same speed as the fresh supply is taken in. The plant at Broadcasting House, London, deals with approximately 260 tons per hour and serves 180 rooms.

In the United States air conditioning is a feature of many of the "crack" express trains, and in Canada it is extensively used in private houses. "Artificial atmospheres of desired temperature and humidity," runs one report, "permit delicate processes to be carried on in factory and laboratory regardless of weather conditions, eliminating losses to owners and workers resulting from seasonal schedules of production."

It would seem that the monotony of repetitive work affects men more than women. "Why is it," asks Dr. Sibyl Horner, "that women alone of the industrial groups can bring themselves to the daily performance of monotonous work without losing what one may call, for want of a better name, their 'interest in life'? They do it," she answers, "by a nice balance between attention and detachment—which is, in effect, a prescription for the prevention of boredom."

Without straining the point too much, it might be safe to say that the cause of the majority of street accidents in which pedestrians and motorists are involved is repetitive work, for walking is usually carried out without conscious thinking and is therefore a kind of automatic process. In a recent year most accidents to walkers were due to apparent inattention to traffic; over eighty-five per cent of the pedestrians involved were killed. Much the same may be said of casualties in the home, which ought to be the safest place in the world but is actually a veritable danger zone. Falls lead the list, and they are usually caused by carelessness, as in the outdoor cases already cited.

Industrial Welfare

It was not until 1875 that Great Britain awakened to the need for investigating diseases due to particular industries. Two instances must suffice. It was discovered that oxide of zinc was an innocuous substitute for white lead in paint, and it is to the honour of France that she was the first country to introduce legislation on the subject. Phosphorus poisoning claimed many victims among the makers of matches until a non-poisonous substitute was found and its use made compulsory. Guards on exposed parts of machinery have prevented innumerable injuries, and the provision of first aid posts has saved many precious lives by enabling workers who have suffered accidents to receive immediate attention on the spot, thus avoiding the dangers inherent in delay.

Deeply impressed by seeing a film on artificial respiration prepared by the Department of Anæsthetics at Oxford University,

Lord Nuffield announced his intention in 1938 to give one or more "iron lungs" to every hospital in the British Empire. The benefactions of this arch-priest of philanthropy have been many and represent millions of pounds sterling. They call attention to the significant fact that not a few makers of wealth have returned a proportion of their gain to the source from which it came. Dives has not spurned Lazarus.

Lord Nuffield, for instance, placed £2,000,000 at the disposal of trustees for the benefit of depressed, or special, areas in the United Kingdom where unemployment was rife, and gave £3,628,000 to Oxford University for medical research and the endowment of a new college for research in social studies. Lord Austin, another maker of motor-cars, gave £250,000 to Cambridge University for scientific research at the Cavendish Laboratory. Andrew Carnegie, who left Scotland as a poor boy and became a steel magnate in the United States, gave away £85,000,000. He declared it a sin to die rich.

Although some of his business methods met with severe criticism, it is computed that John D. Rockefeller, the oil king, spent no less than £150,000,000 on various forms of social service during his lifetime. The Rockefeller Foundation, founded "to promote the well-being of mankind throughout the world," was endowed with £37,000,000; the Rockefeller Institute with £11,000,000, and the General Education Board with £25,000,000.

Rockefeller believed it incumbent on him to get all the money he could, to keep all he could, and to give away all he could. "It is the duty of every man," he once said, "to contribute to the betterment of his race. The power to make money is a gift from God—just as the instincts for art, music, literature—to be developed and used for the good of my fellow men." Although it is difficult to reconcile "the earth is the Lord's and the fullness thereof" with the allegation that at one time the various Rockefeller interests controlled thirty-nine per cent of the natural resources and wealth of the United States, this returning of cash to the common pool may perhaps be regarded as a form of righteousness.

Even so fine an organization as the Foundation, working for the good of all, did not always find its task easy. "Suspicion, distrust, detraction, hatred and threat of war were all too prevalent in the relations of the peoples of the world," wrote Dr.

IMPROVED CONDITIONS

Pithead baths at East Wemyss, Fife, the largest of their kind in Britain. They were constructed to accommodate 2,400 workers, and cost £35,000 to build.

George E. Vincent, the president. "Scientific comradeship and common tasks of hygiene seem almost negligible as bonds of unity. But the difficulty of a task is no excuse for not attempting it. Because it is not possible to predict the early dawn of a millennial peace, there is no good reason for not taking steps which seem to lead towards even a remote era when nations may substitute generous rivalry for deadly conflict. To stimulate world-wide research, to aid the diffusion of knowledge, to multiply personal contacts, to encourage co-operation in medical education and public health are the means by which the Rockefeller Foundation seeks to be true to its chartered purpose

TRAINING MEN FOR RESCUE WORK IN CASE OF DISASTER

The functions of the breathing apparatus worn by a rescue squad being described by means of a chart at a Lancashire station which specializes in the work of training men for such work. Teams of trained rescue workers are immediately available in any case of emergency.

which is to promote, not the exclusive prosperity of any one nation, but 'the well-being of mankind throughout the world'."

It has been said time and time again that the combative instinct of man could be overcome if a substitute were found for the glamour of armed conflict. If death be glamour, 7,067,308 men achieved it in the first World War. The Rockefeller Institute and similar projects believe in welfare, which, rightly understood, is a higher branch of warfare. In the course of a recent report the Director for Natural Sciences of the Rockefeller Institute showed that mankind still had a dozen enemies to be combated, and set them out in the form of questions.

"Can we obtain," he asks, "enough knowledge of the physiology and psychobiology of sex so that man can bring this aspect of his life under rational control? Can we unravel the tangled problem of the endocrine glands and develop a therapy for the whole hideous range of mental and physical disorders which result from glandular disturbance? Can we develop so sound and extensive a genetics that we can hope to breed in the future superior men? Can we solve the mysteries of the various vitamins, so that we can nurture a race sufficiently healthy and resistant? Can

psychology be shaped into a tool effective for many everyday uses? In short, can we rationalize human behaviour and create a new science of man?"

No university in the United Kingdom bears the name of an individual founder. In the United States many seats of learning have been started and endowed by men who held no brief for the supposed bliss of ignorance. Rockefeller founded the University of Chicago; James B. Duke, who made a fortune in tobacco, endowed the seat of learning in North Carolina which perpetuates his name; Leland Stanford founded Stanford University in California, and so on. Probably this form of benevolence has not appealed to Britishers owing to the difficulty of obtaining a charter; although the Wills family liberally endowed Bristol University, and the Palmers and Suttons helped to found that of Reading. America welcomes rather than deprecates competition in education.

A famous editor once stated that repetition is the soul of journalism. He discovered the truth long before modern states woke up to the value of propaganda, which is another name for mass suggestion. Germany brought this form of mind control to a fine, if lying, art. It helped to destroy the soul of a people. When broadcasting came into its own a People's Set, built 'for receiving national stations only, was sold in enormous numbers in the Fatherland. That country, however, did not restrict its radio output to its own language. What it wanted other lands to believe it said in the native tongue of those lands.

Unhappily in totalitarian states most listeners and readers had no means of finding out the truth or otherwise of what they heard and perused. Hitler himself asserted that "the bigger the lie the more readily will it be believed."

Everything was given a Nazi slant. The Nazi Teachers' Association not only assumed the task of "intensifying the teaching of history in the Third Reich" but of "inspiring it with the Nazi spirit." The subject became part and parcel of propaganda, then being developed on a hitherto unheard-of scale. Not that this method of influencing the public mind was novel. Seven or eight years before, "Big Bill" Thompson, Mayor of Chicago, had stirred up a hornet's nest over the question of the use in public schools of text books alleged to be pro-British.

Reading books with the correct bias, issued by the State for primary schools, were introduced in Italy years ago. Their purpose was to make the children good Fascists. In them they were taught that Italy "won the war" with the battle of Vittorio Veneto (assisted, it may be added in the interest of truth, by British, French, Americans and the weather). We read that "Italy, a hundred years ago divided and enslaved, is today one of the great Powers of the world, presenting an admirable spectacle of discipline, work and faith. The heroes and the martyrs of the Risorgimento, of the Great War, and the Fascist Revolution have made our country free, united, prosperous and strong. It is now your turn to grow up healthy in mind and body, to continue the work, so that Italy may once more be a splendid lighthouse of civilization. You must be ready, as were your fathers and grandfathers, if the country calls you, to fly to arms and die serenely should the safety and greatness of your country exact from you this supreme sacrifice."

Minimizing the achievements of other countries is not, of course, confined to the lands cited. Britain has had her noisy orchestra of drum-and-trumpet historians, in which Rudyard Kipling played an unmuted trombone.

TOWER OF LEARNING

The tower of the University of Bristol, one of the newest of England's seats of learning. The University of Bristol obtained its charter in 1909 and owes a great deal to the interest and munificence of the Wills family.

CHAPTER 26

SCIENCE : MIRACLE OR MENACE?

Science is neutral. Man harnesses Nature. Land reclamation ancient and modern.
Coal and oil. Oil for engines on land and sea. Synthetic products. Electricity.
The social side of progress. Slavery ancient and modern. The fight against disease.
Man conquers the soil. Progress in bonds. The evil angel of Man's own making.

UNLESS the world loses the inherent common sense which it has acquired by long and toilsome process, there is little need to fear, much less to dread, Carlyle's "age weighed down by mechanization." Mechanization cannot be overpowering unless mankind makes it so.

Knowledge is of itself neutral—neither good nor evil. In practice it can be turned to either. The first submarine in the British Navy was completed in 1902; thirty years later Great Britain was appealing to the Disarmament Conference at Geneva to abolish undersea craft, and in 1939 Germany was besieging her island enemy with them. Alfred Nobel, the Swedish inventor of dynamite, blasting gelatine, ballistite, and other explosives, realized the irony latent in all discoveries when he left a substantial sum to be used for the purpose of fostering international brotherhood.

Man Outwits Nature

Until it was discovered that latent forces could be turned to good use by machines, and that muscles were really but weak transmuters of energy, man took Nature very much as a matter of course. His conquest of a mountain was determined by a pass; now he tunnels through it with pneumatic tools or builds a gleaming steel highway over it. He burrows to relieve congestion of traffic or for the sake of safety, and soars above land and sea to get to distant places in the minimum of time. As his ships cannot float on land, he digs deep ditches for them if by so doing he can eliminate a circuitous route, hence the Suez and Panama canals.

Nature, at once prodigal and miserly, supplies too much water in one place and too little in another. Man sets to work to make waste profitable by harnessing the overplus, and taking it from where it is not required to where it is a necessity. In ten years the world doubled its water power resources, transforming waste into mechanical energy. "White coal" has become a serious rival of "black diamonds."

Italy, which lacks mineral fuel, has hydro-electric plants. She has corrected seasonal irregularities by making artificial lakes for storage purposes, and after using the water for generating electricity, pumps it to irrigate far-off fields and thus help in the work of reclaiming land hitherto regarded merely as desert from the point of view of agriculture.

The Netherlands represent the supreme triumph of reclamation. Nearly half of the land lies below the level of the sea, which is held in check by massive dykes. The draining of the Zuyder Zee, determined on in 1918 after long consideration, was planned to be completed in 1952. By means of massive earthworks and pumps capable of raising 1,000 million gallons of water per day many thousands of acres have emerged. The bottom of the sea has become the surface of the dry land.

The fertility of Middle Egypt was immensely increased by the building of the Aswan Dam, which can impound 2,400 million tons if necessary. The Makwar Dam, near Sennar, some 170 miles south of Khartoum, irrigates 300,000 acres of the Anglo-Egyptian Sudan. For twelve years men and machines excavated earth, cut canals, erected masonry and ironwork, until the barrage across the Blue Nile was ready to store 140,000 million gallons of water.

Ancient and Modern Engineers

It is believed that within a quarter of a century the output of cotton from the Gezira plain will not be less in value than £20,000,000 a year. The total cost was £12,500,000. Not inappropriately the switch handle used by Lord Lloyd for the opening of the dam was a replica of a statue of Amenemhet III, the builder of an embankment which reclaimed forty square miles from Lake Moeris to the Fayum nearly 4,000 years ago.

The Lloyd Barrage across the Indus at Sukkur enables over 6 million acres of crops in the almost rainless province of Sind to be irrigated annually. Forty-six mechanical diggers excavated about seventy-four tons of earth per minute, equivalent to the exertions of 32,000 men.

Coal is waste wood chemically treated in Nature's laboratory. It is raw material needing little further treatment on the part of man. Half a century before the discovery of America the "sulphurous stone" was reported to Pope Pius II as being burnt by the people of England and Scotland. For long it was employed for furnishing heat and nothing more. Then attention was given to the "fragments that remain," which now number thousands, many of them by-products of by-products, including gas, coke, coal-tar, oils valuable for dyes, perfumes, explosives, preservatives, disinfectants, antiseptics, and much else.

Crude oil is now being distilled from hard coal by low-temperature carbonization, and petrol by hydrogenation. In Germany 100,000 tons of motor spirit per annum are manufactured from brown coal, which has the advantage of being quarried more readily than the black variety, and is therefore less costly.

The nineteenth century was the age of coal; its immediate successor may be that of oil. Yet the substance has been known from remote times, though its origin is still a matter of controversy. It may be as old as the hills. Oil is usually referred to as a mineral, but it is possible that it is derived from an animal or vegetable source, or perhaps from both. Some scientists hold that a tremendous convulsion in far-distant geological times ended the existence of a vast quantity of animal and vegetable life, which became submerged with the sandy formation peculiar to all those districts in which oil is now prevalent.

Other authorities do not agree with the catastrophic theory, but believe that the remains of marine animals and plants and surface vegetation were buried under sedimentary mineral matter during the changes which the earth has undergone. If the petroleum found in the Palæozoic and Tertiary rocks is of the same geological age as the rocks, it may well be that the oil used

WHITE COAL TAKES THE PLACE OF BLACK DIAMONDS

Nature, at once prodigal and miserly, supplies too much water in one place and too little in another. Man sets to work to make waste profitable by harnessing the overplus, and taking it from where it is not required to where it is a necessity. In ten years the world doubled its water-power resources, transforming waste into mechanical energy, as at the great hydro-electric power plant on the Gatineau River, Canada, thanks to the efforts of engineers.

in many a country cottage today is furnishing illumination from a source which originated many millions of years ago. We pause and wonder when we read that the light of some stars started its journey to earth long before the birth of Christ, but the former fact is far more staggering. Though considerably nearer in space, it is immensely more remote in time.

Oil in Ancient Days

Whatever its origin, the so-called mineral oil has more romance attached to it than Aladdin's lamp, which was a mere container. The terms petroleum and naphtha have been used for it with little discrimination. Asphalt was employed by the builder of Nineveh and Babylon to cement walls. Noah's ark was "pitched within and without with pitch," and the little craft of bulrushes that cradled the infant Moses on the waters of the Nile was waterproofed in a similar way. Eratosthenes mentions that "asphaltus is found in great abundance in Babylonia. The liquid asphaltus, which is called naphtha, is found in Lusiana." Pliny tells us of the "Sicilian oil" found at Agrigentum. The sacred fires of sun-worshippers were fed by its gases. China, Japan, Persia and Burma were early sources of production, and in the eighteenth century it was discovered, or re-discovered, in Calabria, Italy.

For hundreds of centuries oil was procured in the most primitive of ways. It was collected in ponds artificially made or skimmed from pools formed as it exuded from the soil.

England is not usually associated with the production of mineral oil, yet the world owes one of its greatest modern industries to the little town of Riddings, in Derbyshire. In 1847, James Oakes, an ironmaster of that place, was boring for coal, when he came upon a stream of oil. He mentioned the matter to his brother-in-law, the future Lord Playfair, who in turn decided to consult James Young, a fellow student at Glasgow University.

Young and a friend erected a refinery, and produced oil for lamps and a heavy oil for lubricating purposes. Then, to their dismay, they found what they thought were solid crystals floating in the petroleum. Playfair reported that they were paraffin, and asked for two candles to be made of the substance. The experiment was somewhat expensive—they cost over one pound each —but Playfair used them to light his desk on the lecture table of the Royal Institution, and prophesied to his audience that before long they would become the common candle of the country. It was so, and whale oil for the purpose of illumination was an affair of yesterday so far as England was concerned. As for the stream at Riddings, it ran dry in two years, but it had revealed a new source of wealth.

Undeterred, Young began to manufacture mineral oil from coal, and secured a patent for his process in 1850. Nine years later Colonel E. L. Drake at Titusville, Pennsylvania, drilled the first practicable oil-well, and until 1885 Pennsylvania furnished over ninety-eight per cent of the crude oil produced in the United States.

By the process known as fractional distillation various refined products of great importance are produced from the crude petroleum, including petrol, illuminating, solar, lubricating, fuel and medicinal oils, perfumes, vaseline, dyes and the explosive known as trinitrotoluene (T.N.T.). In the early days, before the coming of motor-cars, motor-vessels, aeroplanes, tractors and speed-boats, thousands of tons of motor-spirit were poured on open fields and set on fire to get rid of the lightest and most highly inflammable product of petroleum. The natural gas exuded from the oil-wells, once a serious menace, is now converted for use and condensed in increasing quantities into motor-spirit. Solar oil, an intermediate product between illuminating oil and lubricating oil, is extensively used in connexion with the making of gas for illuminating, cooking and power, of perfumery oils, and of liquid paraffin used for medicinal purposes.

Oil for Ships

In all the world's largest liners King Coal, hitherto an absolute monarch in the engine-room, has been forced to abdicate in favour of King Oil. Heavy oil internal combustion engines for marine purposes are common. The first motor passenger liner was M.V. *Aba* (7,937 gross tons), launched at Belfast. The Diesel engine, the most popular type, can be manœuvred and regulated more easily under adverse weather conditions, and the speed of the ship is consequently better maintained in a rough sea. The first Diesel engine to be built in Great Britain dates from 1897.

The success of the Diesel engine for maritime purposes emphasized the possibility of adopting it for transport work on land.

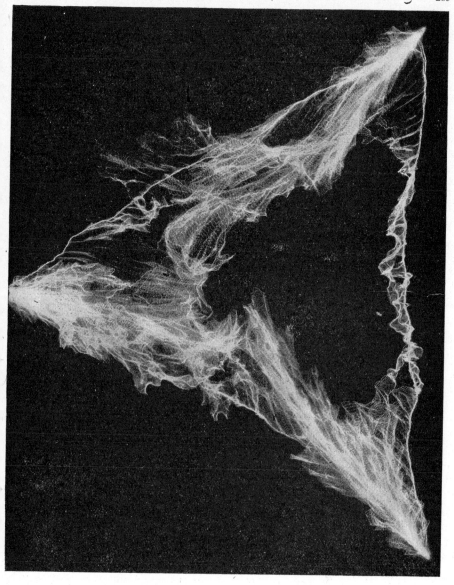

ELECTRIC FLASH OF A MILLION VOLTS

Electrical attraction was known to the ancient Greeks, but did not become the subject of special study till the middle of the seventeenth century, when Gilbert, Queen Elizabeth's physician, first applied the word "electric" to the attractive power of amber and certain other substances. Various electrical experiments and discoveries were made during the eighteenth century by Benjamin Franklin and others, and in 1810 Humphry Davy used electricity for the production of light. Michael Faraday devoted a quarter of a century to research on the subject, and it took a generation or two before the immense possibilities of electricity were realized. Its essentially modern subsidiaries, radio and television, still so recent that they have not ceased to be regarded as wonders, are in the direct line of development from the discoveries of these early investigators, the first of whom was Thales.

PHARAOH AS CIVIL ENGINEER

Amenemhet III, who built a reclamation embankment in Egypt nearly 4,000 years before its successor, the Aswan Dam.

What are termed Mobile Power Houses are used on the Buenos Ayres Great Southern Railway. A Diesel engine-generator of 1,700 horse-power supplies current to electric motors on its own axles and on the bogies of the carriages.

On June 21, 1931, what was termed a "Zeppelin on rails," the invention of Franz Krunkenberg, reached a speed of 143 miles an hour on a trial run between Berlin and Hamburg. Its successor was the *Flying Hamburger*, which in 1932 covered the distance of 178 miles on the same track in two hours twenty minutes. To test the comparative efficiency of the steam locomotive as compared with the performance of the *Flying Hamburger*, the London and North-Eastern Railway ran a train from London to Leeds—186 miles—in two hours thirty-two minutes, an average speed of $73\frac{1}{2}$ miles an hour, attaining on the journey $97\frac{1}{2}$ miles an hour. The schedule of the German train was beaten by thirteen minutes on the return journey, despite added weight and service delays.

On the Union Pacific Railway of the United States the *Zephyr*, a Diesel locomotive of 660 horse-power, stream-lined and

of stainless steel, hauled a train between Denver and Chicago, a run of 1,015 miles, at an average speed of $77\frac{1}{2}$ miles an hour and reached 112 miles an hour. The cost of the 600 gallons of crude oil which it consumed on the journey was extremely low when compared with that of coal. In 1934 the Foden Diesel for omnibuses made its appearance. A Diesel engine for aeroplanes was tried in the United States in 1928 and developed 200 horse-power.

Not only is the chemist the ally of the engineer, but by patient investigation and experiment the successor of the alchemist has increased the production of the soil, protected the crops, eliminated waste in fruits and vegetables by dehydration, and by investigating the requirements of the body has done much to make food safe for democracy. Synthetic sugar can be manufactured from corn, and tea from wild cassava leaves, though it is unlikely that the laboratory will ever rival the field. A woman might not regard it as a compliment if she were told that she was wearing a nice pair of wooden stockings, but rayon is only a by-product of what was once regarded as the waste of the spruce tree. Synthetic alcohol, indigo, camphor, leather, perfumes and flavourings are common. Artificial rubber has been manufactured, though not on a remunerative scale.

It has been computed that rubber enters into at least 40,000 articles, though some may have only a remote connexion with the everyday life of the ordinary individual. London dealings in it often amounted to 20,000 tons a day; in 1900 the total production of plantation rubber was four tons.

The rubber tree has been tamed by man. In the forests of Central and South America it grew wild and untended, the natives hacking and slashing it as and when they required the latex. It has now migrated to distant lands, lives in respectable plantations, and every attention is paid to its health. Millions of acres are given up to the cultivation of the rubber tree in Malaya, the Dutch East Indies, Ceylon, Sarawak, British Borneo, British India, Indo-China and Thailand (Siam).

This stupendous development is due to the pluck of one man, Sir Joseph Hooker, director of the Botanic Gardens, Kew. In 1873 he persuaded the India Office to send Mr. James Collins to the Amazon for the purpose of obtaining seeds of Para rubber. Collins returned with some hundreds of them, but only about a dozen plants were

SYMBOLICAL STATUE IN STAINLESS STEEL

The ugliness associated with factories is gradually disappearing. Serious attempts are made not only to erect places entirely convenient for their main purpose—"functionalism" is the word coined for this—but to render them attractive to the operatives. The above representation of Power, in stainless steel, is on the front of the building of an electric light company, and typifies the function of the structure. Art has found its way into the modern factory.

raised at Kew, and when these were sent to Calcutta they all died. Mr. (later Sir) Henry Wickham and a colleague were next dispatched with the same object. Wickham ascended the Tapajos river in a canoe, made his way into the interior and collected more seeds there.

Two difficulties now presented themselves. Would there be a ship, and if so would the authorities be suspicious? It was necessary to get the 70,000 seeds to England as quickly as possible, otherwise they would lose their vitality. Wickham urged his native boatmen as they had never been pressed before. By an amazing stroke of fortune the Inman liner *Amazonas* was waiting for a cargo. Wickham took a chance, and so did the commander. The former chartered the ship on behalf of the British Government, and the latter took the explorer's word that the bill would be met,

although the cargo consisted of three boxes labelled "Botanical Specimens." The Customs officers at Para were satisfied, and the *Amazonas* crossed the Atlantic in ballast.

In June, 1876, the cargo was discharged at Liverpool, placed on a special train, and within a couple of weeks four per cent of the seeds had germinated in orchid and propagating houses at Kew. Some of the plants were sent to Ceylon, Singapore, Perak and Malaya. Of those planted at Singapore, all but seven died. The survivors were transplanted in more suitable soil and multiplied. For years planters, quite happy in making money out of coffee, would have nothing to do with rubber, but when a slump came they began to think that there was "something in it."

Rubber is the most striking instance of a tree being made to flourish to man's advantage in countries to which it is not

SCIENTIFIC " MAGIC " IN THE WILDS OF AFRICA

With open-eyed wonder and something akin to awe and suspicion, African natives listen to a human voice issuing from what appears to be a traveller's attaché case. Edison made his first crude sketch of a phonograph, later to develop into the gramophone, in August, 1877. Within thirty years Beethoven and Bach were competing with the tom-tom in the African jungle.

ZEPHYR TRAIN THAT MADE A REVOLUTION IN DESIGN

A complete departure from conventional railway practice was brought about by the Burlington Railroad in the United States. Power is provided by a Diesel engine, which is housed in a unit of cromansil, an alloy of chromium, manganese, and silicon, welded into one piece. The remainder of the train is of stainless steel. Streamlining and speed suggest a wind, hence the name Zephyr. It has travelled at a speed of 104 miles an hour.

native. About ninety-five per cent of the world's supply is now obtained from the plantations, and so far as Malaya is concerned mainly from areas that were formerly dense jungle.

Another of the 400 plants producing rubber or rubber-like juices is the evergreen found in Malaya, Sumatra and Borneo from which gutta-percha is obtained. Originally tapped in a way similar to the method employed in the case of rubber, it is now grown on estates, and the gutta-percha is extracted from pruned leaves and twigs from the plant.

The utilization of scrap rubber by reclamation is a fairly recent development. At first the acid process of separating the rubber from foreign matter was employed, but this has largely given place to the alkali process, by which the unwanted matter is either destroyed or dissolved and washed out, and the residue plasticized.

Notoriously prodigal of her natural resources until comparatively recently, the United States furnishes an excellent example of waste through ignorance. For a long time the existence of natural gas was known, but it was not until 1821 that it was used on a small scale for lighting, and over fifty years passed before its commercial

MAN—K

potentialities were fully realized. Today 55,000 miles of piping are required for the transmission of the cheapest fuel and illuminant now known. Some of the wells have a capacity of 35 million cubic feet a day. It is particularly valuable in connexion with fine smelting. Natural gas is found in Australia, Canada, India, China, Japan, Rumania and Russia, in addition to the United States. The use of sewage gas for internal combustion engines has been demonstrated.

Electricity was known to the ancient Greeks, but it was not until 1810 that Humphry Davy used it for the production of light. Another seventeen years elapsed before Robert Davidson ran a car by electric traction. Michael Faraday devoted a quarter of a century to research on the subject, but it took a generation or two before the immense possibilities of electricity were realized. Its essentially modern subsidiaries, radio and television, are still so recent that they have not ceased to be regarded as wonders.

Sometimes we revert to the past and perfect the imaginings of a distant day, as in the case of the turbine. We do not relegate forces to limbo. Steam and electric locomotives run side by side in friendly rivalry.

Steam, electric and oil-driven machines turn the propeller shafts of liners. Oil, gas and electricity give us light, heat and power.

To glance backward may help us to look forward. This is a paradox, like life itself. But the broad view is a corrective of too intense concentration and introspection. It may help one to keep a mental outlook that grows not old. Man has come through many terrible crises. The financial, industrial and commercial depression of the opening/years of the fourth decade of the twentieth century was but an intensified form of the failure to organize the distribution of products scientifically. Maldistribution is to the body politic what malnutrition is to the physical body. It is unmoral and foolish for coffee to be burned in the open fields and closed furnaces of Brazil when other parts of the world would welcome it. The United States, once so proud of her self-sufficiency, has proved nowadays that there can be no Monroe Doctrine where the economic life of the nation is concerned.

There is still a disposition in certain quarters to believe in unending automatic progress. The idea is grateful and comforting, yet a recent writer, albeit a theologian, warns us that "humanity moves in zigzags, in cycles, by way of complication, and indeed degeneration quite as often as, if not more often than, by advance."

Professor J. B. Bury characterized belief in progress as "an act of faith," and gave it as his opinion that "it is impossible to be sure that civilization is moving in the right direction to realize this aim, that is, of a perfectly happy existence of all the inhabitants of the planet."

What is Progress ?

Progress is best appraised in retrospect, when it has ceased to be such. Even then the question of whether the real or alleged moving forward was in the direction of the greatest good to the greatest number is often debatable; mechanical development is valueless or worse unless it makes for the amelioration of human conditions. It must be change for the better. We sacrifice to gain; we cannot consume all the fruits offered at too liberal a feast.

Wireless telephony is a case in point. It has narrowed the world in distance and broadened it in outlook, saved blood and treasure, given pleasure to millions, but made an incalculable number of young people decide that music via the ether is

preferable to harmony by way of their own initiative. From the negative point of view much the same may be said of the gramophone; it eliminates learning and the bugbear of practice. The price exacted is the indefinable but not negligible reward of personal effort and interpretation. Human nature is so constituted that it cannot appreciate something done for it so fully as something it does itself. Of latter-day marvels the cinema is not the least, but glance at the other side of the screen. There you will see, say some prophets, the flicker of the dying embers of the family hearth.

Profit and Loss

When reader and writer are gathered to their fathers will be time enough for posterity to debate on progress as manifested in these three phases of it. We are all prone to forget minus signs in the sum of achievement. "It is admitted," Lord Bryce observed, "that nearly every gain man makes is accompanied by some corresponding loss —perhaps a slight loss, yet a loss." Life itself, as Raphael Meldola puts it, is a "stable instability."

In modern architecture the ornate has given place to the severe, the embellishment of a slower age to the simplicity incumbent on a more feverish existence. The evolution from the squat structure of brick to the lofty skyscraper has been brought about by the use of steel and improvements in its manufacture. Both magnetic and nonmagnetic metals are now super-hardened by exposure to an alternating magnetic field, and it is possible to measure by gauges the stresses in the steelwork of a structure in course of erection.

There is considerable rivalry between steel and reinforced concrete for building purposes. Time alone can solve the test of endurance. If either lasts as long as the Colosseum at Rome, dedicated in A.D. 80, there should be no cause for complaint. Ordinary concrete entered largely into its construction. Its marble casing, like the granite facing of the Great Pyramid, has long since disappeared. For the most part it went to glorify the palaces of medieval nobles. Light interlocking girders and rafters of concrete were used for the pentroofs over the nave and aisles in the restoration of Rheims Cathedral, battered during the first World War.

The United States is already preparing for the time when man will work four hours a day, and many thinkers are giving anxious

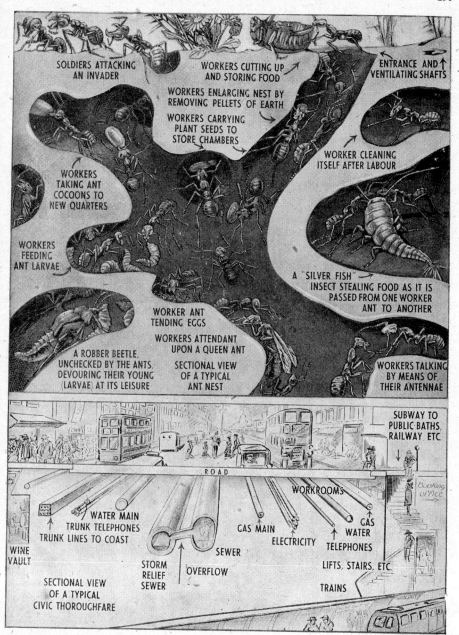

SOLDIERS ATTACKING
AN INVADER

WORKERS CUTTING UP
AND STORING FOOD

ENTRANCE AND
VENTILATING SHAFTS

WORKERS ENLARGING NEST BY
REMOVING PELLETS OF EARTH

WORKERS CARRYING
PLANT SEEDS TO
STORE CHAMBERS

WORKER CLEANING
ITSELF AFTER LABOUR

WORKERS
TAKING ANT
COCOONS TO
NEW QUARTERS

WORKERS
FEEDING
ANT LARVAE

A "SILVER FISH"
INSECT STEALING FOOD AS IT IS
PASSED FROM ONE WORKER
ANT TO ANOTHER

WORKER ANT
TENDING EGGS

WORKERS ATTENDANT
UPON A QUEEN ANT

A ROBBER BEETLE,
UNCHECKED BY THE ANTS,
DEVOURING THEIR YOUNG
(LARVAE) AT ITS LEISURE

SECTIONAL VIEW
OF A TYPICAL
ANT NEST

WORKERS TALKING
BY MEANS OF
THEIR ANTENNAE

SUBWAY TO
PUBLIC BATHS,
RAILWAY ETC.

ROAD

WORKROOMS

Booking
Office

WATER MAIN
TRUNK TELEPHONES
TRUNK LINES TO COAST

GAS MAIN

GAS
WATER
TELEPHONES

ELECTRICITY

WINE
VAULT

SEWER

STORM
RELIEF
SEWER

OVERFLOW

LIFTS, STAIRS, ETC.

SECTIONAL VIEW
OF A TYPICAL
CIVIC THOROUGHFARE

TRAINS

UNDERWORLD OF THE ANT AND OF MAN

*The insect works mainly by instinct, though scientists hold that it possesses glimmerings
of reason. The top section shows a typical ant nest and the activities immediately on
the surface and below it, including defence and the obtaining of food, the storage of
provender, the care of the young, and so on. The bottom portion pictures some of the
uses to which man puts similar territory, partly to relieve traffic congestion in the streets.*

care to the problem of putting to the best use the extended leisure that will be the gift of the machine. In 1870 forty-seven per cent of the workers in that country were agriculturists, a figure which fifty years later had fallen to twenty-six per cent, yet the workers, aided and abetted by mechanical appliances, increased production by thirty-five per cent.

Those who talk glibly of operatives as slaves of the machine will do well to ponder the startling fact that the old-fashioned type of human slavery they probably believed was extinct is still rampant. In 1923 it was deemed imperative to issue decrees making cannibalism a capital crime in the French colonies in Africa and in the Cameroons; slave-traders in the latter were rendered liable to a maximum sentence of ten years. More than a million slaves then existed in Abyssinia taken together with the British mandated territories of South-West Africa and Tanganyika.

The suppression of a lucrative trade of such long standing teems with difficulties. The practical achievements of the Anti-slavery Convention of the League of Nations were so disappointing that a commission of seven persons was set up in 1932 to report on it and to advise the Council how best to expedite the task of completely abolishing slavery and freeing its victims.

The Empire Fights Slavery

On the Okavango river, South-West Africa, it was found that natives were bartered for cattle and sometimes in settlement of debts, and the children became the chattels of the owners of their parents. The practice still prevailed in remote districts of Togoland. The British Commissioner on the north-eastern frontier of Burma reported slavery and human sacrifice in the Naga Hills. Four years later nearly 3,500 slaves were released in the Hukawang Valley, on the frontiers of China and Tibet, thanks to the efforts of a small British expedition. Even today the number of slaves over the whole world is more than five million.

Development in some quarters of the globe has been seriously retarded by diseases that have baffled medical science, but notable progress has been made. For centuries two species of mosquito held man at bay in the conquest of the Isthmus of Panama. Ferdinand de Lesseps was defeated by these noxious insects. It is true that the muddling of the finances played a

part in the crash, but the real cause was unsuspected. The work was inaugurated in 1881, and within seven years over 52 million pounds had been spent. The sanitation was vile, the hospital buildings excellent and usually full to capacity, the source of the besetting malaria and yellow fever unknown. The death roll numbered 40,000; the great engineer collapsed physically and mentally; the plan, for the time, crashed.

War on the Mosquito

When the United States bought the French rights in 1903 they knew the real enemy, though Susruta, a learned Indian physician who lived before the fourth century, had suspected the bite of the mosquito as being the cause of malaria. Among those who shared the discovery were Sir Ronald Ross and Dr. Walter Reed, the one a British citizen and the other an American. Ross found that *Anopheles* carries the germs of malaria, and Reed that *Stegomyia* bore the parasites which cause yellow fever. General G. W. Goethals conquered the isthmus with his diggers and engineering skill; Colonel W. C. Gorgas defeated the insects by sanitation and killing the mosquito larvæ. In ten years there were only 663 deaths, or 1·7 per cent.

It is not always possible to stamp out a disease by the methods adopted by Gorgas. An epidemic of sleeping sickness in the Anglo-Egyptian Sudan was effectively dealt with by other means. After careful investigation the species of tsetse fly responsible for the outbreak was found to live near water, and seldom to go more than a few hundred yards away. The inhabitants of the infested districts were removed to more healthy parts, thanks to the devotion of a band of British officials who built trails and roads and concentrated the natives in villages sufficiently removed from the plague spots.

In Ruanda-Urundi excellent work has been done by defining infected areas, clearing and draining water courses, cutting down vegetation that harbours the tsetse fly, and the enforcement of stringent regulations regarding the movement of canoes and fishing craft. Unfortunately other species of *Glossina* have no such affinity to water, and cannot be dealt with in this way.

In this particular matter progress in one direction has meant retrogression in another, for the disease was once confined to western equatorial Africa. It has been spread by a freer intercommunication. In Tanganyika Territory hookworm and

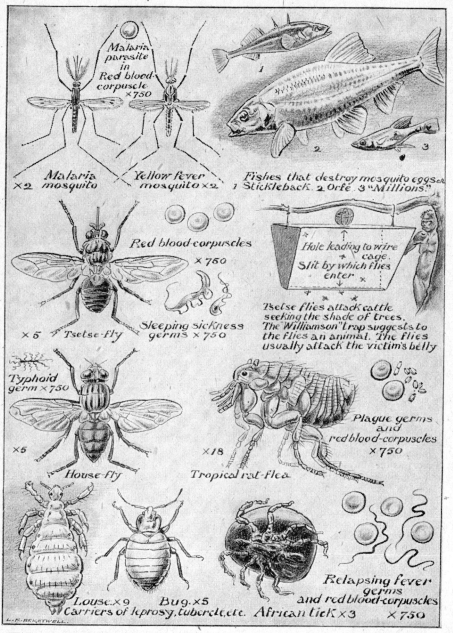

Malaria parasite in Red blood-corpuscle ×750

×2 Malaria mosquito

Yellow fever mosquito ×2

Fishes that destroy mosquito eggs &c. 1 Stickleback. 2 Orfe. 3 "Millions."

Red blood-corpuscles ×750

×5 Tsetse-fly

Sleeping sickness germs ×750

Hole leading to wire cage. Slit by which flies enter

Tsetse flies attack cattle seeking the shade of trees. The "Williamson" trap suggests to the flies an animal. The flies usually attack the victim's belly

Typhoid germ ×750

×5 House-fly

×18 Tropical rat-flea

Plague germs and red blood-corpuscles ×750

Louse ×9   Bug ×5
Carriers of leprosy, tubercle, etc.   African tick ×3

Relapsing fever germs and red blood-corpuscles ×750

L.R.BRIGHTWELL.

IF MAN MUST WAGE WAR, HERE ARE ENEMIES FOR HIM TO FIGHT

"*Life is a fight*," *runs the old Latin proverb. Lip service was for long rendered to the maxim that health is of more worth than wealth. Now that science is becoming democratized and its knowledge more widely spread, the truth, or otherwise, of such time-honoured maxims will be put to the test. Many of man's most deadly enemies are so minute that they cannot be seen with the naked eye, and in this picture they are multiplied (×) many times*

POTENTIAL POWER IN A CLOUD OF SMOKE

The nineteenth century was the age of coal; its immediate successor may be that of oil. Yet the substance has been known from remote times, though its origin is still a matter of controversy. Oil is usually referred to as a mineral, but it is possible that it is derived from an animal or vegetable source, or perhaps from both. Scientists differ on the matter.

spirillum fever are carried by natives passing through infected areas and returning to their tribes. Millions of people gather at fairs and pilgrimages in India, with cholera as an almost inevitable sequel. An annual pilgrimage to Mecca is better managed because devotees have to pass through quarantine.

The problem of contagion is age-long. The Spaniards introduced yellow fever to Europe from America, and the slave-trade with the New World was probably responsible for its appearance on the west coast of Africa. Syphilis may have had an American origin, though some authorities dispute it. There seems to have been an exchange of diseases, for there is reason to believe that the Spaniards infected the American Indians with smallpox and measles.

Lip service was for long rendered to the maxim that health is of more worth than wealth. Now that science is becoming democratized and its knowledge more widely spread, the truth or otherwise of such time-honoured maxims will be put

to the test. One of them, that God made the country and man made the town, suggesting that the broad open spaces are conducive to longevity, is already under suspicion. In Sweden, Denmark, Holland and Japan the urban death-rates are lower than those of rural districts.

A scientific investigation of the soils of a country may be its physical salvation. The food surplus of Palestine is represented by a few vegetables and fruits, whereas formerly the land supported a much larger population by terracing the hills of Judea and Samaria and irrigating the Jordan Valley. It must not be inferred that the cultivators are lazy. Ignorance and not sloth holds them back. That more than the average nine bushels of wheat and five of barley to the acre is possible is shown by an increase of two bushels in the former and of fourteen or fifteen in the latter when modern knowledge has been applied.

The conquest of floods is being tackled. The problem of irrigation, of putting water where it is wanted, is less difficult than that

NEW YORK SKYSCRAPER THAT TOWERS 853 FEET

The evolution of the squat structure of brick to the lofty skyscraper has been brought about by the use of steel and improvements in its manufacture. Both magnetic and non-magnetic metals are now super-hardened by exposure to an alternating magnetic field, and it is possible to measure by gauges the stresses in the steelwork of a structure in course of erection.

of drainage, which is removing water from where it is not wanted. The Huai river drains 50,000 square miles and has no mouth; its victims must have numbered hundreds of thousands. In the floods of 1931 in the Yangtze Valley the maximum depth of water on the fields was nine feet.

The Mississippi is notorious for bursting its banks. So far back as 1717 levees of earth sown with Bermuda grass were built near New Orleans, and there are over 1,500 miles in the present system, which unfortunately the disastrous flood of 1927 proved to be inadequate. Apart from the grievous loss of life and property occasioned by abnormal disasters, soil erosion in the basin of the river aggregates in extreme cases forty tons per acre per year.

In some parts of the world, more particularly in Arizona and New Mexico, floodwater farming is practised, but this is necessarily a precarious method in that silt and too great a rush of water may destroy the entire crop. On the Navajo Reservation many thousands of acres have been culti-

vated in this way during the present century. No plough is used, and the seeds are placed in holes made with a stick.

An adequate water supply is a prime necessity of civilization. The open canals of Egypt, Assyria and Babylonia were no mean feats until the Greeks pierced a mountain with a tunnel nearly a mile long to tap the springs of Mount Ampelus, and the Romans built aqueducts that brought water by gravitation from hills more than sixty miles away. For nearly 2,000 years the aqueduct at Segovia, in Spain, has been carrying water to the town.

The longest modern aqueduct extends for 233 miles, and connects the Sierra Madre mountains with Los Angeles, a feat less wonderful, perhaps, considering the advance of science, than the construction of the cement-lined conduits of granite that crossed rivers, plains and valleys and disappeared underground when Rome was the fulcrum of the Western World. Palmyra, surrounded by desert, was provided with water by means of aqueducts and reservoirs.

MECHANICAL MUSCLES AT WORK ON THE FARM

Cutting, harvesting and threshing wheat at one operation by means of a combined machine. In 1870 forty-seven per cent of the workers in the United States were agriculturists, a figure which fifty years later had fallen to twenty-six per cent, yet the latter, aided and abetted by mechanical appliances, increased production by as much as thirty-five per cent.

In no department of agricultural investigation has progress been more evident than in fertilizers, the food that feeds the food which feeds us. The elements which Mother Earth mainly lacks, or which are exhausted too rapidly by rooted things, are nitrogen, phosphorus, potassium and lime. However destructive a thunderstorm may be, it is also constructive. Every flash of lightning sets up chemical action and causes the nitrogen and oxygen along its path to form oxides of nitrogen, which are washed into the earth by rain. Chilean nitrates have suffered considerably in competition with synthetic fertilizers, for nitrogen is now "mined" from the air.

Bones are an important source of phosphorus for fertilizing purposes. They were formerly burned and the residue treated with sulphuric acid, but direct reduction is now possible by means of an electric furnace. The so-called phosphate rocks are formed from fossil bones, of which there are large deposits in the United States. The world's store of phosphorus is getting appreciably smaller, and if not an immediate source of anxiety to scientists, is certainly leading to considerable thought and experiment. The largest known deposits of potash in the world are to be found in Germany and South America.

Man has advanced far along the road of experience and experiment, yet he may have many long and wearisome miles to cover before he arrives—if ever—at the end of his journey. Once a collector of unconsidered trifles in a world that was still in the making, a tapper of flints that afforded him some measure of protection, he has turned foes into friends, conquered the barriers of mountain, sea and desert, and made Nature herself obey his wishes.

He has learned to fly with the birds, to swim with the fish, to outrun the swiftest horse. He has turned the dead crust of the earth into molten metal, shaping it into craft and engines that carry him and his wares across the globe. He has transformed weeds into flowers that satisfy the desire of the soul for beauty, hacked shapeless stone into statues and cathedrals, and moulded clay and shaped wood into houses to protect him from rain, snow and wind.

Unhappily, man has never been able to enjoy fully the fruits of his labour or enter into possession of his heritage. An evil angel of his own making has stood with drawn sword between him and them.

SAILING IN CONVOY PROTECTED BY THE NAVY

The revival of an old system saved much shipping during the two World Wars. In the first Dutch War of 1652-54, four of the battles that were fought centred about convoys.

CHAPTER 27

THE FIGHT FOR DEMOCRACY

Germany's urge for Lebensraum. Rape of Czechoslovakia. Invasion of Poland. Second World War. Collapse of France. Japan's move for Eastern domination. America, arsenal of democracy. Germany invades Russia. International Aims of the Atlantic Charter. Humanity's quest for peace. Man's conquest of himself.

THE world has yet to discover a non-belligerent means of holding in check a nation bent on conquest. This accounts for the amazing paradox of millions of people anxious to beat their spears into pruning-hooks being compelled in self-defence to wage war and violate their most sacred longings.

The school of thought which believes that no State has the right to interfere with the government of another received a rude shock when it became increasingly obvious that Germany was bent on gathering all her nationals, or those she regarded as such, into one fold and at the same time was crying for *Lebensraum*—living space. The democracies, wishful for peace at almost any price provided it was paid by the other fellow, were taken at a grave disadvantage when the Third Reich made preparation for total war a national industry. Marshal Pilsudski of Poland warned France in 1933 that Germany was rearming and went so far as to suggest that a preventive war might be better than the major conflict which he saw looming darkly on the horizon.

There are those who postulate that the Germans are an inferior race, or at least a people with so thin a veneer of real culture that the wild beast in them has not been sufficiently tamed to warrant their mixing in decent society; a society that, whatever its faults, has slowly arrived at a sense of human values.

The studied setting at nought of international law, the repudiation of obligations solemnly contracted, the brutal invasion of countries on the lying pretext of protecting them against the depredations of friendly neighbours, the using of homeless and helpless refugees as screens to cover the advance of armed hordes, and the machine gunning of civilian non-combatants from aircraft are the evidence brought forward for this contention. The compulsory removal of hundreds of thousands of men, women and children from one territory to another and forcing them to labour at whatever task is assigned to them is no more than a reversion to slavery of a most revolting kind.

After the bloodless reoccupation of the Rhineland in 1936 and the invasion of

Austria in 1938, Hitler and his band of international gangsters—there is no more appropriate term—were encouraged to believe that they could help themselves to any country they coveted.

Democracy is too often silenced when it asks awkward questions by being told that it is not in the public interest to give a reply. If the matter is pressed it may receive attention in a secret session of parliament, which may satisfy members but bars out the people who elected them. We know very little of what happened at Munich in September, 1938, when a final attempt to appease Hitler was made by Britain and France. The stark and terrible sequel to "peace in our time" promised by Mr. Neville Chamberlain, the Prime Minister, was the seizure of Czechoslovakia in 1939 and the confiscation by Germany of 1,582 aeroplanes, 2,175 guns, 469 tanks, 43,876 machine guns, over 1,000,000 rifles and 300,000 shells. The statistics are Hitler's.

With Satanic cunning the Führer had led the Continent to assume that Nazi doctrines were diametrically opposed to Bolshevism. On that belief, on the fanning into flame of passions aroused by what he regarded as the iniquity of the Treaty of Versailles and the shibboleth of the Germans being the Master Race, he jackbooted to power. Then he came to terms with the protagonist of Bolshevism, Stalin.

Not until the second World War was crackling and spreading like a prairie fire did the altruistic democracies begin to see that there was little, if any, difference between leader and led. The conflict was begun on September 1, 1939, by the German invasion of Poland. Two days later Britain and France, who were pledged to assist the Poles, joined in. So far as the Allies were concerned the war was waged against a government. Pamphlets were rained down from the sky on Berlin streets to reassure the citizens of that fact.

EXODUS OF THE SECOND WORLD WAR

In order to avoid the possibility of wholesale massacre as a result of air raids by the Germans, the British Government arranged for the evacuation of vast numbers of children and their mothers. By the beginning of 1940 over 1,161,000 had been accommodated in various parts of the kingdom. Children were also removed from many coastal areas.

BACK TO THE DAYS OF THE CAVE MAN

A cave shelter from air raids in Kent, formerly worked for sand for brickmaking. In Malta and on the British south-east coast tunnels in the rock were used for a similar purpose.

The consummate cruelty of the armed forces, using human shields, bombing lightships and neutral fishermen, sinking ships without warning and other barbaric methods soon made it obvious that the conflict was also a clash of peoples. There are orders that countermand those of officers, however highly placed. They are the orders of humanity. A British soldier or a French poilu would rather be shot at dawn than injure pitiful old women or helpless children. These things were done deliberately as part of the principles of legitimate warfare according to the Nazis. Eye-witnesses of unimpeachable character attest them. To strike terror was the first article of the vindictive and callous creed of National Socialism. It was a reversion to type; the type of the primeval forest.

With the thought of her 1,500,000 dead in the last tussle still a vivid and heart-breaking memory, France sought to wage a war with the fewest possible casualties. For that reason she clung to the Maginot Line of steel and concrete fortresses that ran from Basle to Montmédy, and from thence in a considerably weaker extension to the sea. She hesitated to launch a vigorous offensive on account of the cost, even when

Germany was hotly engaged battering her way on the great Polish plain.

It is true that General Gamelin made an attack in the neighbourhood of the forest of Warndt and that his guns dominated industrial Saarbrücken, but he failed to follow up his initial effort, and when Poland collapsed after almost a month of unrelieved slaughter he suddenly withdrew, having done little to relieve the pressure on his Ally. Poland's 150,000 square miles were partitioned between Germany and Russia which had decided at the eleventh hour to take part in the division.

At the end of November, 1939, the Soviet armies invaded Finland, which put up a desperate and heroic defence until March 13, 1940, when the republic was compelled through sheer weakness to accept Russia's peace terms. They included the surrender of territory that Russia thought necessary to make her north-western frontiers secure.

In the following month Denmark and Norway were invaded by Germany without warning. A feeble attempt to help Norway was made by the Allies. Their 12,000 men, for the most part ill-equipped, were vastly outnumbered and speedily withdrawn, though British squadrons exacted a heavy

AFTERMATH OF A GERMAN AIR RAID ON LONDON

A gigantic crater caused by a high-explosive bomb. During the series of air attacks known as the Battle of Britain, which lasted from August to October, 1940, no fewer than 2,375 German aircraft were destroyed and many damaged over Great Britain in daylight alone.

toll of enemy warships and convoys and themselves sustained serious losses before the country was finally evacuated in June. In the opening phase the Allies were put at a hopeless disadvantage by having no aerodrome nearer than the United Kingdom, hundreds of miles away. Narvik, the iron-exporting port in the north, was captured and abandoned; at once a victory and a defeat. The enemy remained in possession.

On May 10 Germany started a blitz-krieg—lightning war—against the Low Countries and Luxemburg. Five days later the Nazis occupied Holland, and a salient had been driven into the French lines at Sedan. The bulge grew bigger. General Weygand, Foch's Chief of Staff, hastily recalled from Syria, took over the command from General Gamelin. Much was expected of him; little was achieved. He failed to close the gap. Aided by masses of tanks, aeroplanes and mechanized cavalry, the Germans pushed towards the Channel

ports, reaching Abbeville and Boulogne. On the 28th Belgium capitulated.

Only by fighting the most desperate rear-guard actions, the constant bombardment of the enemy forces, and the exercise of incredible exertions on the part of the Royal Navy and hundreds of odd merchant and private craft were 335,000 members of the Allied forces evacuated from Dunkirk, minus their material. Nothing like it had happened in history.

Snatched as brands from the burning the men were sometimes compelled to wait on the open sand-swept beaches for three days with little or no shelter from attack by enemy aircraft. Britain had to organize and equip her expeditionary force anew. Before she could do so Italy, waiting like a footpad in the dark, declared war and stabbed France in the back.

In a final attempt to save her from herself, for the French Government had become defeatist and had taken on a frame of mind

SHATTERED SHELL OF A FOURTEENTH-CENTURY CATHEDRAL

The Germans boasted that on the night of 14–15 November, 1940, they dropped nearly 450 tons of bombs on Coventry. The casualties totalled some 200 killed and 800 injured. The cathedral, a beautiful example of the Perpendicular style of architecture, was wrecked.

which made it appear senseless to continue the struggle, Mr. Winston Churchill, who had succeeded Chamberlain as Prime Minister, made a daring proposal. He suggested that the governments of the two nations should form a Franco-British Union, with a single War Cabinet and a formal association of their two parliaments.

It was not to be. Weygand feared a revolution and refused to bring up reserves. For a brief moment the idea of transferring the French Government to North Africa was entertained, then dismissed. Outvoted in his own cabinet, thanks to an injudicious choice of defeatist ministers, Paul Reynaud resigned. His place as Prime Minister was taken by Marshal Pétain, the hero of Verdun in the first World War but now a man over eighty years of age with an inclination to dictatorship. He sought what he held to be an honourable peace, but with dishonourable men, and was worsted.

The Republic was rent asunder. The whole of the western coastline and more than half of the country was occupied by the Germans, who charged £2,270,000 a day for the privilege. To prevent units of the French fleet falling into the hands of the Nazis, warships that had co-operated to defeat a common enemy turned their guns against each other off Oran and Mars-El-Kebir following the refusal of the admiral to surrender or demilitarize his ships.

Pétain's sympathy with totalitarian methods of government soon became evident. He took the title of Head of the French State. The Constitution of 1875 was abolished; the Third Republic was added to the list of things that had been. It was as dead as the Babylonian Empire. "Liberty, Equality, Fraternity," the watchword of France since the days of the Revolution when she had burst her bonds asunder, was erased as though a dirty smudge. The words had no place in the new régime, which adopted "Labour, Family, Fatherland" as the new motto of the French nation.

Why France Collapsed

The defection of France was due to several causes. The alleged security afforded by the Maginot Line had helped to form what came to be known as the Maginot mind, with the comforting but erroneous belief that all was well when it was otherwise. Big business rather admired Nazi and Fascist methods; ordinary folk hated them. The many parties worked for their own interests rather than for the State. Many influential people believed in making concessions to Hitler. For months before the French collapse long trains loaded with French iron ore wended their way through Belgium to Germany and returned with coal. "A great nation," said Mr. Winston Churchill, "was rotted from within before it was assaulted from without."

Italy Takes a Hand

Italy, thinking Greece easy prey, treacherously invaded her through Albania without declaring war. Aided by British attacks on the Duce's naval forces, which never essayed other than run-away battles, and by the Royal Air Force, the Greeks fought with the valour of their ancient heroes and flung the enemy across the frontier. In March, 1941, the Italians launched a mighty offensive with 120,000 men. At the end of five days their losses were estimated at about 15,000 dead and 35,000 wounded or captured. In North and East Africa General Sir Archibald Wavell disintegrated the new Roman Empire after an abortive attempt had been made by Italy to invade Egypt with an eye on the Suez Canal.

Britain held the command of the Mediterranean although robbed of French help. On one occasion the Fleet Air Arm attacked the Italian naval base at Taranto and severely damaged three battleships, two cruisers and two fleet auxiliaries. This daring exploit, carried out on the night of November 11–12, 1940, left Mussolini for the time being with only three effective capital ships.

Japan, which had earned for herself the stigma of being known as the Germany of the East, became fully associated in 1940 with what was called the Axis. This political alliance between Germany and Italy had originated in 1936 during the Abyssinian War, mainly in opposition to Britain, France and Russia, and developed into a political and military alliance in May, 1939. When Hitler announced what he termed the New Order, a Monroe Doctrine for Europe, Japan declared a similar policy for East Asia, and showed, by menacing measures taken in Indo-China after the secession of France, that she was still eager for other worlds to conquer, despite setbacks in her war with China. This "incident," as Japan was pleased to term it, had been raging since 1937, following the conquest of Manchuria, which had become the puppet State of Manchukuo.

The leading tenet of the New Order was

MOVING FORTRESSES IN THE MAKING

Eighteen-ton tanks in course of production. After the evacuation of Dunkirk, with the loss of much valuable material, Britain had to organize and equip her expeditionary force anew. This was accomplished by almost incredible exertions on the part of the workers.

tersely summed up by President Roosevelt when he explained in March, 1941, that the Nazi forces were not seeking mere modifications in colonial maps or in minor European boundaries, but the destruction of all collective systems of government on every continent, including America; "they seek to establish systems of government based on the regimentation of all human beings by a handful of individual rulers who seized power by force."

As the President commented, it was neither new nor order. The guiding principle was to make conquered countries the milch cow on which to fatten Germany. Or, to use another simile, the Reich was the mother planet around which nations not entitled to be called leader-peoples would revolve as satellites. Adherents to or sympathisers with the Axis included Spain, Hungary, Rumania and Bulgaria. In the case of the first two countries the object was brought about by political pressure; in the last two it was achieved by a combination of political pressure and military occupation.

It would appear less difficult to secure whole-hearted co-operation in war than in peace. The United States gradually began to realize that British sea power was a far more practical means of defending America than the hypothetical 300-mile safety zone around the coast of the continent claimed by the Panama Congress of October, 1939. In return for fifty destroyers of somewhat ancient type, Britain leased to the United States certain strategic bases in the West Indies and elsewhere, and in 1941, by the terms of the Lease-and-Lend Act, all munitions of every kind that the great western republic could spare were placed at the disposal of Britain, Greece, China and governments in exile. The President called it "all-out aid," and declared that help would be increased, and yet again increased, until total victory had been won. Of the 11,800 aircraft ordered by Britain from the United States 3,400 had been delivered by the middle of March, 1941.

The United States became what Mr. Roosevelt called the arsenal of democracy.

American isolation was at an end. It was significant that a newspaper correspondent in Washington cabled to London that co-partnership talk was rife in the United States about a future world society in which the keys would be held by the English-speaking peoples. This suggestion put Aristide Briand's advocacy of European union at the Assembly of the League of Nations in 1929 completely in the shade, an idea which had already been given an evil twist by Hitler in his New Order.

Shot-gun Politics

Murder as an instrument of national policy had already been resorted to by the Nazis before they set the world aflame. In 1934 King Alexander of Yugoslavia, Louis Barthou, Foreign Minister of France, M. Duca, Foreign Minister of Rumania and Chancellor Dollfuss of Austria had been assassinated by Nazis or their agents. Hitler's purge of his own party, a blood bath in which hundreds were killed, had also taken place in that red year. Murder on a ruthless and wholesale scale was rained from the sky by German aircraft on the civilians of every country with which the Führer was at war.

Thousands of people were butchered in Great Britain alone, and enormous damage was done to property in London, Coventry, Liverpool, Birmingham, Bristol, Clydeside, Belfast, Plymouth and other populous centres. When it was found that the Royal Air Force exacted too heavy a toll in day-time, Goering altered his tactics to night bombing, when the attacking planes had much their own way. Included in the pre-sumably military objectives were hospitals and places of worship. Up to the beginning of February, 1941, 2,659 churches had been bombed, including nine cathedrals, that of Coventry being left no more than a blackened ruin.

After the defeat of France, the object most dear to Hitler's heart was the landing on the British Isles of a German expe-ditionary force. In August, 1940, news of Nazi troops assembled on French beaches ready for embarkation, but frus-trated by British aircraft was released for publication by the Ministry of Information after consultation with the Air Ministry. It was subsequently cancelled. A somewhat similar story to the effect that in the follow-ing month transports and barges loaded with troops were wrecked by the Royal Air Force appeared in many American news-papers. That masses of craft were prepared for the purpose was proved by a succession of air raids carried out by Britain on what were officially known as invasion ports—the harbours of Holland, Belgium and occupied France.

The formation of the volunteer Home Guard, the constant warning by prominent statesmen and others of the likelihood of such a descent, and the erection of fortifica-tions round the coast were additional proofs that Hitler's preparations were something more than a threat or an artful scheme to compel Great Britain to retain an enor-mous army in the homeland.

Mussolini's set-backs in North Africa, Greece and Albania could scarcely be tol-erated if Hitler wished to retain his ally. Unless help from Germany was forth-coming he would be utterly consumed. The battle of Cape Matapan, on March 28, 1941, was doubtless brought about by Ger-man pressure, for the Italian Fleet was not much given to "airing itself," to use one of Nelson's expressive terms. The excursion was, in all probability, a ruse to distract attention from convoying operations across the Mediterranean. The immediate result was that while Italy lost three 10,000-ton heavy cruisers and two destroyers, and sus-tained damage to a battleship, a 6-inch gun cruiser, and a large destroyer at Admiral Sir Andrew Cunningham's hands, German armoured divisions under General Erwin Rommel effected a landing in Cyrenaica. Denuded of troops sent to Greece owing to Hitler's threatening attitude in the Balkans, the victorious army of the Nile, not yet recovered from its arduous task, was forced back. It retained its firm grip, however, on the coastal stronghold of Tobruk.

Balkans Under Hitler

On April 6, without declaring war, Hitler struck at Greece and Yugoslavia. His troops crashed through by sheer weight of men and metal. Yugoslavia fell in a matter of days, though the unflinching Serbs in their mountain fastnesses continued to maintain a spirited guerrilla warfare. In Greece the Allies, contesting every yard of territory and fighting fierce rearguard actions, were unable to stem the ever-rising tide of invasion. An armistice was signed by Greek commanders without the sanction of the Government. Officially informed that further sacrifices on the part of the Forces of the Empire, as they were called, would be in vain, some 45,000 British soldiers and

BUILDING FUSELAGES FOR STIRLING BOMBERS

Immense impetus was given to the manufacture of munitions by the air attacks on Britain. In the conquest of Western Europe the Germans were aided by masses of tanks, aircraft and mechanized vehicles that had been prepared while the democracies sought appeasement.

WOMEN HELP TO WAGE TOTAL WAR

Women of the Auxiliary Territorial Service in battledress running to action stations. At the beginning of the second World War they numbered about 20,000, a strength that grew as the conflict progressed, as did that of the women's auxiliary naval and air forces.

airmen were evacuated with heavy losses on the part of the Navy and the Merchant Service. King George of the Hellenes transferred his seat of government to the island of Crete, where Allied soldiers, reinforced from Greece, were established. On April 27, no more than three weeks after the beginning of the campaign, the Nazis goose-stepped into Athens. The swastika flag was unfurled on the Acropolis. From then on the inhabitants of the peninsula began to starve. German ruthlessness was applied to the stomach, an organ held by them in high regard. The cruelty of the conquerors was matched by the unconquerable spirit of the vanquished descendants of Leonidas.

Less than a month later the Germans invaded Crete by air. Again there was valorous resistance, but the defenders had insufficient fighter planes, and their aerodromes were captured. Fortune continued to frown. Once again, as in Norway, France, and Greece, Allied troops had to be carried off on the broad backs of ships. Over

14,500 of the 27,550 soldiers who had landed were got away. Another campaign was lost, and a further base provided for the Axis from which to menace the British in North Africa and the Near East, where political and military intriguers had plotted in Iraq and Syria. The revolt in Iraq was speedily suppressed by troops from India and Palestine. It took six weeks to win Syria, which, with the Lebanon, passed from the control of Vichy to that of Free France, afterwards termed Fighting France. German influence in Iran was quashed by prompt measures a little later.

Hitler next turned to rend his Russian "friend." For years he had pretended that Germany was the bulwark against the menace of Bolshevism. Then he had decided that the ideology of the Soviets was not so black as it was painted, and came to terms with Stalin. Now it suited his purpose to regard the Union as a collection of menacing barbarians. Moscow in German hands, and peace would speedily

READY TO RESIST INVASION BY SEA AND AIR

The invasion of Britain was projected by Napoleon but frustrated by the vigilance of the Royal Navy. Hitler made vast preparations for a similar attempt, a measure answered by Britain by the erection and manning of coastal batteries and other means of defence, and the bombing of ports used for the collection of German craft. It led to the formation of the Local Defence Volunteers, afterwards known by the happier name of Home Guard.

follow. Such was his belief. A mighty offensive was launched on June 22, 1941, without any word that the two-year-old pact had become another scrap of paper. The front stretched from the Arctic to the Black Sea. Finland, seeing an opportunity to regain her old frontiers, threw in her lot with the Reich. Britain, casting aside all political differences, sided with Russia. Great slices of territory were torn away, including most of the prosperous Ukraine; cities fell, towns were captured. Many of the factories developed as part of the programme of the Five-Year plans were deliberately set on fire by the Russians after the machinery had been wrecked or removed. The "scorched earth" policy of China was adopted with ruthless energy. Anything and everything likely to be of service to the enemy was destroyed without compunction. Human habitations and the homes of industry were put to the torch. Guerrilla bands sprang up like the dry bones in the valley of which Ezekiel tells, to become not an exceeding great army, but groups that attacked with amazing skill when and where they were least expected. Bitter defeats were sustained, yet when hope was failing and the Russians were regarded as totally unable to do anything of the kind, Marshal Timoshenko launched a counter-offensive that did much to restore a critical situation. Although Sevastopol fell and the Crimea was conquered, the autumn of 1942 found the Russians facing their foes with stolid fortitude. According to General Sikorski, the Polish Commander-in-Chief, German losses in all theatres since 1939 totalled 1,500,000 dead and 3,000,000 wounded and sick. The exiled Polish Government and Russia had put aside their differences, leaving the vexed question of the future frontier of their respective territories to be settled after the termination of the war.

Japan Prepares to Pounce

Just as Italy had waited like a jackal to attack France when the Republic was almost at its last gasp, so Japan played a waiting game before striking. Probably with Japanese connivance, a dispute had arisen between French Indo-China and Thailand (Siam) regarding frontiers, and the Land of the Rising Sun, having already demanded permission to land troops in Indo-China, had offered to mediate. Her award was that certain territory in Cambodia was to be demilitarized and ceded to Thailand, whose western neighbour, like that of Indo-China,

was Burma, while her southern frontier marched with that of British Malaya. Japan made good her footing in the French possession, ready to pounce.

While her representatives were talking peace in Washington, on December 7, Japanese air forces to the number of about 150 planes attacked the American naval base at Pearl Harbour and flying-fields in the Hawaiian Islands. A United States battleship blew up, another capsized, three destroyers, a minelayer, and a target-training ship were sunk. The killed and wounded numbered over 2,300. Shanghai and the British concessions at Tientsin and Shameen were occupied. Thailand and Malaya were invaded. Midway Island, Guam, Wake Island, Nauru and the Philippines were attacked. Steaming off the west coast of Malaya, the British battleship *Prince of Wales* and the battle-cruiser *Repulse* were bombed and torpedoed from the air and destroyed. Kowloon was evacuated and the garrison transferred to Hong Kong, which held out until the limit of endurance was reached. It surrendered on Christmas Day, 1941. Sarawak was conquered. The lonely outposts of Guam and Wake Island were compelled to submit; they could do no other. Forestalling the Japanese, Australian and Dutch forces quickly occupied Portuguese Timor.

The Atlantic Charter

Mr. Winston Churchill, Britain's Prime Minister, had promised help "within the hour" should the United States be attacked. In the previous August he and President Roosevelt had met at sea, drawn together by mutual regard, the growing practical sympathy of America with the Allies in the hard-fought struggle, and the threatening attitude of Japan. They issued a declaration of principles which became known as the Atlantic Charter; eight points that may be of far-reaching consequence in the years ahead. They are as follows:

"Their countries seek no aggrandizement, territorial or other;

"They desire to see no territorial changes that do not accord with the freely expressed wishes of the people concerned;

"They respect the right of all peoples to choose the form of government under which they shall live, and they wish to see sovereign rights and self-government restored to those who have been forcibly deprived of them;

"They will endeavour, with due respect for

CANADIAN TROOPS PUTTING TANKS THROUGH THEIR PACES

The tank was a British invention and received its baptism of fire in September, 1916, during the battle of the Somme. The second World War saw great developments in the land battleship, which the Germans used in very large numbers from the outset.

their existing obligations, to further enjoyment by all States, great or small, victor or vanquished, of access, on equal terms, to the trade and to the raw materials of the world which are needed for their economic prosperity;

"They desire to bring about the fullest collaboration between all nations in the economic field, with the object of securing for all improved labour standards, economic development, and social security;

"After the final destruction of Nazi tyranny, they hope to see established a peace which will afford to all nations the means of dwelling in safety within their own boundaries, and which will afford assurance that all men in all lands may live out their lives in freedom from fear and want;

"Such a peace should enable all men to traverse the high seas and without hindrance;

"They believe that all the nations of the world, for realistic as well as spiritual reasons, must come to the abandonment of the use of force. Since no future peace can be maintained if land, sea, or air armaments continue to be employed by nations which threaten, or may threaten, aggression outside of their frontiers, they believe, pending the establishment of a wider and permanent system of general security, that the disarmament of such nations is essential. They will likewise aid and encourage all other practicable measures which will lighten for peace-loving peoples the crushing burden of armaments."

The reference to "existing obligations" was an unhappy qualification. What agreements filed in the permanent or temporary chancelleries of the nations still awaited honouring? The first of Dr. Woodrow Wilson's fourteen points was "open covenants and no secret diplomacy in the future." To that the common people had pinned their faith and been disillusioned. President Roosevelt's predecessor had also postulated the removal, "as far as possible," of all economic barriers, adequate guarantees for the reduction of national armaments and absolute freedom of navigation at all times outside territorial waters, except at times when seas might be closed to particular nations by international action.

Japanese landed on islands that directly threatened Australia. The defences of Malaya were overcome ; Singapore surrendered unconditionally; Burma was invaded and occupied. Off Java a whole squadron of Allied warships was wiped out, and the Netherlands East Indies fell to the prowess of the attackers, but in the Coral Sea the United Nations were the victors, the Japanese losing an aircraft carrier, three heavy cruisers, one light cruiser, and several supply ships. The seizure of the French island of Madagascar was frustrated by the landing of British naval and military forces. General Sir Claude Auchinleck forestalled Rommel's Libyan offensive against Tobruk, and the enemy's front was broken. Then the tide of battle turned, thanks to the use of superior armoured forces, leading to the loss of Tobruk, and the capture of many prisoners and much valuable material. The Axis crossed the Egyptian frontier and again continued their offensive. Meanwhile vigorous air attacks were made by the Allies on important industrial centres in Germany, as on Cologne in May, 1942, when 1,130 planes attacked the city, only forty-four of them being lost.

Democracy Gets to Work

In spite of temporary set-backs, the moral strength of democracy was unabated, and its physical strength multiplied by leaps and bounds. Munitions of every kind—ships, tanks, guns, planes—left the stocks in unheard-of quantities, America and Britain not only supplying their own needs, but supporting the magnificent struggle of their Russian allies by a continual stream of the materials of war. The titanic struggle in Eastern Europe relentlessly sapped the strength of the Axis powers, and as the end of 1942 approached, the German advance, long held up by the heroic defence of Stalingrad, seemed to be turning into a retreat. The carrying of the war back into Western Europe was foreshadowed by a simultaneous expulsion of the Axis from Egypt and Cyrenaica, and a combined Anglo-American occupation of the western half of North Africa, with the goodwill of the French local governments. At last the long story of disaster and disappointment seemed at an end, and the blind faith that in the darkest days had never been over-whelmed was finding its justification in a reasoned prospect of the final overthrow of the forces of darkness. It was not yet day, but the bitter memory of the sorrow of the night had given place to a glad confidence in the joy to come in the morning.

Right through the long centuries of man's failures and achievements we have seen him chasing the will-o'-the-wisp of permanent peace. Must it always prove to be nothing more substantial than a wandering marsh light, at once elusive and fascinating? If history proves anything it surely shows that the impossibility of today is the possibility of tomorrow. The opportunity for peace to show her prowess is long overdue. Recent wars have settled nothing and unsettled everything. Text-books are bestrewn with records of broken treaties, pacts, agreements, eternal friendships, leagues and what not. The four quarters of the globe are littered with dead men's bones by reason of these failures to fulfil the plighted troth of the written word.

Civilization's Debit Account

Yet in many other directions humanity has thrived on frustration. Labour and social conditions have been vastly improved, the slave trade has disappeared in many countries, deadly diseases have been virtually stamped out or held in check. War remains immune. But let this significant fact be noted. Epidemics have invariably marched with the armies, stalking them with stealth, and civilians have not been immune. During and following the first World War millions died of influenza and typhus. After Germany had brought France to her knees in the Franco-Prussian War, over 126,000 of her nationals died of smallpox. Cholera played havoc in Austria and Prussia when they fought in 1866, and while the American Civil War was being waged the northern armies lost four times as many men by disease as in battle. The Napoleonic conflicts left France physically weak for many years. During the Thirty Years War, the total loss of life from all causes in Germany has been put as high as two-thirds of the population. The advance of medical science has done much to lessen the death roll, but war never decreases human misery. For instance, there were about 2,000 sailors, soldiers and airmen in hospitals in the United Kingdom immediately before the first World War; when the armistice was signed there were some 333,000. Abroad

CLOSE QUARTERS IN A BRITISH SUBMARINE

The conflict which began in 1939 was largely waged by engineers and technicians, thanks to the development of the internal combustion engine. The Germans based their hopes of cutting the sea communications and supply lines of the United Nations on the U-boat.

over 244,800 patients awaited complete or partial recovery, or death. The belligerents together lost 8,000,000 men; the wounded totalled 21,000,000. The glory of war is shadowed when such facts are known.

Men of War on Peace

Men whose names are writ large on the pages of history and who were primarily associated with the waging of battle have pointed out the stupidity of armed conflict. Napoleon, in his hours of bitter introspection and exile at St. Helena, confessed that the more he studied the world, the more was he convinced of the inability of brute force to create anything durable. His great antagonist, the first Duke of Wellington, remarked to Lord Shaftesbury that war was a most detestable thing, adding that if his listener had seen but one day of war he would pray God that he might never see another. Field-Marshal Sir William Robertson, Chief of the Imperial General Staff from 1915-18, asserted that he had spent nearly half a century on matters connected with war, and had come to the

conclusion that it was a futile thing, for it neither ensured peace nor composed differences.

Many and varied have been the projects to render mankind immune from periodic bouts of wholesale murder. Over nine and a half centuries ago, in 990 to be exact, various ecclesiastical synods in France, by various pains and penalties, sought to protect non-combatants, including animals, from warring factions. The plan was known as the Peace of God. One council, that of Narbonne, went wholly pacifist, and banned the shedding of blood of one Christian by another, which was declared to be crucifying Christ anew. Tribunals were to be set up which would settle grievances that had hitherto been decided by the sword. Unhappily, the warriors thought on lines that were not parallel to those of the Church, and the armed men went on with their fighting.

The Truce of God

Thirty-seven years later another experiment was made, this time called the Truce of God. If war could not be ended, perhaps it

PRISONERS IN PROCESSION AFTER A HARD-FOUGHT BATTLE

Enormous numbers of prisoners, especially Italians, were taken by the United Nations in the Libyan campaigns. Those captured in the Allied advance in the autumn of 1942 amounted to nearly eighty thousand—obviously delighted their part in the war was over.

INTRODUCING THE NEW ORDER IN RUSSIA

A family in the Ukraine, when overrun by the Germans, forced to draw a harrow by their conquerors. Hitler's New Order for Europe largely centred on providing food and munitions of war for Germany, whose inhabitants were regarded as the Master Race.

could be confined to certain days of the week. First of all Sunday was to be deemed sacred. Then the number of fighting days were cut down to three a week, and even these were not available if certain Saints' Days occurred. There was to be a cessation of hostilities throughout Lent and Advent. Pope Urban II ordained the truce throughout Christendom at the Council of Clermont in 1095, and at the same time urged the first of the series of Crusades that transferred the dreaded evil from the west to the east.

Light on the Great Design of Henry IV of France, the monarch who wished every peasant to have a fowl in his pot on Sundays, filters through opaque windows. It would appear that the Duke of Sully was the author of this plan for the federation of Europe, which included in its objects the reduction of the power of the House of Austria, and the expulsion of the Turk. The Tsar of Russia, although regarded as an infidel, was to be afforded an oppor-

tunity to join the association. Should he refuse he was to be given the same rough treatment as was to be meted out to the Sultan, and his possessions confined to those in Asia. No insurmountable religious difficulties were foreseen, but new sects, or opinions, would not be tolerated. To enforce the Great Design an army of 270,000 foot soldiers and 50,000 cavalry, and a navy of 120 vessels were deemed requisite, the cost to be borne by members of the league "in proportion to their several abilities."

These particulars were not given to the world until 1662, over twenty years after Sully's death. The scheme, however imperfect, attracted William Penn, who, in his *Essay Towards the Present and Future Peace of Europe*, has this to say on the matter:

"I confess I have the passion to wish heartily that the honour of proposing and effecting so great and good a design might be owing to England, of all the countries in Europe, as something of the nature of our expedient was, in design and preparation to the wisdom, justice and valour of Henry the Fourth of France, whose superior qualities raising his character above those of his ancestors or contemporaries deservedly gave him the style of Henry the Great. For he was upon obliging the princes and estates of Europe to a politic balance, when the Spanish faction, for that reason, contrived and accomplished his murder by the hand of Ravaillac. I will not then fear to be censured for proposing an expedient for the present or future peace of Europe, when it was not only the design but glory of one of the greatest princes that ever reigned in it. This great king's example tells us it is fit to be done."

Penn and the Redskins

Penn's idea was the establishment of a court of arbitration such as afterwards came into being at The Hague. His colony of Pennsylvania, an estate which then comprised some 55,000 square miles, set a pattern for other plantations, and the famous treaty which he made with the Redskins by which they agreed to "live in love with William Penn and his children as long as the sun and moon give light" was faithfully kept for many years after the peaceful Quaker, and those associated with him, had been laid to rest. Philadelphia, which means "the City of Brotherly Love," was founded by Penn in 1682.

An agreement signed in 1817 by Richard Rush, Secretary of State, and Sir Charles Bagot, British Minister at Washington, limiting the naval force on Lake Ontario to a vessel of not more than 100 tons and mounting a single 18-pounder cannon, still obtains, and the boundary between the United States and Canada, a frontier of some 3,800 miles, is without any kind of defence. Sometimes the tempers of the two nations have been severely tried, but that is all. The amicable arrangements have stood the test.

Tennyson saw a vision of the federation of the world; Woodrow Wilson and millions of humble folk believed that international peace would be cemented by the League of Nations; the greater part of the whole civilized world now awaits the blue prints that various committees are developing. One school of thinkers bases its hopes on a loose internationalism; another on the possibility of a union of the English-speaking peoples; a third on a great European federation. Maybe Victor Hugo's prophecy of 1849 may still be fulfilled:

"A day will come when a cannon-ball will be exhibited in public museums, just as an instrument of torture is now, and people will be amazed that such a thing could ever have been. A day will come when these two immense groups, the United States of America and the United States of Europe, will be seen placed in the presence of each other, extending the hand of fellowship across the ocean, exchanging their produce, their industries, their arts, their genius, clearing the earth, peopling the desert, improving creation under the eye of the Creator, and uniting, for the good of all, these two irresistible and infinite powers, the fraternity of men and the power of God."

That mankind is interdependent is a fundamental truth. It was painfully evident when the British Navy and the Royal Air Force blockaded enemy countries and the Axis Powers sought by means of a vigorous counter-blockade carried out by U-boats, mines, raiders and long distance aircraft to starve Britain into surrender. In a single month over 400,000 tons of shipping were sent to the bottom by Germany. Though races may differ in colour as in culture, in religion as in government, in methods as in manners, the day of the self-contained and fiercely self-sufficient country is over.

How Man Needs Man

We are literally "members one of another." The far corners of the earth and the intervening spaces contribute to the welfare of all. No country, or nation, or empire has all the gifts. If Great Britain had to depend for gold on the amount found within the confines of her own island territory she would have to revert to barter. If the gold-miner were compelled to live in his diggings, remote from the outside world and unable to get access to it, he would starve, though he owned a nugget worth a fortune. Even the primitive wants of the natives of Labrador were affected by the upheavals of 1914 and 1939. An inadequate appreciation of universal requirements, of the fundamental unity of mankind, has led to the perpetuation of grievous wrongs and crimes against humanity.

The world's greatest need is sympathy, which is another word for understanding. Indulge in it for a moment. In all likelihood the chair in which you are sitting is made of wood that was hewn many thousands of miles from your home. Perhaps it was part of a mahogany tree that grew 100 feet high

PILOT AND CO-PILOT IN A WHITLEY BOMBER

Whitley long-range heavy bombers were provided with power-operated gun turrets in the nose and tail. Their fuel capacity and powerful Rolls-Royce Merlin engines gave them so wide a range of operations that they were able to leave bases in Great Britain and operate in Western Germany and Northern Italy, where they successfully carried out many important attacks on military and industrial objectives centred in cities and ports.

in a dense forest in Honduras. A host of helpers whom you have never seen, whose names you will never know, contributed to your comfort. There were the men who blazed a trail through the dense undergrowth, who erected the scaffolding round the great girth of the trunk, who swung the hatchet, who hauled at the tackle to get the fallen giant on to the timber wagon, and who led the oxen. These are but a few of the workers in the preliminary stages of the making of your furniture who enable you to enjoy your ease.

You, for your part, have contributed your quota towards their livelihood as well as of those who go down to the sea in ships, who run railways and other transport, who sell timber, who make chairs, who distribute them and who sell them. To complete the complicated account would take many columns of figures; to tell the story of any article in daily use many pages of words. Even then the whole would not be told, because the tramp steamer has its own glowing romance of officers and crew, owners and agents, shipwrights and engineers, moulders and forgers, miners of iron ore and of coal, to say nothing of the builders of docks, port authorities, harbour masters, keepers of lighthouses, watchers on lightships and those who buoy channels, survey the coasts and make charts. Thus you might continue until you were lost in a maze of fact and wonder at the jig-saw puzzle of civilization.

Man's last great conquest will be himself.

NEW MAGNA CHARTA FOR ALL NATIONS

President Roosevelt and Mr. Winston Churchill when they made the great declaration of principles on the future of the world known as the Atlantic Charter. Its eight points were drawn up and agreed upon by them at their meeting on the high seas in August, 1941.

INDEX

(Page numbers in italics refer to illustrations)

317

ACKNOWLEDGMENTS

The thanks of the publishers are due to the following for the use of illustrations reproduced in this book:—
The Mount Wilson Observatory; The Field Museum of Natural History; The British Museum; The British Museum (Natural History); The American Museum of Natural History, N.Y.; The London Museum; The Oriental Institute of the University of Chicago; and Dr. Upham Pope.